TURBOBLOWERS

Theory, Design, and Application of Centrifugal and Axial Flow Compressors and Fans

A. J. STEPANOFF Ph.D.

Melville Medalist, A.S.M.E.

Ingersoll-Rand Company

NEW YORK · JOHN WILEY & SONS, INC.

LONDON · CHAPMAN & HALL, LIMITED

Library of Congress Catalog Card Number: 55-6546
PRINTED IN THE UNITED STATES OF AMERICA

PREFACE

The last fifteen years have witnessed an unprecedented development and an increase in the field of application of turbomachinery for the compression of gases and vapors. This is evidenced by the increase of individual sizes of units, and an increase of pressure ratios realized in one casing. Horsepower of the drivers went up accordingly. High premiums set for efficiency of large units, particularly in Europe, led to perfection of hydraulic design to the point that in single-stage units efficiencies of 90 per cent are approached, thus equaling those established in the field of centrifugal pumps years before. At the same time the theoretical reasoning underlying the blower design has shown a definite trend toward unification of the fundamental hydrodynamic relationships for all turbomachines and away from the indirect thermodynamic basis commonly adopted in the past. An immediate result of this trend was that extensive experience accumulated in several related fields, markedly in the centrifugal pump field, became available and was profitably applied to the blower design.

This book deals with hydrodynamic and thermodynamic aspects of the turboblower design. Mechanical problems are being solved differently by several manufacturers and are adequately covered by the trade literature. This book aims to present the state of the art of building of turbocompressors in this country and abroad.

It is my firm conviction that the thermodynamic aspects of compression of gases cannot be adequately treated without the concept of "available energy." Several important deductions known and confirmed by observations cannot be arrived at by the use of internal energy or enthalpy functions alone, whereas they follow simply and logically with the aid of available energy function.

The theoretical treatment of the axial flow impeller is based on the actual "fluid deflection angles" rather than airfoil lift coefficients. In this method axial flow machines appear as an extreme type in a continuous row of hydraulic types. The forced vortex pattern of flow through the axial flow stage is a logical development in this design procedure. The airfoil theory of the axial flow impeller is introduced only to acquaint the reader with the terminology and show its limitation. In high-pressure multistage axial flow compressor design the trend is definitely away from the airfoil theory and free vortex pattern of flow, thus a detailed discussion of this method of design is hardly justified. Besides, there is ample literature on the subject in the form of numerous reports of several government agencies and engineering schools.

No space is allowed in this book for the description of the testing procedure and calculation of results as these are adequately covered by Power Test Codes of the American Society of Mechanical Engineers PTC 10-1949 and PTC 11-1946. These codes are accepted by the Compressed Air and Gas Institute (90 West St., New York 6, New York) and the National Association of Fan Manufacturers, Inc. (2159 Guardian Building, Detroit 26, Michigan). The reader should become familiar with the publications of these two organizations, which contain a great deal of useful information not duplicated in this book.

I am indebted to The Ingersoll-Rand Company, Mr. D. R. Lowry, President, Mr. M. C. Davison, Vice President, and to Mr. Hanns Hornschuch, Engineer-in-Charge, Blower and Pump Engineering Department, whose help and encouragement made this book possible. The manuscript was critically reviewed by Mr. H. A. Stahl of Ingersoll-Rand Company and Mr. R. J. Sweeney, Consulting Engineer, who have furnished numerous corrections and improvements.

Although great care has been exercised to check the manuscript and proofs, errors may be discovered. I will appreciate it if they are called to my attention. I also invite criticism of the views presented in the book or suggestions that may lead to its improvement.

A. J. STEPANOFF

Phillipsburg, New Jersey
January 1, 1955

CONTENTS

CHAPTER 1

Selected Topics from
Fluid Mechanics

A theoretical treatment of the flow through turbomachines is difficult because most of the channels comprising such machines have variable and irregular sections and a curved mean path. Some of the channels are in a circular motion with power applied to or taken from the flow. Simple relationships established in fluid mechanics for idealized conditions, if applied directly to such flow, may not only give an incorrect quantitative answer but may also result in a false qualitative mental pattern of flow.

In this chapter a number of subjects are treated which are either missing or not sufficiently emphasized in books on fluid mechanics. In several instances limitations of principles established in fluid mechanics, when applied to conditions of flow as found in turbomachines, are stressed.

In every case it is convenient to disregard the compressibility of the fluid and consider the fluid of constant density, such as water or air at low pressures. Since a great amount of information about fluid flow has been established with water, examples from hydraulics and hydraulic machinery (pumps) will be quoted, when helpful. Also, in some instances, familiar terms from hydraulics will be used, such as hydraulic gradient, hydraulic efficiency, and hydraulic radius, rather than introducing new terms for gas flow.

1.1 ENERGY GRADIENT

To start and maintain flow in a channel, stationary or moving, there must be a drop in total energy content in the direction of flow below its initial level at zero flow. The graphical representation of the total energy along the path of flow is the energy gradient. This should be distinguished from the hydraulic gradient, which shows only static pressures at different points of the path (Fig. 1.1). The hydraulic gradient may have a local drop and rise along the path, but the energy gradient drops continually and it determines the direction of flow.

1

In actual pipe flow the energy gradient drop represents hydraulic losses along the flow path.

An idealized flow can be imagined to be produced by hydraulic (or pressure) gradient drop with the energy content remaining constant; for instance, the discharge from a vessel through a nozzle. But in every case where real fluids are concerned the process will follow the direction indicated by the energy gradient drop.

The presence of a pump in a system of conduits produces a jump in the energy gradient, but the flow is still maintained by the energy gradient drop ahead of the pump, through the pump, and beyond the pump. *In a movable channel, such as an impeller of a blower, the energy gradient drop is referred to the energy level when there is no flow.* When the flow starts, energy is absorbed by the flow at such a rate that the total energy remains, at all times and at all points, below its zero flow level. The use of the energy gradient concept simplifies a number of problems connected with the flow through a turbomachine and will be elaborated further in later chapters (Figs. 1.2, 1.4).

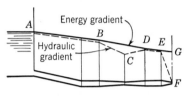

Fig. 1.1. Energy and hydraulic gradients.

1.2 TRANSITION OF PRESSURE IN FLUIDS IN MOTION

In a stationary body of fluid, pressure intensity is transmitted equally in all directions. In moving fluids, a difference in pressure may exist along the path of the flow and also across the section of the channel as a result of the dynamic forces developed by the flow. Pressure changes along the path of flow are a result of a change in kinetic energy as given by Bernoulli's equation, the total energy of each streamline remaining constant.

Variation of pressure across a channel, however, can occur in such a manner that some streamlines will increase their pressure without decreasing their velocities, thus increasing their total energy, or the constant in Bernoulli's equation. But, since the total energy of the flow across the channel section remains the same, such an increase of pressure energy of one group of streamlines takes place at the expense of the pressure energy of the remaining streamlines.

The transition of pressure energy takes place on the molecular scale without actual mixing of streamlines, in the same manner as it happens in a stationary fluid, and is similar to the heat propagation by conduction. Both pressure energy and heat energy are due to molecular kinetic energy and are interchangeable, as is well known in thermo-dynamics of gases.

When the pressure energy exchange is effected by shifting or mix-ing of streamlines the process is similar to convection. There is still another mode of pressure transition which takes place without exchange of particles or mixing of streamlines, and that is by means of traveling pressure waves.

The flow of pressure energy from a higher to a lower level takes place naturally like heat flow from a higher to a lower temperature, whereas the flow of pressure energy in the reverse direction usually takes place under the dynamic forces developed in a curvilinear or rotary motion. As soon as the tangential component of the velocity is taken out of the flow by special means, such as guide vanes or a straight length of pipe, pressures are immediately equalized by a natural flow of the pressure en-ergy from a higher to a lower level without mixing of the streamlines, that is, by conduc-tion. Conduction is responsible for the constant pressure across the section of a channel with a steady flow assumed in hydraulics. Examples of conduction and con-vection of pressure energy follow.

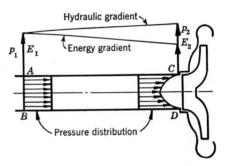

Fig. 1.2. Hydraulic and energy gradi-ents along impeller approach.

Figure 1.2 shows a straight-pipe approach to an impeller of a centrifugal blower. At the section AB, sufficiently removed from the blower, pressure p_1 is uniform across the section and a normal pipe velocity distribution prevails. At sec-tion CD, near the blower, the pressure p_2, as measured at the pipe wall, is higher than at section AB. But since the energy gradient decreases from AB to CD, the higher pressure at CD can appear only at the expense of the middle streamlines. A paraboloid of pressure dis-tribution is developed at CD with the pressure higher at the periphery (and lower at the center) than the average original pressure. The absolute velocities at the periphery are higher than those in the middle as a result of the addition of a tangential component due to rotation of the stream. This pressure exchange takes place without mixing of streamlines or by conduction.

In Chapter 3, it will be shown that prerotation in the inlet pipe is caused by the tendency of the fluid to follow a path of least resistance on its way to enter impeller channels. This tendency becomes evident when the prerotation is in a direction opposite to that of the impeller. This occurs usually at blower capacities exceeding the normal capacity.

The process is reversed at the discharge of an axial flow blower. At the impeller discharge, pressure and velocities are higher at the periphery than at the hub. In the stationary vanes the tangential component of the absolute velocity is taken out of the flow and pressures are equalized across the whole discharge pipe area. The exchange of pressure energy in the diffusion casing takes place without mixing of streamlines (by conduction), as visually observed by Schmidt (reference 1), by introducing smoke and sparks at a blower inlet.

Higher velocities and pressures near the outer wall of a turn observed by Adler (reference 2) for laminar flow may serve as an illustration of the pressure transition by conduction, as there is no mixing of streamlines in the laminar flow.

Transition of pressure by convection takes place, for instance, in an elbow. Beyond the turn, pressure and velocities are higher at the outer wall of the turn, the increase in energy being made at the expense of streamlines near the inner wall. This process is not efficient and is always followed by losses or degeneration of pressure energy into heat. Beyond the turn a uniform pressure is reestablished, partly by convection, partly by conduction.

1.3 VORTEX MOTION

Movement of fluid in a circular path is known as a vortex motion. All particles of fluid describing circles of the same radius form stream cylinders. Particles of the same stream cylinder move with the same tangential and angular velocity. These velocities may vary from one cylinder to another. *Variation in the linear or angular velocity determines the pressure distribution along the radius, or the shape of the free surface if the vessel containing the liquid is open to atmosphere.*

The condition of equilibrium requires that, for each particle, the centrifugal force must be balanced by the pressure or static liquid column at the same point.

$$\frac{dp}{dr} = \frac{\gamma v^2}{gr} = \frac{\gamma}{g}\omega^2 r \tag{1.1}$$

where p is pressure at radius r; v is the tangential velocity; and ω is the angular velocity.

If the variation of angular velocity with radius is known, substitution of this value of ω into equation 1.1 will permit integration, and the pressure distribution along the radius will be obtained. In Table 1, results of the integration of equation 1.1 are tabulated for a velocity

TABLE 1. VORTEX MOTION

Curve No. on Figs. 1.3a and 1.3b	Angular Velocity Distribution $\omega = C_r r^m$	Peripheral Velocity Distribution $vr^n = C$	Pressure Distribution $\int dp = \int \frac{\gamma}{g}\omega^2 r\, dr$	Type of Vortex	Remarks
1	$\omega = C_1 r^{-\infty}$	$vr^{\infty} = C_1$	$\frac{p}{\gamma} = C_1^2 + h_1 = \text{constant}$	$\omega = 0$, stationary	
2	$\omega = C_2 r^{-5/2}$	$vr^{3/2} = C_2$	$\frac{p}{\gamma} = -\frac{C_2^2}{3gr^3} + h_2$		ω is higher toward center for 1, 2, 3, 4, 5, and 6
3	$\omega = C_3 r^{-2}$	$vr = C_3$	$\frac{p}{\gamma} = -\frac{C_3^2}{2gr^2} + h_3$	$h_3 + \frac{p}{\gamma} + \frac{v^2}{2g} = \text{constant, free vortex}$	
4	$\omega = C_4 r^{-3/2}$	$vr^{1/2} = C_4$	$\frac{p}{\gamma} = -\frac{C_4^2}{gr} + h_4$		
5	$\omega = C_5 r^{-1}$	$vr^0 = C_5$	$\frac{p}{\gamma} = \frac{C_5^2}{g}\log r + h_5$	$v = \text{constant}$	
6	$\omega = C_6 r^{-1/2}$	$vr^{-1/2} = C_6$	$\frac{p}{\gamma} = \frac{C_6^2 r}{g} + h_6$	$\frac{v^2}{r} = \text{constant} = \text{centrifugal force}$	
7	$\omega = C_7 r^0$	$vr^{-1} = C_7$	$\frac{p}{\gamma} = \frac{C_7^2 r^2}{2g} + h_7$	$\omega = \text{constant, forced vortex}$	$\omega = \text{constant}$
8	$\omega = C_8 r^{1/2}$	$vr^{-3/2} = C_8$	$\frac{p}{\gamma} = \frac{C_8^2 r^3}{3g} + h_8$	Super-forced vortex	
9	$\omega = C_9 r$	$vr^{-2} = C_9$	$\frac{p}{\gamma} = \frac{C_9^2 r^4}{4g} + h_9$	Super-forced vortex	ω is higher toward periphery for 8, 9, and 10
10	$\omega = C_r r^m$	$vr^{-(m+1)} = C$	$\frac{p}{\gamma} = \frac{C^2 r^{2(m+1)}}{2(m+1)g} + h$	A general form of vortex equation	

distribution given by an equation:

$$\omega = Cr^m \tag{1.2}$$

or

$$vr^n = C \tag{1.3}$$

where

$$n = -(m + 1)$$

Different values of m result in different types of vortices. The free vortex and forced vortex described in textbooks on hydraulics are special cases of this series. The first one is determined by a condition

$$vr = C_3 \tag{1.4}$$

and the pressure distribution is obtained from

$$h + \frac{p}{\gamma} + \frac{v^2}{2g} = E = \text{Constant} \tag{1.5}$$

which states that all particles possess the same amount of energy. If such a vortex is superimposed upon an axial flow with a uniform velocity, equation 1.5 will require either that no energy be added to the liquid or that energy be added at a constant rate. Such a pattern of flow is sometimes assumed for axial flow pumps and for compressors.

In a forced vortex the angular velocity is constant, or

$$\omega = \text{Constant} \tag{1.6}$$

This means that the liquid is revolving as a solid body. After the liquid is set in motion, disregarding losses, no power is required to maintain such a vortex. The pressure distribution curve is a square parabola; see Fig. 1.3a, curve 7. Forced vortex motion may be superimposed upon a radial outward flow; the resulting motion is a spiral forced vortex. Such a pattern of flow is found in centrifugal pumps and blowers. Disregarding losses, particles at the periphery carry the total amount of energy applied to the liquid. *To make possible a radial outward flow against higher pressures the energy gradient must be below the forced vortex pressure paraboloid* (Fig. 1.4). The forced vortex pressure paraboloid represents a state of static equilibrium for a forced vortex in the same manner as a horizontal plane does for a stationary liquid. To produce flow the energy gradient must fall in the direction of flow below its value at zero flow.

If a forced vortex is superimposed upon a uniform axial flow in a cylindrical conduit an axial spiral forced vortex is obtained. This type of flow is observed in axial flow pumps and blowers. Power is

applied to maintain this flow.   Particles carry different amounts of
energy at different radii, with a maximum at the periphery.

A free spiral vortex motion is observed when water flows through
a hole in the bottom of a vessel.   The vortex usually starts naturally,
some initial disturbance giving the direction of rotation.   Water
moves spirally toward the opening, friction limiting velocities near
the axis to some finite values.

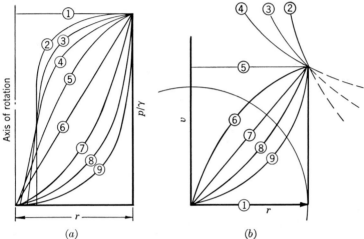

(a)   (b)

Fig. 1.3.   (a) Vortex pressure distribution elevation; (b) vortex velocity distribution, $vr^n = C$, plan view.

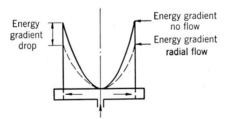

Fig. 1.4.   Energy gradient, forced vortex.

Other forms of vortices can be produced with axial flow impellers
having different vane curvature and vane twist along the radius.   *All
these vortices are stable and without cross flows, as all satisfy equation 1.1,*
but means of producing various vortices in this manner are not equally
efficient.

Although, for simplicity, the discussion of the subject of vortices
in this article is confined to liquids, the results obtained and points
emphasized apply directly to all fluids and hence to compressible gases.

1.4 HEIGHT OF GAS COLUMN

The object of all gas-pumping turbomachinery is to raise the gas pressure from the inlet pressure p_1 to the discharge pressure p_2. Several important relationships between the factors affecting the performance of the gas-pumping machinery become particularly simple if the work of compression of gas is thought of as straight lifting of a given weight of gas at the inlet pressure (p_1) and temperature (T_1)

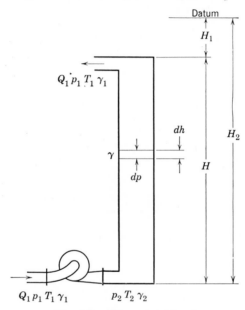

Fig. 1.5.   Blower total head.

to a height H feet where gas is discharged at the same pressure and temperature (Fig. 1.5).   Then the useful output of a turbomachine, or gas horsepower, will be expressed by a formula

$$\text{Gas horsepower} = \frac{WH}{550}$$

where, W is the weight of pumped gas in pounds per second; and H is height in feet.   Height in feet is referred to as "head," a term borrowed from centrifugal pump practice where pumps are frequently used for actual lifting of liquids.   Head H in feet, which represents the output of a turbomachine in foot-pounds per pound of gas includes the gain in kinetic energy or "velocity head" at discharge nozzle in addition to a static head (height of a straight lift).   Usually the velocity head is small or is equal to zero when inlet and outlet nozzle velocities are the same. In the following discussion the velocity head will be disregarded.

In this article it will be shown how the head H of a turbomachine can be calculated from the known inlet and outlet pressures and temperature gradient along the gas column without knowing anything about the mechanism or process of compression. For the purposes of this article all reference to the turbomachine could be omitted, and the gas column could be considered as stationary, like an air column in the atmosphere.

In an actual column of gas, H feet high, the gas density varies from γ_1 at the top to γ_2 at the bottom (Fig. 1.5). The pressure p_2 represents the actual weight of gas per square foot of column-base area. This depends upon the gas temperature at various elevations. The connection between the total head in feet and the net differential pressure in pounds per square foot for incompressible liquids is

$$p_2 - p_1 = \gamma H \tag{1.7}$$

For compressible fluids the same relationship holds in differential form.

$$dp = \gamma \, dh \tag{1.8}$$

To integrate this equation the specific weight γ can be expressed in terms of pressure p from the equation of state

$$pv = \frac{p}{\gamma} = RT \tag{1.9}$$

where R is the gas constant; T is the absolute temperature; and v is the volume of 1 lb. of gas. Then equation 1.8 becomes

$$\frac{dp}{p} = \frac{dh}{RT} \tag{1.10}$$

The temperature of gas at the bottom of the column (blower discharge) is higher than that at the top of the gas column (blower inlet). Assume that temperature varies at a constant rate along the column* so that

$$\frac{dT}{dh} = \lambda \tag{1.11}$$

Combining equations 1.10 and 1.11 and eliminating dh, we obtain

$$\frac{dp}{p} = \frac{1}{\lambda R} \frac{dT}{T} \tag{1.12}$$

* It so happens that for the first few miles above the earth's surface the rate of temperature decrease of the atmosphere is very nearly constant.

Integrating gives

$$\lambda R \log p - \log T = C$$

or

$$\frac{p^{\lambda R}}{T} = C = \text{Constant} \tag{1.13}$$

which is equivalent to

$$\frac{p_1^{\lambda R}}{T_1} = \frac{p_2^{\lambda R}}{T_2} \tag{1.14}$$

Substituting $T = p/(\gamma R)$ from equation 1.9 into equation 1.13 gives

$$\frac{p^{\lambda R} \gamma R}{p} = C$$

or

$$\frac{\gamma}{p^{1-\lambda R}} = \frac{C}{R} = \text{Constant} \tag{1.15}$$

Taking $1 - \lambda R$ root of both sides of equation 1.15 reduces it to

$$\frac{p}{\gamma^{1/(1-\lambda R)}} = \left(\frac{R}{C}\right)^{1/(1-\lambda R)} = \text{Constant} \tag{1.16}$$

or

$$\frac{p}{\gamma^n} = pv^n = \text{Constant} \tag{1.17}$$

where

$$n = \frac{1}{1 - \lambda R} = \text{Constant} \tag{1.18}$$

The height of the gas column in terms of pressures p_1 and p_2 is obtained by substituting into equation 1.14 for T_2 its value from

$$T_2 - T_1 = \lambda(H_2 - H_1) \tag{1.19}$$

which is the integrated form of equation 1.11.

$$H = H_2 - H_1 = \frac{T_1}{\lambda}\left[\left(\frac{p_2}{p_1}\right)^{\lambda R} - 1\right] \tag{1.20}$$

Eliminating λ between equations 1.20 and 1.18 leads to

$$H = \frac{T_1 R}{(n-1)/n}\left[\left(\frac{p_2}{p_1}\right)^{(n-1)/n} - 1\right] \tag{1.21}$$

In Chapter 3 it will be shown that for a given blower size and speed, and with different gas temperature and density distribution along the column, the height of the gas column will remain the same. At the same time the total weight of the gas column or the pressure at the bottom of the column will depend upon the rate of temperature change along the column. Thus, if $\lambda = 0$ in equation 1.11, $n = 1$ in equation 1.18. The temperature is constant along the column. This corresponds to an isothermal compression.

If $\lambda = 1/c_p$, equation 1.18 yields $n = k = c_p/c_v$, where c_p and c_v are specific heats at constant pressure and constant volume respectively. The process becomes adiabatic. With $n > k$, heat is added to the gas (hydraulic and disk friction losses) and the process becomes polytropic. For cooled compressors $n < k$. In every case, to use equation 1.21 for calculation of the head H for a given set of conditions, the temperature gradient is assumed constant along the gas column or $\lambda = $ constant in equation 1.11. This in turn means that c_p and n are constant along the path of compression.

In thermodynamics, equation 1.21 represents the work of compression in foot-pounds per pound in a steady flow process of a given gas (R, n, and T are known) from a pressure p_1 to a pressure p_2. *The fundamental property of head in feet H as applied to the turbomachinery (pumps, blowers, compressors) is that for a given machine at a selected speed the head produced does not depend upon the nature of fluid, its inlet temperature, or whether it is cooled or not in the process of compression.* This immediately suggests the convenience of rating blowers in terms of head rather than by a compression ratio or pressure rise.

In the following chapters it will be shown, both in theory and in practice, that the physical dimensions of a blower are directly connected with its performance in terms of head in feet; also, classification of blowers according to hydraulic performance is based upon the head in feet. For that reason the term head is introduced at this stage. It should be remembered, however, that numerically and dimensionally the head produced in feet is equal to the work on the gas in foot-pounds per pound of gas.

REFERENCES

1. Schmidt, "Some Screw Propeller Experiments," *J. Am. Soc. Naval Engrs.*, Vol. 40, No. 1, 1928, p. 15.
2. Adler, "Strömung in gekrümmte Rohren," *Z. angew. Math. Mech.*, Vol. 14, Oct., 1934, p. 257.
3. Stepanoff, *Centrifugal and Axial Flow Pumps*, Wiley, 1948, Chapter 1.

CHAPTER 2

Definitions and Terminology

2.1 CLASSIFICATION

Gas-pumping turbomachinery comprises a wide variety of machines
known to the trade under several names such as fans, blowers, compressors and superchargers. In all of them gas is compressed and
moved by dynamic action of the rotating vanes of one or several
impellers which imparts velocity and pressure to the flowing gas.
The division between these classes is drawn rather arbitrarily on the
basis of the degree of compression, the physical proportions, and the
method of manufacture. The principle of operation and the theoretical treatment, however, is the same for all types.

Fans are used to handle large volumes of gas and usually operate
at relatively low speeds. The increase of gas density in fans seldom
exceeds 7 per cent, and, for air, this amounts to a pressure rise of
about 1 p.s.i., or 27.7 in. of water. The casing and impeller are generally constructed of sheet steel.

Figure 2.1 shows a centrifugal blower, and Fig. 2.2 represents an
axial fan. In the centrifugal blower the flow through the machine is
essentially radial, whereas in the axial fan the general direction of flow
is axial. For small fans and low pressure units the stationary straightening vanes are frequently omitted (Fig. 2.3).

Blowers produce a pressure rise up to 40 p.s.i. gage (at atmospheric
inlet), whereas compressors cover a higher pressure range. This
demarcation line between the two classes is arbitrary and indefinite,
and both terms are used indiscriminately to describe medium pressure
units.

In Europe the term turboblower is applied to all uncooled machines
including multistage with pressure ratios of 2.5 to 3.0. For higher
compression ratios water cooling is generally provided and units are
referred to as turbocompressors.

A blower may be called an "exhauster" if it is used to remove gas
from a process or container and to discharge it at essentially atmos-

12

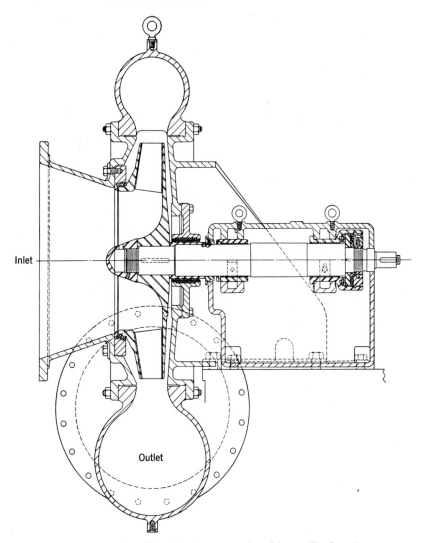

Fig. 2.1.   Centrifugal single-stage volute blower (De Laval).

pheric pressure.   If a blower is used to raise the pressure in a system that is already above atmospheric pressure, it may be called a "booster," as for example the natural gas pipe line blowers.

The great variety of blowers built for various applications may be reduced to a few basic hydraulic types.   The difference in design details is dictated mostly by the service and mechanical requirements. Every blower consists of two principal parts: an impeller, which forces the gas into rotary motion by impelling action of the vanes, and the casing, which directs the gas to the impeller and leads it away at a higher pressure. Before the gas leaves the casing its velocity is reduced and partially converted into pressure by diffuser action. There are several methods of converting the velocity of gas issuing from the impeller. Figure 2.4 shows a "vaneless diffuser," consisting of two parallel disks. Theoretically, gas continues to travel through a vaneless diffuser at the same angle as it leaves the impeller, the value of velocity being reduced in the inverse ratio of the inlet and outlet diameters. Figure 2.5 shows a diagram of the "vaned diffuser." In

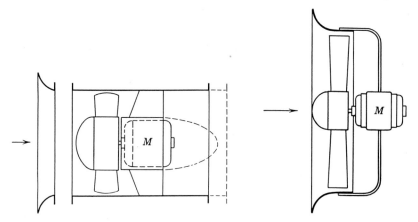

Fig. 2.2.   Single-stage axial fan with outlet vanes.

Fig. 2.3.   Propeller fan with motor on outlet side.

this type the direction and value of velocities from the impeller are controlled by means of vanes, which results in a more efficient conversion of velocity into pressure. In a volute casing, gas from the impeller is collected at a constant velocity in a volute channel and all diffusion is accomplished in the discharge nozzle.

The impeller may be mounted directly on a motor shaft extension, Fig. 2.4, or it may be mounted on a shaft supported by two bearings and driven through a flexible or rigid coupling. To prevent loss of gas, the casing is fitted with suitable seals between the rotating element and the casing. The majority of blower impellers have vanes that are curved backwards. High speed superchargers and centrifugal air compressors for aircraft gas turbines have radial vanes to withstand the centrifugal force due to high rotational speed. Figure 2.6 shows an impeller with forward curved "cup-shaped" vanes; it belongs to a class by itself. This type wheel produces, in addition to cen-

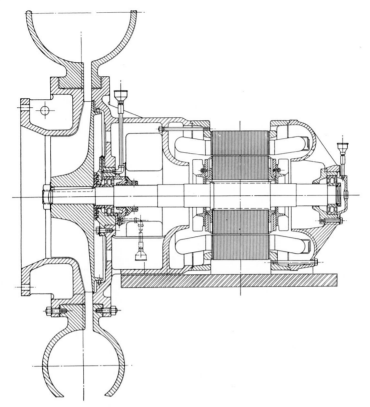

Fig. 2.4.   Single-stage blower with vaneless diffusion casing.
(Allis-Chalmers)

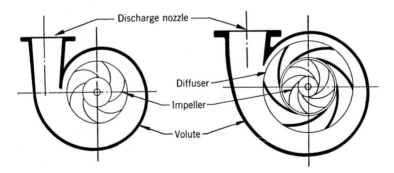

Fig. 2.5.   Diagram of volute and vaned diffuser casing.

trifugal action, an acceleration by the impulse action of the numerous blades. Impellers may be of the enclosed type with vanes enclosed between two "shrouds," Fig. 2.1, or they may be of the open type in which the front shroud is omitted to simplify mechanical production of the impeller, Fig. 2.4. Depending on whether gas is admitted on one side of the impeller or both sides, impellers are designated as "single inlet or double inlet" (Figs. 2.1 and 2.7).

An impeller is designated as "radial" if the shrouds are essentially normal to the shaft axis and only slightly curved at the entrance. Such impellers usually have plain or cylindrical vanes. In an axial

Fig. 2.6.   Sirocco impeller with cup-shaped vanes (American Blower).

blower, fan, or compressor, impeller vanes are contained between two cylindrical surfaces and the gas approaches the impeller and leaves the casing essentially in an axial direction. Mixed flow impellers occupy an intermediate position in the continuous row of hydraulic impeller types from radial to the axial flow. These have vanes of double curvature and are sometimes referred to as Francis type, after James B. Francis who introduced such vanes in the early water turbines known by his name.

The impeller profile, as represented by the ratios b_2/D_2 and D_1/D_2 for radial and mixed flow impellers, and hub ratio D_h/D_2 for axial flow impellers, is closely associated with the impeller hydraulic type. In the above ratios, b_2 is the width of the impeller opening at dis-

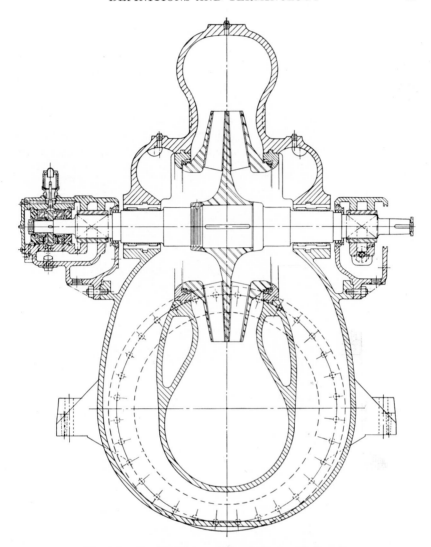

Fig. 2.7. Double-inlet centrifugal blower (De Laval)

charge; D_2 is impeller outside diameter; D_1 is the impeller inlet diameter; and D_h is the hub diameter. Later a term "specific speed" was introduced as a type number. It is directly connected with the blower performance and indirectly always suggests a certain impeller profile. Although the blower casing has no part in the pressure generation, it is designed to suit individual impeller types, thus reflecting specific speed in its controlling proportions.

2.2 BLOWER PERFORMANCE

Blower performance is usually represented by means of characteristic curves showing variations of pressure rise, efficiency, and blower
power input versus capacity at constant speed, Fig. 2.8. Capacity
or flow rate is expressed in cubic feet per minute (c.f.m.) at inlet
pressure and temperature. Several important relationships between
the factors affecting the blower performance and design become simpler
if the work of compression is thought of as straight lifting of a given

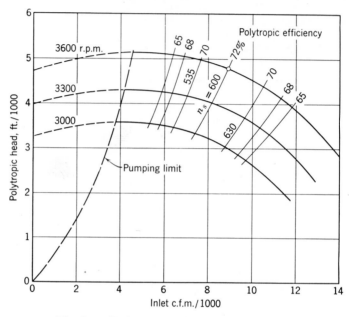

Fig. 2.8. Performance of a single-stage blower.

weight of gas at inlet pressure and temperature to a height H ft., where
the gas is assumed to be discharged at the same pressure and temperature. Then, the useful output of a blower, or gas horsepower (g.hp.)
will be expressed by a formula

$$\text{Output g.hp.} = \frac{W \times H}{550} \qquad (2.1)$$

where, W is weight of gas in pounds per second delivered by the blower,
and H is the total head in feet.

The total head in feet includes, in addition to the static head
(straight lift), the gain in kinetic energy, or velocity head, at dis-

charge nozzle. This part of the head is usually small, or is equal to zero when inlet and discharge velocities are the same.

The total head H in feet, is also equal to the work of compression in feet-pounds per pound of gas.

The head, in feet, produced by an impeller depends only on the impeller diameter and its rotative speed (impeller peripheral velocity) but does not depend upon the nature of gas, its density, nor its inlet temperature and pressure. Head in feet cannot be measured directly on test, but it can be calculated very closely from the observed inlet and discharge pressures and temperatures, using theoretical formulas as will be shown later.

In the early stages of blower development, pumping air was the main application. It was customary to express the work of compression as a pressure rise $p_2 - p_1$ p.s.i. referred to normal or standard air at atmospheric pressure at inlet. A term "equivalent air pressure" (e.a.p.) was used for the performance curves. Use of such curves for any other gas, or different inlet conditions, required a considerable amount of calculation.

For high pressure work, particularly in connection with superchargers, pressure ratio $r = p_2/p_1$ is used as one of the performance characteristics plotted against capacity which is also reduced to one of several dimensionless forms. Such characteristic curves also involve additional calculations when they are to be used for any other application.

The latest trend is to plot the total head in feet (polytropic head, defined below) which, in connection with polytropic efficiency, represents most accurately the true performance of a blower.

The advantages of representing blower performance in terms of head in feet, rather than e.a.p., or pressure ratio, will become apparent when discussing the laws governing blower performance and design methods.

2.3 EFFICIENCY

(a) **Definitions.** The blower efficiency is defined as a ratio of the energy output to the energy input,

$$\text{Efficiency } e = \text{Energy output/Energy input} \qquad (2.2)$$

or

$$e = WH/550 \text{ b.hp.} \qquad (2.3)$$

The energy input is equal to the driver output and is referred to as brake horsepower (b.hp.). *The true blower efficiency is a definite physical quantity depending upon the degree of perfection of hydraulic and mechanical design.* Its accurate determination involves some problems: one is connected with the calculation of a true head from inlet and outlet pressures; and another, with the measurement of the energy input in the case of large units with steam turbine drive. Both are discussed later.

This efficiency is called "total" or "gross" blower efficiency to distinguish it from several "partial" efficiencies used by designers, which are of little interest for the users of blowers.

The partial efficiencies are:

$$\text{Mechanical efficiency } e_m = \frac{\text{Brake horsepower} - \text{Mechanical losses}}{\text{Brake horsepower}}$$

$$(2.4)$$

where mechanical losses include bearing, mechanical seal, and impeller disk friction losses. The numerator of equation 2.4 represents power absorbed by the flowing gas from the impeller.

$$\text{Volumetric efficiency } e_v = Q/(Q + Q_L) \qquad (2.5)$$

where Q is the measured volume of flow; and Q_L is the volume of leakage through the sealing rings which is by-passed back to the impeller inlet.

$$\text{Hydraulic efficiency } e_h = H/(H + h_L) \qquad (2.6)$$

where H is the head in feet available at the blower discharge and h_L represents hydraulic losses through the blower passages, including skin friction and eddy losses.

The partial efficiencies are connected to the total efficiency as follows:*

$$e = e_m e_v e_h \qquad (2.7)$$

Note that the three partial efficiencies account for losses of volume (or weight of flow), head, and power, the only quantities which enter into the formula defining the blower efficiency. *None of the above losses or partial efficiencies depend appreciably upon the nature of gas or process of compression, whether cooled or adiabatic.*

(**b**) **Commercial Efficiencies.** There is no way to measure the blower head H in feet, directly during the test; the head is calculated from the observed discharge and inlet pressures and temperatures. Depending upon the formulas used for head calculation, several "commercial" efficiencies are obtained.

* For proof of this relationship, see reference 1, p. 39.

Assuming isentropic compression, i.e., no heat added or subtracted externally, and neglecting heat added internally owing to hydraulic losses, the head can be calculated by the use of a thermodynamic formula expressing the work done in foot-pounds per pound of gas (equal to the head in feet) compressed adiabatically.

$$H_{ad} = \frac{RT_1}{(k-1)/k} \left[\left(\frac{p_2}{p_1} \right)^{(k-1)/k} - 1 \right] \tag{2.8}$$

where R is the gas constant.

T_1 is inlet temperature, absolute.

k is ratio of specific heats c_p/c_v.

p_1 is inlet pressure, absolute.

p_2 is discharge pressure, absolute.

For uncooled blowers the true head H is somewhat higher than that given by equation 2.8 on account of unavoidable hydraulic losses which raise the temperature above that reached with isentropic compression; hence the density of the gas is less and the same discharge pressure would correspond to a higher head in feet. *Therefore "adiabatic efficiency" is lower than the true output/input efficiency.* For a low compression ratio $r = p_2/p_1$, the difference is small, the error increasing for higher compression ratios and lower hydraulic efficiency. Figure 7.6 shows the relation between adiabatic and polytropic efficiencies for different compression ratios. Polytropic efficiency, defined later, is very closely equal to the hydraulic efficiency of the blowers.

The "isothermal" formula for calculating the blower head is usually used in connection with cooled blowers, and efficiency based on isothermal head is referred to as "isothermal efficiency."

$$H_{\text{iso}} = RT_1 \log_e (p_2/p_1) \tag{2.9}$$

The calculated isothermal efficiency is considerably below the "true" output/input efficiency of the blower because cooling never brings the discharge temperature to that at the inlet. Therefore the true density is lower and the head is higher than given by the above formula. Cooling in high pressure blowers may be justified economically because, for a given discharge pressure, a lower head H in feet is required. This results in reduced speed or a smaller impeller, thus effecting power reduction.

If the adiabatic formula 2.8 is applied to the calculation of head for a cooled blower, the adiabatic efficiency will be considerably higher than the true output/input efficiency because the true head developed by the impeller, to produce a given pressure rise, is considerably lower than that allowed for by the adiabatic formula.

The true output/input efficiency of an uncooled blower is very closely determined by using the "polytropic" head equation.

$$H_p = \frac{RT_1}{(n-1)/n}\left[\left(\frac{p_2}{p_1}\right)^{(n-1)/n} - 1\right]$$ (2.10)

where n is the polytropic exponent in the polytropic equation of state.

$$p_1 v_1^n = p_2 v_2^n = \text{Constant}$$ (2.11)

If the inlet and discharge pressures and temperatures are measured on a test, the exponent n can be calculated from the thermodynamic relationship,

$$\frac{T_1}{T_2} = \left(\frac{p_1}{p_2}\right)^{(n-1)/n}$$ (2.12)

To calculate the polytropic head for a blower for which the discharge temperature is not known, n is obtained from a formula established in thermodynamics (Chapter 7).

$$\frac{n-1}{n} = \frac{k-1}{k} \cdot \frac{1}{e_p}$$ (2.13)

where, k is the adiabatic exponent, and e_p is the polytropic efficiency of the blower estimated from previous experience. In calculating the polytropic efficiency e_p from test data, mechanical losses are subtracted from the b.hp.

For blowers with external coolers (intercooling) between several stages of one unit, the polytropic efficiency can be determined in the same manner as that for the uncooled blowers by measuring the output of each group of impellers before and after the intercooler and treating them as independent blowers. Intercooling is used in the United States to a limited extent only.

Although both adiabatic and isothermal efficiencies may differ from the true output/input efficiency by as many as ten points, they will show correctly the relative degree of hydraulic perfection when they are used for comparing blowers of different makes for the same requirements. This is so because using the same formula for calculating the blower output the numerator in the formula for the efficiency will be the same for each blower. Thus the true output/input efficiencies will be in the inverse ratio of b.hp. or direct ratio of adiabatic or isothermal efficiencies as the case may be.†

2.4 AFFINITY LAWS

Design and selection of blowers for a given set of conditions involve use of "affinity laws," which give relationships between the blower head, capacity, speed, and size. These laws, established experimentally, have a rigorous theoretical background and represent a special application of the laws of dynamic similarity.

a. If the speed of a given blower is changed, its head H will vary directly as the square of the speed and its capacity (c.f.m. at impeller outlet) will vary directly as the speed. Cubic feet per minute at inlet will vary approximately as the speed, the exact volume depending upon the compression ratio between impeller outlet and inlet. For small speed variations, efficiency of the blower stays approximately the same, therefore the b.hp. (brake horsepower) requirements of the driver vary approximately as the cube of the speed. The above relationships are expressed by the following formulas:

$$\frac{H_1}{H_2} = \frac{n_1{}^2}{n_1{}^2} \qquad \frac{Q_1}{Q_2} = \frac{n_1}{n_2} \qquad \frac{\text{b.hp.}_1}{\text{b.hp.}_2} = \frac{n_1{}^3}{n_2{}^3} \qquad (2.14)$$

where n is the speed in r.p.m.; Q is the capacity (c.f.m.); subscript 1 refers to the original speed; subscript 2 refers to the new speed.

Figure 2.8 shows a blower head-capacity characteristic at three speeds plotted by applying the affinity laws to each point on the head-capacity curve.

b. If two geometrically similar impellers (i.e., of the same specific speed) are operated at the same speed then their heads are in the ratio of their impeller outside diameters squared; their capacities (c.f.m.), in the ratio of the impeller diameter ratio cubed; and b.hp., the fifth power of the same ratio, or

$$\frac{H_1}{H_2} = \left(\frac{D_1}{D_2}\right)^2 \qquad \frac{Q_1}{Q_2} = \left(\frac{D_1}{D_2}\right)^3 \qquad \frac{\text{b.hp.}_1}{\text{b.hp.}_2} = \left(\frac{D_1}{D_2}\right)^5 \qquad (2.15)$$

c. When the diameter of an impeller, at a given speed, is reduced, its head decreases in the ratio of impeller diameters squared; the c.f.m. reduces directly as the impeller diameters; and b.hp. is reduced as cube of the impeller diameters. These relationships are approximate only, the accuracy decreasing for larger impeller cuts. Actually

† The shaft efficiency defined by the Test Code PTC 10-1949 is equivalent to the "adiabatic total efficiency" in the author's terminology.

the head and capacity drop a little faster than the above rules would indicate, therefore some excess diameter should be allowed when calculating the impeller cut.

It will be shown in later chapters that the blower performance is determined primarily by the impeller outlet design and the affinity laws apply really to the capacity or volumes of gas at impeller discharge. Therefore, applying these relationships to the inlet volume introduces an inaccuracy which may be tolerated for the preliminary calculations; but the design is always based on the volume at impeller discharge.

If performance of a blower is expressed in terms of equivalent air pressure $p_2 - p_1$ (e.a.p.) or the pressure ratio $r_1 = p_2/p_1$, the effect of speed can be determined by expressing pressure rise in terms of head, in feet, using equations 2.8 or 2.10 first, then stepping up the head according to the affinity laws to determine a new pressure ratio $r_2 = p_2'/p_1'$, from which the e.a.p. can be obtained.

$$\frac{H_1}{H_2} = \frac{(r_1^{(k-1)/k} - 1)}{(r_2^{(k-1)/k} - 1)} = \frac{X_1}{X_2} = \frac{n_1^2}{n_2^2} \tag{2.16}$$

It is customary to denote the bracketed factors by X; its values can be found tabulated in handbooks on compressed air.

2.5 SPECIFIC SPEED

All blower impellers can be grouped hydraulically according to specific speed which is used as a "type number." Specific speed is calculated by the formula

$$n_s = \frac{(\text{r.p.m.})(\text{c.f.m.})^{1/2}}{H^{3/4}} \tag{2.17}$$

where, r.p.m. is the rotative speed in revolutions per minute, and c.f.m. is capacity in cubic feet per minute.

For slide rule calculations the same formula can be presented in the form

$$n_s = \frac{\sqrt{\sqrt{\sqrt{H}}}}{H} \text{ r.p.m. } \sqrt{\text{c.f.m.}} \tag{2.18}$$

and operations are performed in the order indicated.

For design purposes, c.f.m. in the above formulas should be taken at the impeller discharge; however, for a preliminary selection c.f.m. at the blower inlet may be used as an approximation.

The specific speed of all geometrically similar impellers is the same and does not change when the speed of the blower is varied, being closely associated with the impeller profile proportions. For multi-stage blowers, specific speed is referred to the head per stage. For a comparison of specific speed of a double-inlet impeller with that of single inlet, the capacity of the first is divided by 2 or its specific speed should be divided by $\sqrt{2}$. All important design and performance characteristics are closely connected with the specific speed.

From equation 2.17 it follows that, for the same head-capacity requirements, higher specific speed blowers will run at a higher speed and will be of smaller physical dimensions. Low specific speed impellers are characterized by narrow impellers with low D_1/D_2 ratio (Fig. 4.1).

When specific speed is used as a type number its value at the best efficiency point (b.e.p.) is used. Values of specific speed along the head-capacity curve decrease to the left of the b.e.p. and the value is equal to zero when the capacity is zero. To the right of the best efficiency point, specific speed increases and becomes infinite when the head is zero. Points connected by affinity laws for similar impellers of different speeds or sizes are points of the same specific speed and are referred to as "corresponding points." In Fig. 2.8, points of the same efficiency are of the same specific speed.

2.6 PUMPING LIMIT

There is a minimum capacity for each blower, at every speed, below which the blower operation becomes unstable. This instability is accompanied by a characteristic noise known as "pumping." The pumping limit is determined largely by the impeller discharge angle, and for the average blower it lies in the neighborhood of 50 per cent of the capacity at the best efficiency point. The primary cause of this behavior lies in the shape of the head-capacity curve which, after reaching a maximum at about half of the rated capacity, begins to "droop" toward the zero-capacity point. When the capacity is reduced below this point, the pressure in the discharge pipe exceeds that produced by the blower and the flow tends to reverse momentarily. However, as soon as the flow is further reduced the pressure drops in the discharge pipe and the blower begins to discharge into the pipe again. Such pulsations in pressure and capacity are magnified by the response of the compressible gas in the discharge system.

CHAPTER 3

Theory of
the Centrifugal Impeller
for Incompressible Fluid

INTRODUCTION

The pressure rise in a blower is produced by dynamic means. Fluid particles leave the impeller at higher pressure and increased velocity compared with those at entrance to the impeller. These effects do not depend upon the nature or state of the fluid; i.e., its pressure, temperature, and density, if expressed in foot-pounds of work absorbed by the fluid per pound, or if measured in feet of head produced by the impeller. The design of the impeller and casing passages should allow for the reduction of the specific volume of the fluid as it passes regions of increased pressure. Thermodynamics furnishes the relationships between the variables involved to establish the volume of the fluid passing through the important controlling passages of the impeller and casing. It is more convenient to develop the theory of the impeller action for an incompressible fluid and later apply the corrections necessary to account for compressibility of the actual fluid.

3.1 VELOCITY TRIANGLES

A study of the several component velocities of flow through an impeller is best carried out graphically by means of velocity vectors. The shape of such vector diagrams is triangular, and they are called velocity triangles. They can be drawn for any point of the flow path through the impeller, but usually attention is focused on the entrance and discharge part of the impeller vanes, and the velocity triangles are called entrance and discharge triangles.

It is necessary to distinguish between absolute and relative velocities. The relative velocity of flow is considered relative to the impeller. The absolute velocity of flow is taken with respect to the casing and is always equal to the vectorial sum of the relative velocity and the peripheral velocity of the impeller. Any point on the impeller will describe a circle about the shaft axis and will have a peripheral velocity,

$$u = \frac{\pi D}{12} \times \text{r.p.s.} \qquad \text{or} \qquad u = \frac{D \times \text{r.p.m.}}{229} \text{ ft. per sec.}$$

where D is the diameter of the circle in inches.

Figure 3.1a shows an entrance triangle, and Fig. 3.1b, a discharge triangle. The following notation is adopted.

u = peripheral velocity of impeller (ft. per sec.).
w = relative velocity of flow (ft. per sec.).
c = absolute velocity of flow (ft. per sec.).

Subscript 1 refers to the entrance; subscript 2 to the discharge. Tangential components of relative and absolute velocities are given another subscript, u. Components of the absolute velocity normal to the

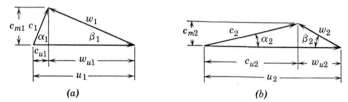

(a)   (b)

Fig. 3.1.   (a) Entrance velocity triangle (b) discharge velocity triangle.

peripheral velocity are designated as c_{m1} and c_{m2} for entrance and discharge diagrams. This component is radial in a radial impeller and axial in an axial impeller. It will be referred to, in general, as meridional and will have the subscript m.

Unless specifically stated, all velocities are considered average velocities for the section normal to the general direction of flow at a specified point. This is one of the approximations made for theoretical studies and practical design which is not true in practice. A uniform velocity across a channel section does not exist for actual fluids even in the case of straight pipe flow.

3.2   THEORETICAL HEAD OF THE CENTRIFUGAL IMPELLER

An expression for the theoretical head of a centrifugal impeller is obtained by applying the principle of angular momentum to the mass of fluid going through the impeller passages. This principle states that the time rate of change of angular momentum of a body with respect to the axis of rotation is equal to the torque of the resultant force on the body with respect to the same axis.

Let us consider a mass of fluid filling the space between two adjacent impeller vanes (Fig. 3.2). At time $t = 0$ its position is abcd, and after a time interval dt its position has changed to efgh. Denote the mass of an infinitely thin layer of fluid *abef* just leaving the impeller channel *dm*. This mass is equal to the mass of fluid just entering the channel in the same interval of time *dt*, as represented by *cdgh*. The part *abgh* of the fluid contained between the two impeller vanes does not change its moment of momentum in time interval *dt*; thus the change in moment of momentum of the whole content of the channel is given by the change of moment of momentum of the mass *dm* entering the impeller (*cdgh*) and mass *dm* leaving the impeller (*abef*). This change of moment of momentum is equal to the moment of all external forces

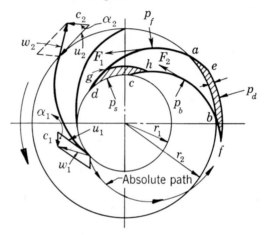

Fig. 3.2.   Forces and velocities in an impeller.

applied to the fluid contained between the two impeller vanes. The moment of external forces being denoted by T, the above is stated mathematically by

$$T = \frac{dm}{dt} \left(r_2 c_2 \cos \alpha_2 - r_1 c_1 \cos \alpha_1 \right) \tag{3.1}$$

The external forces applied to the fluid contained between the vanes are: (1) the difference in pressure on two sides of each vane (p_f and p_b); (2) pressures p_d and p_s, on the faces *ab* and *cd* of the elementary fluid section respectively, which are radial forces and have no moment about the axis of rotation; and (3) hydraulic friction forces, which oppose the relative flow and produce torque in addition to that exerted by the impeller vanes.   Friction forces are neglected in idealized flow.*

* In an actual blower friction forces F_1 and F_2 have a moment about the axis, thus requiring power from the shaft.   Therefore, not all the applied torque is converted into head.

The term dm/dt, when extended to all impeller channels, represents the constant time rate of mass flow through the impeller which is $Q\gamma/g$. Substituting this into equation 3.1 and multiplying both sides of it by ω, the angular velocity of the impeller, we obtain

$$T\omega = \frac{Q\gamma}{g} (r_2 c_2 \cos \alpha_2 - r_1 c_1 \cos \alpha_1) \qquad (3.2)$$

The left-hand side of equation 3.2 represents power input P applied to the fluid by the impeller vanes. Substituting $u_2 = \omega r_2$, $c_2 \cos \alpha_2 = c_{u2}$, $u_1 = \omega r_1$, and $c_1 \cos \alpha_1 = c_{u1}$ into equation 3.2, we obtain

$$P = \frac{Q\gamma}{g} (u_2 c_{u2} - u_1 c_{u1}) \qquad (3.3)$$

Assuming that there is no loss of head between the impeller and the point where the total dynamic head is measured, this power is available as the blower output of an idealized machine.

$$Q\gamma H_i = \frac{Q\gamma}{g} (u_2 c_{u2} - u_1 c_{u1}) \qquad (3.4)$$

Eliminating $Q\gamma$ we get an expression for head.

$$H_i = \frac{u_2 c_{u2} - u_1 c_{u1}}{g} \qquad (3.5)$$

Since all hydraulic losses between the points where the actual total dynamic head of a blower is measured have been disregarded, the head H_i is a theoretical head; the equation is known as Euler's equation.

If the fluid enters the impeller without a tangential component, or if $c_{u1} = 0$ (radially for a radial impeller and axially for an axial flow impeller), Euler's equation reduces to

$$H_i = \frac{u_2 c_{u2}}{g} \qquad (3.6)$$

By geometric substitutions from the velocity triangles, Euler's equation 3.5 is transformed into another form more convenient for some discussions. From the velocity triangles we find

$$w_2{}^2 = c_2{}^2 + u_2{}^2 - 2u_2 c_2 \cos \alpha_2$$
$$w_1{}^2 = c_1{}^2 + u_1{}^2 - 2u_1 c_1 \cos \alpha_1$$

Making use of these, Euler's equation becomes

$$H_i = \frac{c_2{}^2 - c_1{}^2}{2g} + \frac{u_2{}^2 - u_1{}^2}{2g} + \frac{w_1{}^2 - w_2{}^2}{2g} \qquad (3.7)$$

The first term represents a gain of the kinetic energy (K.E.) of the flow through the impeller. The second and third terms jointly represent an increase in pressure from the impeller inlet to the outlet. It is futile to attach any physical meaning to the second and third terms individually. Thus the second term does not represent entirely gain in pressure of the flow due to centrifugal force because there are no particles of the fluid moving with the peripheral velocities u_1 and u_2. Similarly the third term does not represent an increase in pressure due to conversion of the relative velocity from w_1 to w_2, as it should be realized that no diffusion can take place in a curved channel, stationary or moving. In the case of axial flow impellers there is no definite channel containing velocities w_1 or w_2. Although the third term is shown positive, it is really a subtractive term. Rearranging the second and third terms, this becomes apparent.

$$H_i - \text{K.E.} = \frac{u_2{}^2 - w_2{}^2}{2g} - \frac{u_1{}^2 - w_1{}^2}{2g}$$

which can be transformed back to the form of equation 3.5.

$$H_i - \text{K.E.} = \frac{c_{u2}u_2 - c_{u1}u_1}{g} - \frac{c_2{}^2 - c_1{}^2}{2g}$$

In general, although a velocity can be represented by its components, energy can be expressed only in terms of the resultant or absolute velocity (equation of momentum) because *energy is not a vector quantity*. According to equation 3.5 the head (both pressure and K.E.) is built-up gradually as both c_{u2} and u_2 are increased steadily.

If, in equations 3.1 and 3.2, c_1 and c_2 represent actual absolute velocities of all fluid particles and α_1 and α_2 are their true directions, P in equation 3.3 will represent the actual power input to the fluid by the impeller. In that case the theoretical head H_i, as given by equations 3.5, 3.6, and 3.7, will be the actual theoretical head of the impeller, or the input head. The term input head will be used in preference to actual theoretical head to avoid confusion, as different theories give different theoretical heads. However, for a given impeller, the input head H_i is a definite quantity independent of the formulas used for its calculation. In practice, however, the true velocities of flow and their directions are never known. Theoretical studies of impeller performance are based on the velocity triangles drawn on the vane angles, and the theoretical head is calculated by means of Euler's equations 3.5 or 3.7. Using velocities from such velocity triangles leads to a considerably higher head than the input head. To distinguish the two theoretical heads, the velocity triangles drawn on the vane angles will be called Euler's velocity triangles, and the head calculated by using velocities and angles from Euler's velocity triangles will be termed Euler's head and denoted by H_e.

If velocities from Euler's velocity triangles are inserted in equation 3.3, P will not represent the actual power input to fluid, the equality will be destroyed, and the equation will lose its meaning. Euler's velocity triangles are used mostly for graphical determination of the impeller vane shape, particularly in mixed flow and axial flow impellers.

3.3 THEORETICAL CHARACTERISTIC CURVES

By taking Euler's head equation in its simplest form as given in equation 3.6, it can be shown that it is the equation of a straight

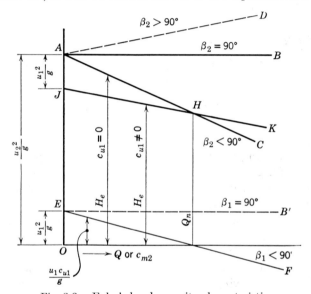

Fig. 3.3.   Euler's head-capacity characteristics.

line which will give the variation of Euler's head with capacity. Substituting

$$c_{u2} = u_2 - w_{u2} = u_2 - \frac{c_{m2}}{\tan \beta_2}$$

into equation 3.6, we obtain

$$H_e = \frac{u_2^2}{g} - \frac{u_2 c_{m2}}{g \tan \beta_2} \qquad (3.8)$$

In equation 3.8, c_{m2} is proportional to the capacity since Q is equal to the product of c_{m2} and the area normal to c_{m2}. Thus equation 3.8

represents a straight line that intersects the head axis at u_2^2/g and the c_{m2} axis at $u_2 \times \tan \beta_2$ (Fig. 3.3). The slope of this line depends on the value of the angle β_2. When $\beta_2 = 90°$, the head-capacity line is parallel to the axis of capacities, and $H_e = u_2^2/g = \text{Constant}$. For $\beta_2 < 90°$, the head decreases as the capacity increases. With $\beta_2 > 90°$ the head increases with the capacity. This can be realized only by impulse action with an impeller similar to the Pelton water wheel reversed, as the absolute velocity leaving the impeller c_2 is greater than the peripheral velocity u_2 (Fig. 3.4).

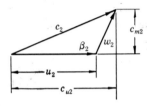

Fig. 3.4. Discharge triangle for $\beta_2 > 90°$.

When the approach to the impeller eye is such that fluid has prerotation before being acted upon by the impeller, the subtractive term in equation 3.5 is not equal to zero and the head-capacity curve is obtained as follows. Let $u_1 c_{u1}/g = H_1$. Applying the same trigonometric substitution as used in equation 3.8, we get

$$H_1 = \frac{u_1^2}{g} - \frac{u_1 c_{m1}}{g \tan \beta_1} \tag{3.9}$$

This equation is of the same type as equation 3.8 and represents a straight line cutting the head axis at u_1^2/g, which is parallel to axis of capacities for $\beta_1 = 90°$, and which decreases for $\beta_1 < 90°$ (line EF, Fig. 3.3). The Euler's head, line JK, is obtained by subtracting ordinates of the line EF from those of line AC.†

In practice the discharge angles β_2 vary between $25°$ and $90°$, the normal range being $55° > \beta_2 > 40°$.

In an idealized turbomachine the input is equal to output, or b.hp. equals g.hp. The shape of the theoretical power curve is obtained by multiplying equation 3.8 by Q, or $K c_{m2}$, where K is a constant for a given machine and can be accounted for by a proper selection of scales. Then

$$\frac{\text{g.hp.}}{K} = \frac{u_2^2 c_{m2}}{g} - \frac{u_2 c_{m2}^2}{g \tan \beta_2} \tag{3.10}$$

When $\beta_2 = 90°$, equation 3.10 represents a straight line passing through the origin. For $\beta_2 < 90°$, it is a parabola below the above

† At zero capacity the subtractive term u_1^2/g in Euler's equation requires full impeller angular velocity for the flow approaching the impeller eye. This can never be realized in actual impellers under the most favorable conditions.

straight line and tangent to it at the origin (Fig. 3.5). With $\beta_2 > 90°$ the power curve is also a parabola tangent to the first straight line but lies above it. The latter shape of the power curve is never realized in actual pumping machinery. Whereas the discharge angle β_2 is selected to meet the required head-capacity characteristics, the entrance angle is determined from the velocity triangle, depending upon the impeller capacity, profile, and speed as will be shown in Chapter 5.

3.4 EFFICIENCIES

All the head in a centrifugal blower is generated by the impeller. The rest of the parts contribute nothing to the head but incur inevi-

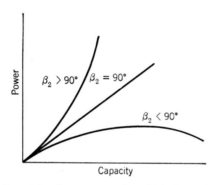

FIG. 3.5.   Power to produce Euler's head.

table losses—hydraulic, mechanical, and leakage. All losses of head which take place between the points where the inlet and discharge pressures are measured constitute hydraulic losses. These include skin friction losses along the fluid path from the inlet to the discharge nozzle, losses due to sudden change in area or direction of flow, and all losses due to eddies whatever their causes. *Hydraulic efficiency is defined as a ratio of the available total dynamic head to the input head,* or

$$e_h = \frac{H}{H_i} = \frac{H_i - \text{Hydraulic losses}}{H_i} \tag{3.11}$$

The ratio of the input head to Euler's head will be referred to as vane efficiency, or

$$(H_i/H_e) = e_{va} \tag{3.12}$$

In Fig. 3.6, AED is Euler's velocity triangle and AFD the input velocity triangle. The area AFB is proportional to the impeller input because $H_i = u_2 c_{u2}'/g$ and $Q = c_{m2} A_2$, where A_2 is the impeller discharge area normal to c_{m2}. Then

$$P = Q\gamma H_i = \frac{u_2 c_{u2}'}{g} \times c_{m2}\gamma A_2 = \frac{c_{u2}' c_{m2}}{2} \times K$$

In the above, K is a constant for a given machine and r.p.m.

Similarly, the area AEC is proportional to the input to produce Euler's head. Then the ratio of the two areas is the vane efficiency.

$$AFB/AEC = H_i/H_e = c_{u2}'/c_{u2} \qquad (3.12a)$$

This is similar to the cylinder or indicated efficiency of a steam engine which is defined as the ratio of the actual indicator diagram (corresponds to area AFB in our case) to the theoretical Rankine or Clausius pressure-volume diagram (area AEC on Euler's triangle).‡

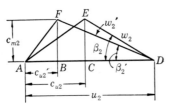

Fig. 3.6. Euler's and input velocity triangles.

Besides the losses of head there are *losses of capacity* in each turbo-machine known as leakage losses. These take place through the clearances between the rotating and stationary parts of the machine. The capacity available at the discharge nozzle is smaller than that passed through the impeller by the amount of leakage. The ratio of the two is called the volumetric efficiency.

$$Q/Q_i = Q/(Q + Q_L) = e_v \qquad (3.13)$$

where Q_L is the amount of leakage.

Mechanical losses include *loss of power* in bearings and the disk friction. Disk friction loss is hydraulic in nature but is grouped with the mechanical losses since it is external to the flow through the machine and does not result in a loss of head. *The mechanical efficiency is the ratio of the power actually absorbed by the impeller and converted into head and the power applied to the shaft,* or

$$e_m = \frac{\text{Brake horsepower—Mechanical losses}}{\text{Brake horsepower}} = \frac{Q_i \gamma H_i}{550 \text{ b.hp.}} \qquad (3.14)$$

‡ The product of $e_h e_{va} = e_{man}$ has been named manometric efficiency by several writers and defined as $H/H_e = e_{man}$. This has no physical meaning and frequently has been confused with hydraulic efficiency.

The difference between Euler's head H_e and the input head H_i is not a loss, therefore the ratio H_i/H_e could be termed vane effectiveness rather than vane efficiency. However, the vane efficiency will be used for convenience.

The relationship between the partial efficiencies defined above and the gross or total efficiency e can be obtained from

$$e = \frac{Q \; \gamma H}{550 \; \text{b.hp.}} \tag{3.15}$$

by substituting for Q its value $Q = e_v Q_i$, for H its equivalent $H = e_h H_i$, and for b.hp. its value from equation 3.14,

$$e = e_v e_h e_m \tag{3.16}$$

which is the expression sought.

3.5 IMPELLER APPROACH AND PREROTATION

To study the effect of the impeller approach channel upon the impeller performance it is better to take into consideration part of the inlet pipe because impeller reaction on the flow may extend a considerable distance ahead of the impeller. The flow toward the impeller, through the impeller, and beyond the impeller is caused by the drop of the energy gradient below its level at zero flow.§ The drop in energy gradient permits fluid to proceed through the impeller against a gradually increasing head. *Following the energy gradient the fluid selects a path of least resistance to get to and through the impeller and out of the casing.* The fluid acquires prerotation to enter the impeller passages with a minimum disturbance, and the direction depends on the impeller vane entrance angle β_1, the capacity going through, and the impeller peripheral velocity—all three of which determine the entrance velocity triangle.∥

It is evident that resistance to flow is minimal if the liquid enters the impeller channel at an angle approaching the vane angle β_1. For a given impeller speed, there is only one capacity at which the fluid will approach the impeller meridionally, or without prerotation; see Fig. 3.7a. At a capacity considerably smaller than normal, the fluid should acquire prerotation in the direction of impeller rotation to be

§ It should be realized that liquids and gases cannot transmit tension, therefore cannot be "pulled" or "sucked" but only "pushed" by the excess pressure from behind. Any devices that suck fluids accomplish only a local reduction of pressure, thus establishing an energy or hydraulic gradient necessary to produce flow.

∥ The principle of least resistance is quite general when applied to the flow of energy; it is nothing more than a restatement of the second law of thermodynamics. Human beings and animals follow it by instinct; for instance, taking the shortest distance between two points, or boarding a moving train by running in the direction of the train motion. The latter is analogous to prerotation of flow in the impeller approach at partial capacities. In this connection it is interesting to point out that the flow of human crowd through the restricted passages follows the pattern established in fluid mechanics (reference 4).

able to enter the channel at an angle approaching β_1; see Fig. 3.7b. But at a capacity greater than normal, a prerotation in the opposite direction is necessary for the fluid to satisfy the "least resistance" requirement. The behavior of the fluid in actual blowers follows this pattern, modified somewhat by the effect of the inlet nozzle and inlet pipe design. *Note that the rotation of the fluid in the impeller approach is not derived from the impeller, as it is evident that an impeller cannot impart fluid rotation opposite to its own—a condition frequently observed at capacities above normal* (references 1 and 2).

If the inlet pipe of a single-stage blower is such that a forced vortex can be set up, the total head produced by the impeller at partial capacities will be appreciably reduced.

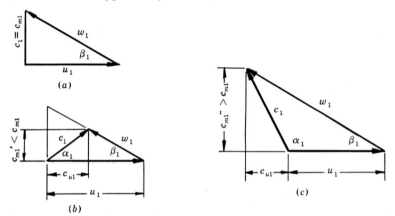

Fig. 3.7.   Entrance velocity triangles.

It will be observed that the energy gradient drop is greater along the streamlines in the middle of the inlet pipe than along the streamlines near the pipe walls. Thus, higher velocities are expected in the middle of the impeller eye. At low capacities, approaching zero, the difference between the velocities in the inlet pipe becomes more pronounced. This gives the impeller an opportunity to increase the tangential component of the velocity of flow near the periphery of the impeller eye by viscous drag of the fluid. *Thus, the energy of the streamlines near the pipe wall may increase and there may be no energy gradient drop available to maintain the flow along these streamlines. As a result, the flow near the impeller periphery may be reversed at capacities approaching zero. Such a back-flow has been observed by several investigators.*

If the fluid approaching the impeller eye acquires prerotation in the direction of impeller rotation, the impeller will be deprived of the opportunity to impart that much of the tangential component to the flow and the entrance part of the impeller vanes will be inactive, taking no power from the shaft. This condition reduces the input head and consequently the available total head. It is immaterial whether prerotation is caused by the shape of the channel approach or by the exaggerated vane entrance angle. Lower input head will result, and the subtractive term in Euler's equation 3.5 will not equal zero.

Blowers are frequently provided with special guide vanes to control the direction of flow in the impeller approach to vary the impeller characteristics. To reduce the impeller output (head capacity) prerotation is given in the direction of the impeller's own rotation. Prerotation in the opposite direction increases the impeller head and capacity. This subject is treated in greater detail in Chapter 15.

The direction of the flow in the impeller approach is impossible to estimate accurately from the configuration of the channel of approach, but it is rarely meridional (without prerotation).

3.6 DISCUSSION OF EULER'S CHARACTERISTICS AND EULER'S VELOCITY TRIANGLES

(a) **Head-Capacity Characteristics.** For simplicity, assume no prerotation in the impeller approach. Euler's equation of head 3.8 represents a straight line intersecting the head axis at $H_e = u_2^2/g$ and the axis of capacities at $Q_{max.} = A_2 u_2 \tan \beta_2$. A_2 is the impeller discharge area normal to c_{m2}, and, since it is constant for a given machine, it can be omitted from the above relationship by incorporating it in a proper scale selection. *The head-capacity characteristics, shown in Fig. 3.8, are plotted on suitable dimensionless scales for a given impeller discharge angle β_2 and apply to machines of all specific speeds and sizes using the same angle β_2 and consistent in design elements.*

The specific speed is used here as a type number for actual machine

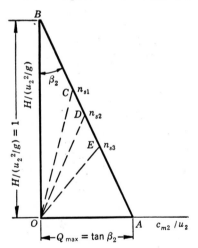

Fig. 3.8. Euler's head-capacity characteristics.

at the best efficiency point (b.e.p.) only, and is determined by the conditions of minimum hydraulic losses. All points corresponding to the b.e.p. of different specific speeds (n_{s1}, n_{s2}, n_{s3}, etc.) are located on line BA, the specific speeds increasing from B to A. Similarly, Fig. 3.9 shows Euler's discharge velocity triangles OCB, ODB, OEB for several capacities and applies to several specific speeds with their b.e.p. at points C, D, E, and so on. Each point on line AB (Fig. 3.9) represents a different specific speed and fixes all important impeller characteristics.

Thus line AB on Fig. 3.9 represents the head-capacity curve for blowers of all specific speeds using the same angle β_2 in the same manner as AB on Fig. 3.8 but to a different scale. Conversely, by connecting points C, D, E, and so on, to point O on Fig. 3.8, discharge velocity triangles OBC, OBD, and OBE are obtained if the scales for

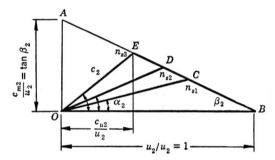

Fig. 3.9. Euler's discharge velocity triangle.

head and capacity are selected so that the angle OBA is equal to β_2. *By using suitable scales, Euler's head-capacity diagram and the discharge velocity diagrams become identical.* This is an important property because certain features not clear on one diagram become more apparent on the other.

(**b**) **Dimensionless Scales.** The following dimensionless scales (ratios) will bring both the head-capacity and the discharge velocity diagrams to the same scale. The meridional velocity c_{m2} will represent the capacity. On the head-capacity diagram, Fig. 3.10, heads are expressed as ratios to shut-off head, or

$$\psi_e = \frac{H_e}{u_2^2/g} = \frac{u_2 c_{u2} g}{g u_2^2} = \frac{c_{u2}}{u_2} \tag{3.17}$$

which will be called the head coefficient. Then, on the velocity diagram, heads will be represented to the same scale by use of the ratio

$$\psi_e = c_{u2}/u_2$$

All velocities on the velocity diagram will be taken as ratios to u_2; thus

$$c_{m2}/u_2 = \phi_e \qquad (3.18)$$

will be the meridional velocity on the velocity diagram and will represent capacity on both diagrams. This ratio is called the capacity coefficient. The peripheral velocity will be $u_2/u_2 = 1$. The shut-off head on the head-capacity diagram is also equal to unity. The maxi-

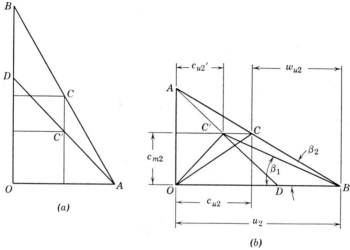

Fig. 3.10. (a) Euler's and input head-capacity curves; (b) Euler's and input discharge velocity triangles.

mum capacity and maximum meridional velocity are equal to

$$(c_{m2}/u_2)_{\max} = \tan \beta_2 \qquad (3.19)$$

(c) **Vane Efficiency.** The input head-capacity curve DA for a given β_2 is drawn on Fig. 3.10a. Both Euler's head-capacity curve BA and input head-capacity curve DA meet at zero head.¶

The direction of line DA can be determined by locating one point on this line. This point can be estimated, for instance, by assuming or calculating the hydraulic efficiency for the best efficiency point of one existing machine of any specific speed. Then line DA will represent the input head-capacity curve for this particular impeller. Moreover, it will represent the input head-capacity characteristic of machines of all specific speeds having the same discharge vane angle β_2.

¶ This assumption is made by several writers (reference 3).

The ratio of ordinates for any capacity will be the vane efficiency or $e_{va} = DO/BO$. This is equal for machines of all specific speeds using the same β_2 and consistent otherwise. Figure 3.10b represents Euler's velocity triangle drawn to the same dimensionless scale as Fig. 3.10a. By transferring point D from Fig. 3.10a to Fig. 3.10b, line DA becomes the locus of all c_{u2}' values for the input-velocity triangles $OC'B$ shown for one point C. The vane efficiency then is

$$e_{va} = H_i/H_e = c_{u2}'/c_{u2} \qquad (3.20)$$

and is constant for all capacities for blowers of all specific speeds forming a continuous series in their hydraulic design.

3.7 FLOW THROUGH THE IMPELLER

The reason impeller vanes cannot apply, and fluid cannot absorb the power required to produce Euler's head, will be seen from the following considerations.

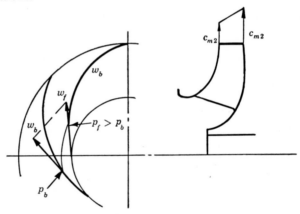

Fig. 3.11. Velocity distribution in an impeller channel.

(*a*) **Pressure Distribution.** In order to transmit power to the fluid, pressure p_f on the leading or front face of the vane should be higher than pressure p_b on the back of the vane (Fig. 3.11). Any force exerted by the vane on the fluid has an equal and opposing reaction from the fluid, and this can exist only as a pressure difference on two sides of impeller vanes. The immediate effect of such a pressure distribution is that relative velocities near the back of the impeller vanes are higher than those near the front of the vane. The velocity triangle, Fig. 3.1b, will show that, for a given vane angle, the head produced is lower with higher meridional velocities. Therefore the higher relative velocity at the back of the vane will result in lower heads and the total integrated head will be lower than that calculated for an average velocity of flow.

(*b*) **Velocity Distribution.**   Another cause for velocity distortion, which takes place even in an idealized machine, is the effect of turns in the impeller approach and impeller profile.   In radial flow and mixed flow impellers the fluid must make nearly a full 90° turn before it is acted upon by the vane.   The final result of uneven velocity distribution is again a reduction of the maximum head possible; see Fig. 3.11.

(*c*) **Relative Circulation.**   The relative velocity distribution through an impeller channel is affected also by the relative circulation of the

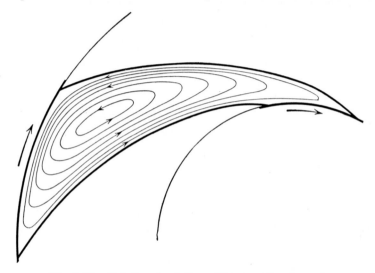

Fig. 3.12.   Relative circulation within impeller channel.

fluid due to the inertia effect of frictionless fluid particles; see Figs. 3.12 and 3.13.   The particles retain their orientation in space as shown in Fig. 3.14.   Here, particle *AB*, shown as a sphere, has an arrow *AB* marked on its body and pointing radially outward from the center.   After half a revolution the same particle will have its arrow pointing toward the center, and after a complete revolution the arrow again will be pointing away from the center.   The particle, while following the impeller in its translatory movement around the axis, fails to turn with the impeller.   This results in a turning movement relative to the impeller.   Superimposition of flow through the impeller increases the velocity at the back of the vane and reduces the velocity at the front face of the vane.   The result is a component in the tangential direction opposite to c_{u2} at the discharge (Fig. 3.15) and an additional component in the direction of c_{u1} at the entrance (Fig. 3.16). All these effects reduce the input head. Although the particle within the impeller channel remains irrotational, it travels in a translatory motion in a circular path and therefore is subject to centrifugal force which causes outward flow through the impeller. Evidently the rela-

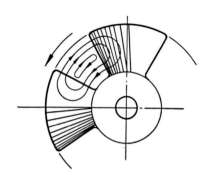

Fig. 3.13. Relative circulation within impeller channels of axial flow pump.

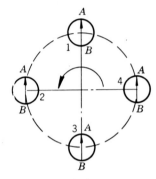

Fig. 3.14. Relative motion of particles is opposite to impeller rotation.

tive circulation is less with a greater number of vanes, hence the input head and the useful head are higher for a greater number of vanes. Also, it is reasonable to expect that relative circulation is smaller in a narrow impeller than in a wide one. For the same impeller diameter, the total head is greater with a narrow impeller (lower specific speed).

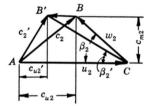

Fig. 3.15. Discharge velocity triangle.

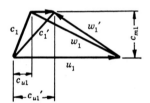

Fig. 3.16. Entrance velocity triangle.

The surface friction of shrouds has a decided effect on suppressing the relative circulation within the impeller channel and in imparting rotary motion to the fluid, thereby increasing the tangential component of the absolute velocity c_{u2} and the absolute velocity c_2. Special tests have shown that higher absolute velocities exist near the shrouds at the impeller discharge.

(d) **Actual Discharge Angle.** A study of Figs. 3.15 and 3.16 will reveal that the relative circulation of fluid within the impeller vanes has the effect of decreasing the fluid discharge angle from vane angle β_2 to β_2'. The inlet angle β_1, on the other hand, is increased to β_1', allowing more prerotation than indicated on Euler's velocity triangle. With actual fluids, power cannot be applied by the vane if the fluid moves in a path having the same relative angle β_2 as the vane itself. In that case the fluid would move outward with the same velocity as the vane sweeps radial distances while turning. In an established flow, whether rotary or straight as in open channel flow, a body must move faster than the established velocity of flow in order to exert any force on the liquid flowing in the same direction. In other words, the vane must have "impelling" action.

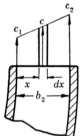

It is important to realize that changing the vane angle from β_2 to β_2' will mean only that the liquid will again lag behind the vane and discharge at a smaller angle $\beta_2'' < \beta_2'$.

(e) **Non-Active Part of Vane.** In an actual blower or an idealized one, the pressure difference on the two faces of a vane disappears at the vane tips where the two streams from adjacent impeller channels join. This means that not all the vane is equally active; in fact, the vane discharge tips have to be inactive since no pressure difference exists there. To unload vane discharge ends, the angle β_2 must be reduced.

Fig. 3.17. Velocity distribution at impeller discharge.

(f) **Theoretical Head with Non-Uniform Meridional Velocity.** Assuming that the radial velocity varies linearly from c_1 at one shroud to c_2 at the other shroud (Fig. 3.17) the author has shown (reference 2) by a simple integration that the theoretical head H_t is represented by the following equation:

$$H_t = \frac{u_2{}^2}{g} - \frac{u_2 c_m}{g \tan \beta_2} \left[1 + \frac{(c_2 - c_1)^2}{12 c_m{}^2} \right] \qquad (3.21)$$

This differs from the equation 3.8 by the bracketed factor which is greater than unity and indicates that when the meridional velocity is not uniform the theoretical or ideal head (no losses) is lower than that based on the average velocity. When $c_2 = c_1 = c_m$ the second term of the bracketed factor becomes zero and equation 3.21 reduces to equation 3.8.

To get an idea of the magnitude of the reduction of head due to this cause, equation 3.21 will be made dimensionless by dividing all terms by $u_2{}^2/g$; the dimensionless head will take the form given by equation 3.17.

$$\psi_t = \frac{H_t}{u_2{}^2/g} = 1 - (1 - \psi_e)\left[1 + \frac{(c_2 - c_1)^2}{12c_m{}^2}\right] \qquad (3.22)$$

Then, taking a value of 0.50 for ψ_e, based on the uniform radial velocity, this is a reasonable value for a straight centrifugal impeller, and equation 3.21 becomes

$$\psi_t = 1 - 0.5\left[1 + \frac{(c_2 - c_1)^2}{12c_m{}^2}\right] \qquad (3.23)$$

Assuming further that $c_2 = 2c_1$ and $c_m = (c_2 + c_1)/2 = \frac{3}{2}c_1$, the bracketed factor becomes $28\frac{8}{27}$ and the value of $\psi_t = 0.482$, which is 0.965 of its original value based on the uniform radial velocity.

For lower values of the dimensionless head $\psi_e = 0.25$, which is a reasonable figure for an axial impeller; the reduction of the theoretical head under the above assumed conditions is more pronounced, the value of ψ_t reducing to

$$\psi_t = 1 - 0.75 \times 28\frac{8}{27} = 0.224$$

which is 0.895 of its value for a uniform axial velocity. Figure 14.7 shows a measured velocity distribution in an axial flow compressor. Note that after the fourth stage the ratio of maximum to a minimum axial velocity is about 2:1 and that the experimental correction factor on Fig. 14.6 to account for the uneven axial velocity distribution is of the order arrived at in the above numerical example.

REFERENCES

1. Schmidt, "Some Screw Propeller Experiments," *J. Am. Soc. Naval Engrs.*, Vol. 40, Feb., 1928, p. 16.
2. Stepanoff, *Centrifugal and Axial Flow Pumps*, Wiley, 1948, pp. 41, 52.
3. Lichtenstein, "Method of Analyzing the Performance Curves of Centrifugal Pumps," *Trans. A.S.M.E.*, Vol. 50, No. 3, 1928, p. 3.
4. Otte, "Strömung von Menschenmengen durch Engpässe," *Z.V.D.I.*, Bd. 95, 1953, S.240,241; Also: Daeves u. Flachsbart, *Z.V.D.I.*, Bd. 94, 1952, S.880,881.

CHAPTER 4

Vortex Theory
of Euler's Head
for Incompressible Fluid

4.1 RADIAL IMPELLER

Flow through the impeller can be considered as consisting of two components; a circular motion around the axis, as a result of the impelling action of the vanes, and through-flow or meridional flow caused by the energy gradient drop. The circular component of flow forms a vortex motion. The type of vortex depends on the velocity and pressure distribution and can be established from a study of Euler's equation. For simplicity, consider first a straight radial impeller in which the flow approaches the impeller eye without prerotation. Euler's equation for this case, Fig. 3.1b, is

$$H_e = \frac{u_2 c_{u2}}{g} = \frac{u_2{}^2}{g} - \frac{u_2 c_{m2}}{g \tan \beta_2} = \frac{u_2{}^2}{g} - \frac{u_2 w_{u2}}{g} \qquad (4.1)$$

Only tangential velocities appear in equation 4.1, indicating that all head is produced by vortex action in planes normal to the axis of rotation. It will be shown that this is true, in general, for all turbomachines, including straight axial flow.

When the flow is zero ($w_{u2} = 0$), Euler's head becomes

$$H_e = u_2{}^2/g = 2(u_2{}^2/2g) \qquad (4.2)$$

and the total head at any radius r is equal to

$$H_e = 2(u^2/2g) \qquad (4.2a)$$

where u is the peripheral velocity at radius r. This head is equally divided between static and kinetic heads. Such energy distribution along the radius is typical for a forced vortex and is represented by a square parabola OA in Fig. 4.1. When flow starts, the head drops by an amount $u_2 w_{u2}/g$, where w_{u2} is proportional to the flow. *This drop of head is the energy gradient drop needed to produce flow, because even an idealized machine (no losses) cannot start flow against a head higher than or equal to its zero flow head.* It is also evident that a further drop of energy gradient is necessary to increase the flow or produce a higher capacity. Thus the total head drops from AE to CE on Fig. 4.1 The value of $u_2 w_{u2}/g$ decreases with decreasing radii, and the head variation along the radius is represented by a parabolic curve OC. In a straight radial impeller the relative velocity and vane angle vary little along the radius, and the tangential component of the relative velocity (w_{u2}) will also vary little. Assuming w_{u2} to be constant along the radius, the energy gradient drop $u_2 w_{u2}/g$ will vary as u_2 or

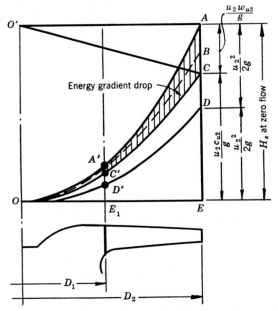

Fig. 4.1. Euler's head, radial flow impeller.

will increase directly as the distance traveled by the flow ($O'C$ on Fig. 4.1). This is analogous to the hydraulic gradient drop in pipe flow of constant velocity. However, in this case the drop in hydraulic gradient represents hydraulic loss along the pipe, whereas in a centrifugal blower impeller the drop in energy gradient is a condition that is necessary to realize flow and that results in an equal reduction of the impeller input. As the capacity increases, the energy gradient drop increases and Euler's head decreases.

The energy gradient drop $u_2 w_{u2}/g$ can be considered a turbine reaction of the impeller. While pumping, an impeller acts as a turbine runner. With the head $u_2 w_{u2}/g$ applied to the impeller eye and the direction of flow as it exists in the blower impeller, the direction of rotation due to turbine reaction will be the same as that of the blower.

The torque developed by the turbine action will act in the same sense as the applied torque. As a result, the impeller power input is reduced by the value of $u_2 w_{u2}/g$ (Fig. 4.2). There being no losses in an idealized machine, the turbine reaction returns to the shaft the energy put into it by the flow caused by the energy gradient drop.

The turbine reaction of an impeller is analogous to the armature reaction of a direct-current generator. Figure 4.3 shows a relationship between the voltage E (corresponding to the blower head) and current I (corresponding to the blower capacity) for a direct-current

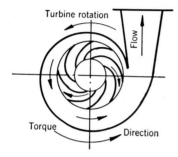

Fig. 4.2. Turbine reaction of impeller.

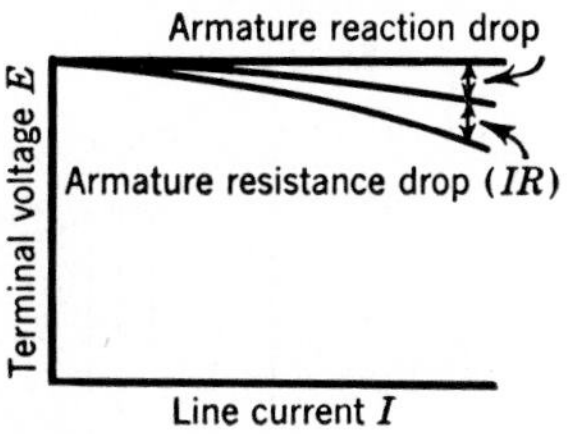

Fig. 4.3. Regulation curve of a direct-current generator.

generator. The general appearance of $E\text{-}I$ curves resembles that of the $Q\text{-}H$ curve representing Euler's equation in Fig. 3.3.

For any rate of flow,

$$\frac{u_2^2}{g} = \frac{u_2 c_{u2}}{g} + \frac{u_2 w_{u2}}{g}$$

$$\frac{u_2^2}{g} = \text{Impeller action} + \text{Turbine reaction}$$

(4.3)

Note the similarity of the algebraic expression for the first and second terms of the right-hand part of equation 4.3 representing pumping action and turbine reaction.*

If prerotation is allowed in the impeller approach, Euler's equation takes the form

$$H_e = \frac{u_2 c_{u2}}{g} - \frac{u_1 c_{u1}}{g} = \frac{u_2^2}{g} - \frac{u_2 w_{u2}}{g} - \frac{u_1 c_{u1}}{g}$$

* Applying the same reasoning to a turbine runner, it can be stated that the runner, while rotating under applied head, generates a centrifugal head analogous to the back-electromotive-force of an electric motor. The flow through the runner is determined by the difference between the head applied and the centrifugal head developed by the runner.

hence

$$\frac{u_2^2}{g} = \left(\frac{u_2 c_{u2}}{g} - \frac{u_1 c_{u1}}{g}\right) + \left(\frac{u_2 w_{u2}}{g} + \frac{u_1 c_{u1}}{g}\right)$$

$$= \text{Impeller action} + \text{Turbine reaction}$$

Figure 4.4 represents the same relationship graphically.

Thus, with prerotation the pump action is reduced by $u_1 c_{u1}/g$, but the turbine reaction is increased by the same amount.

Figure 3.3 shows the variation of H_e with capacity. This is given by the straight line AC below line AB for constant u_2^2/g. The line AB can be approached theoretically with vane angles approaching

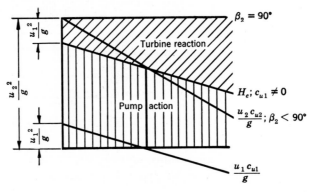

Fig. 4.4. Pumping action and turbine reaction with prerotation allowed.

90° as a limit. The head-capacity curve above line AB for vane angles $\beta_2 > 90°$ (AD on Fig. 3.3) is impossible as no energy gradient is available to produce the flow. It has been pointed out in Chapter 3 that impulse action is required to produce a rising characteristic. This principle is difficult to realize in the pumping turbomachinery.

In contrast to the impulse action, all centrifugal pumping machines operate on a pressure or reaction principle, a term used in reference to hydraulic and steam turbines which represent a closed system under pressure. The total energy is partly pressure and partly kinetic, whereas in impulse turbines all energy is converted to kinetic energy of high velocity jets, which impinge upon the buckets at atmospheric pressure.

If the flow approaching the impeller eye is not radial, or if prerotation is allowed, Euler's equation 4.1 will change to

$$H_e = \frac{u_2 c_{u2}}{g} - \frac{u_1 c_{u1}}{g} \tag{4.4}$$

It will be noticed that the second or subtractive term is similar to the first term. Following the same reasoning applied to the first term will reveal that the subtractive term represents the part OC' of the parabolic head curve OC (Fig. 4.1), and thus the total head will be obtained as the difference $CE - C'E' = H_e$.

For each capacity there is a parabolic curve, located somewhere between OA and OE, representing the head variation along the impeller radius. The line OE is reached at zero head or when $w_{u2} = u_2$ in equation 4.1.

By using Euler's head equation in the expanded form,

$$H_e = \frac{u_2^2 - u_1^2}{2g} + \frac{c_2^2 - c_1^2}{2g} + \frac{w_1^2 - w_2^2}{2g} \tag{4.5}$$

it can be shown that each component part of the total head as it appears in this equation represents a vortex motion. By making use of the geometrical relationships

$$c_1^2 = c_{u1}^2 + c_{m1}^2 \qquad w_1^2 = w_{u1}^2 + c_{m1}^2$$

$$c_2^2 = c_{u2}^2 + c_{m2}^2 \qquad w_2^2 = w_{u2}^2 + c_{m2}^2$$

equation 4.4 can be changed to

$$H_e = \frac{u_2^2 - u_1^2}{2g} + \frac{c_{u2}^2 - c_{u1}^2}{2g} + \frac{w_{u1}^2 - w_{u2}^2}{2g} \tag{4.6}$$

Only tangential velocities appear in this equation, and the radial velocities at entrance and discharge, not equal in general, cancel out. This shows again that all changes in velocities as a result of impeller action take place in planes normal to the axis of rotation producing a vortex motion. With radial approach $c_{u1} = 0$ and $w_{u1} = u_1$, equation 4.5 reduces to

$$H_e = \frac{u_2^2}{2g} + \frac{c_{u2}^2}{2g} - \frac{w_{u2}^2}{2g} \tag{4.7}$$

As the capacity approaches zero, w_{u2} approaches zero, and c_{u2} approaches u_2. So at zero flow

$$H_e = \frac{u_2^2}{g} = \frac{u_2^2}{2g} + \frac{c_{u2}^2}{2g} \tag{4.7a}$$

showing that at zero capacity the total head is equally divided between static head and kinetic energy. At zero head, $c_{u2} = 0$ and $w_{u2} = u_2$; then

$$H_e = \frac{u_2^2}{2g} - \frac{w_{u2}^2}{2g} = 0 \tag{4.7b}$$

showing that the flow is meridional, under energy gradient, and there is no vortex produced by the impeller.

4.2 AXIAL FLOW IMPELLER

In an axial flow compressor, fluid particles leave the impeller at the same radius at which they enter. Applying Euler's equation 4.5 to a point on the impeller periphery and noting that $u_2 = u_1$, we get

$$H_e = \frac{c_{u2}^2 - c_{u1}^2}{2g} + \frac{w_{u1}^2 - w_{u2}^2}{2g} \tag{4.8}$$

Again assuming first that the liquid approaches the impeller without prerotation ($c_{u1} = 0$, and $w_{u1} = u_1$), equation 4.8 reduces to

$$H_e = \frac{u_2^2}{2g} + \frac{c_{u2}^2}{2g} - \frac{w_{u2}^2}{2g} \tag{4.8a}$$

Substituting $c_{u2} = u_2 - w_{u2}$, we obtain

$$H_e = \frac{u_2^2}{g} - \frac{u_2 w_{u2}}{g} \tag{4.9}$$

Because this is exactly the same as equation 4.1, it indicates that the process of generating head is the same in axial flow blowers as it is in radial flow blowers. In both, head is generated through the vortex motion and the flow through the impeller is caused by the energy gradient drop $u_2 w_{u2}/g$. The head distribution along the radius is shown on Fig. 4.5, where curve AA' shows the head at different radii with zero flow. This is a square parabola. Curve CC' shows the head variation for one rate of flow (w_{u2}). AC is the energy gradient drop at the periphery. Ordinates between curves AA' and CC' represent the energy gradient drop for differing radii. It will be shown later in this chapter that for a normal design both w_{u2} and u_2 vary directly as the radius. Therefore the energy gradient drop $u_2 w_{u2}/g$ varies directly as the square of the radius (curve $O'C$), and the curve of heads OC is a square parabola. This is a characteristic of a forced vortex when all particles rotate with the same angular velocity.

Although the head distribution along the radii is similar for radial and axial pumps, there is an important difference between the final results of the two. In a radial impeller all particles reach the same maximum head at the periphery of the impeller. In an axial flow impeller, fluid particles enter and leave at the same radii and the heads produced at different radii are different, being maximum at the periphery and minimum at the hub. The impeller total head is an integrated average. The hydraulic integration of the head over the whole

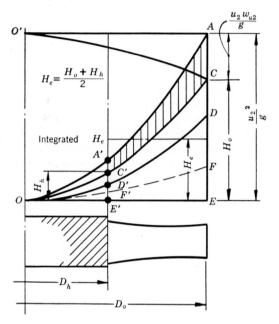

Fig. 4.5. Euler's head, axial flow impeller.

impeller area takes place in the discharge casing, where the tangential component of the absolute velocity is converted into pressure and the pressure is equalized over the whole area of the discharge pipe. In an efficient diffusion casing, this equalization of pressure occurs without mixing of streamlines, as demonstrated with axial blowers by admitting smoke and sparks into the suction (reference 1). Evidently the pressure equalization takes place by conduction (see Chapter 1). Figure 4.6 shows a diagram of hydraulic integration. The volume of the

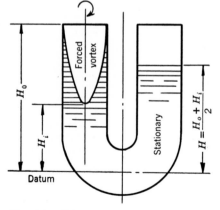

Fig. 4.6. Diagram of hydraulic integration.

liquid in the two legs of the U-tube is the same. In the left leg, liquid is in rotation. The column of liquid at the center of the left leg supports a higher head H in the right-hand leg of the tube. The integrated head of the impeller in Fig. 4.5 is equal to the average of the head at the hub (H_h) and the head at the periphery (H_o). This follows from the geometrical properties of a square paraboloid.

$$H_e = (H_h + H_o)/2 \qquad (4.10)$$

If the fluid approaches the impeller with prerotation, Euler's head for an axial flow impeller is given by equation 4.4 which is the same as for the radial impeller. The subtractive term is of the same appearance as the first term and represents a square parabola of suction heads at different radii $(FF'$, Fig. 4.5$)$. The net Euler's head at different radii is represented by ordinates between the curves CC' and FF'. The curve of the net Euler's head will remain a square parabola.

4.3   FORCED VORTEX AXIAL FLOW IMPELLER

(a) **Inlet and Outlet Pitch, Pitch per Second.** All theoretical discussion, and practical design of axial flow compressors and fans, is based on the assumption of constant axial velocity through the impel-

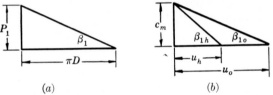

(a)   (b)

Fig. 4.7.   (a) Inlet pitch; (b) inlet velocity triangle for axial flow impeller.

ler. The axial velocity of approach to the impeller and beyond the impeller is assumed to be equal to that through the impeller. This assumption is reasonable with a normal design except for the effects of frictional drag at the casing and impeller walls. Such distribution has been actually observed on axial flow blowers. To maintain a uniform axial velocity the impeller vane should have the same inlet pitch at different radii. The latter is defined as $P_1 = \pi D \tan \beta_1$, where P_1 is inlet pitch; D is impeller diameter; and β_1 is the vane entrance angle, Fig. 4.7a.

There is a definite relationship between the axial velocity c_m at normal capacity and pitch P_1. From the entrance velocity triangle, Fig. 4.7b,

$$c_m/u_o = \tan \beta_{1o} \quad \text{and} \quad c_m/u_h = \tan \beta_{1h} \qquad (4.11)$$

where subscript o refers to the outside diameter, and h refers to the hub. But

$$u_h = \pi D_h \times \text{r.p.s.} \qquad u_o = \pi D_o \times \text{r.p.s.} \qquad (4.12)$$

and

$$\tan \beta_{1h} = P_h/(\pi D_h) \qquad \tan \beta_{1o} = P_o/(\pi D_o) \qquad (4.13)$$

$$c_m = P_h \times \text{r.p.s.} = P_o \times \text{r.p.s.} = P_1 \times \text{r.p.s.} = P_{1s} \qquad (4.14)$$

Thus, to maintain a constant axial velocity c_m, the vane inlet pitch at all radii should be constant.

To provide impelling action, the impeller vane angles should increase gradually from inlet toward discharge or the vane pitch should increase. To maintain the same axial velocity along the radii the pitch for all radii should remain constant to assure the same degree of impelling

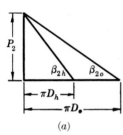

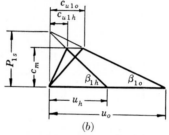

(a) Fig. 4.8. Outlet pitch.

(b) Fig. 4.9. Axial flow impeller entrance triangle with prerotation.

action for several streamlines of different radii. Thus by definition (Fig. 4.8)

$$P_2 = \pi D_h \tan \beta_{2h} = \pi D_o \tan \beta_{2o} \qquad (4.15)$$

and, multiplying by the revolutions per second, we obtain

$$P_2 \times \text{r.p.s.} = u_h \tan \beta_{2h} = u_o \tan \beta_{2o} = P_{2s} \qquad (4.16)$$

P_{2s} may be called discharge pitch per second, a term which will be used in discussing axial flow impeller geometry. Similarly $P_1 \times$ r.p.s. $= P_{1s}$ may be called inlet pitch per second. With an axial inlet velocity, $P_{1s} = c_m$ at normal capacity.

If some prerotation is allowed ahead of the impeller, and the vane entrance angles are so selected that the entrance pitch is constant along the radius, the entrance velocity triangle will be as shown on Fig. 4.9 where $P_{1s} > c_m$ at normal capacity.

The differences $P_{1s} - c_m$ and $P_{2s} - c_m$ are frequently referred to as axial slip. This term is misleading as slip is usually associated with loss of capacity and corresponding drop in volumetric efficiency.

However, with axial flow blowers there is no connection between $P_{1s} - c_m$ and volumetric efficiency. Thus at half-normal capacity the slip $(P_{1s} - c_m)/c_m$ may be more than one half, but a blower gross efficiency considerably over 50 per cent is quite common. Also, at a capacity over the normal, $P_{1s} - c_m$ is negative while the efficiency is decreasing after reaching a maximum at the normal capacity.

(*b*) **Forced Vortex Action.** A constant pitch P_1 at entrance and P_2 at discharge, where $P_2 > P_1$, assures a forced vortex motion of the liquid by the impeller. Assuming an axial inlet, it follows from con-

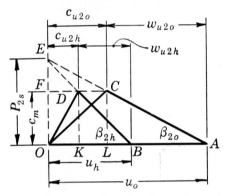

Fig. 4.10.   Discharge velocity triangle, axial flow impeller.

sideration of two pairs of similar triangles, *OEB* and *EFD*, *OEA* and *EFC*, Fig. 4.10, that

$$c_{u2h}/u_h = c_{u2o}/u_o = (P_{2s} - c_m)/P_{2s} \qquad (4.17)$$

hence

$$c_{u2h}/r_h = c_{u2o}/r_o = \omega' \qquad (4.18)$$

where ω' is the angular velocity of the absolute flow leaving the impeller which is constant for all streamlines at different radii. This is the requirement for a forced vortex. From similar triangles *EBO* and *DBK*, *EAO* and *CLA* (Fig. 4.10),

$$\frac{w_{u2h}}{u_h} = \frac{w_{u2o}}{u_o} = \frac{c_m}{P_{2s}} \quad \text{and} \quad \frac{w_{u2h}}{r_h} = \frac{w_{u2o}}{r_o} = \omega''$$

also

$$\omega' + \omega'' = \omega \qquad (4.19)$$

ω'' is the relative angular velocity of flow, also constant for all streamlines.

The forced vortex regime is maintained at all capacities or all values of c_m. Zero head ($c_u = 0$) occurs simultaneously at all streamlines at

$c_m = P_{2s}$. Also, zero capacity takes place at the same time at all points on different radii when $c_m = 0$.

To summarize: *Euler's head in an axial flow blower can be generated by a forced vortex motion. To produce a forced vortex the impeller has to be of constant pitch along the radius, the pitch increasing from inlet to discharge. The pitch at the inlet edge fixes the axial velocity at normal capacity. The ratio of the pitch per second at discharge P_{2s} to the axial velocity c_m is a measure of the impelling action of the vane and will be referred to as an impelling ratio.*

$$P_{2s}/c_m = Impelling\ ratio \qquad (4.20)$$

For the axial flow impellers without prerotation, the impelling ratio becomes the pitch ratio, since

$$P_{2s}/c_m = P_{2s}/P_{1s} = P_2/P_1 = \tan \beta_2/\tan \beta_1 \qquad (4.20a)$$

The impelling ratio varies with the capacity, increasing as the capacity is decreasing. It is equal to unity at zero head point since the axial velocity c_m at that point is equal to P_{2s}. There is no impelling action when the impelling ratio is equal to unity.

Thus, when there is no slip ($P_{2s} - c_m = 0$), there is no impelling action, and impelling action is increasing as the slip is increasing.

(c) **Mixed Flow Impellers.** It has been shown that the action of impellers is the same in a straight radial flow and a straight axial flow impeller. This action consists in producing a forced vortex that is superimposed on a radial outward flow in the straight radial flow impeller and upon a uniform axial flow in the straight axial flow impeller. The mixed flow impellers occupy an intermediate position between the above two types. Therefore all the deductions for radial and axial flow impellers apply as well to the mixed flow types. The meridional velocity at the entrance c_{m1} is not equal to that at discharge; normally $c_{m1} > c_{m2}$. In drawing the discharge angles, the same procedure is followed as in Fig. 4.10 for axial flow impellers, the impelling ratio P_{2s}/c_m being selected. It should be noted that with mixed flow impellers a vane having a prescribed impelling ratio may have a discharge angle at the hub lower than the entrance angle $\beta_{2h} < \beta_{1h}$. This depends on the relative values of c_{m2} and c_{m1} and impeller profile.

The impelling ratio as defined by equation 4.20 applies equally to the radial impellers. The pitch per second at discharge P_{2s} for radial impellers is defined in the same manner as for axial flow impellers.

$$P_{2s} = u_2 \tan \beta_2$$

and the impelling ratio is

$$\frac{P_{2s}}{c_{m2}} = \frac{u_2 \tan \beta_2}{c_{m2}} = \frac{\tan \beta_2}{\dfrac{c_{m2}}{u_2}} = \frac{\tan \beta_2}{\phi_e} \tag{4.20b}$$

where ϕ_e is capacity coefficient, defined by equation 3.18.

The impelling ratio increases as the specific speed at b.e.p. decreases. The impelling ratio is discussed further in Chapter 6, in connection with other design elements incorporated in the author's diagram of turbomachine characteristics represented in Fig. 6.10.

(d) **Free Vortex Pattern of Flow through the Axial Flow Impeller.** The forced vortex pattern of flow, as a basis of the impeller action on the fluid, is not the only one possible when applied to straight axial flow machines. A free vortex pattern of flow for axial flow blowers is assumed by many writers on the subject mostly in connection with airfoil theory. According to this, the tangential velocity distribution along the radius follows the law

$$c_{u2}r = \text{Constant} \tag{4.21}$$

This is arrived at by assuming that the same head is generated at all radii, or

$$uc_{u2} = gH = \text{Constant} \tag{4.21a}$$

which is Euler's head equation with an axial inlet velocity. Both assumptions are motivated by reasoning that only at these conditions is the flow stable or free from cross flows. In Chapter 1 it has been shown that a free vortex is only one mode of circular motion of fluids out of a great many possible modes, all of which are stable. There are several objections to a free vortex flow pattern as a basis for the theoretical reasoning of the axial flow impeller action, some of which have been pointed out in more recent writings on the subject (reference 2).†

1. Free vortex motion of fluid at the impeller discharge can exist at one point on the head-capacity curve only. If Fig. 4.11a represents Euler's velocity triangle, at the design point,

$$c_{u2h}r_h = c_{u2o}r_o = \text{Constant} = C \tag{4.22}$$

† A statement by C. W. Smith, of General Electric Company, may serve as an example. "The Vortex Theory (free vortex) is not the best on which to base a design, at least in its present simple form." *Minutes of Axial Flow Compressor Meeting of June 26 on German Articles*, primarily by Bruno Eckert and Group P.40 published by Navy Department, Code 445A, Bureau of Ships, 1946, Washington 25, D. C.

which means that the tangential component is inversely proportional to the radius. Then at partial capacity c_{u2o} becomes greater than c_{u2h}, and the regime approaches a forced vortex; Fig. 4.11b. At zero capacity the flow becomes a forced vortex. At capacities over the rated, c_{u2o} becomes zero, whereas c_{u2h} does not; Fig. 4.11c. At a still greater capacity, c_{u2o} becomes negative.

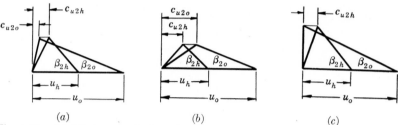

(a)   (b)   (c)

Fig. 4.11. (a) Discharge velocity triangle at rated point, free vortex; (b) velocity triangle at partial capacity; (c) velocity triangle at capacity over the normal.

2. Actual test curves show that at capacities below one half of normal (Fig. 4.12) the total head H is equal to or exceeds u_h^2/g. This is a maximum possible theoretical head at the hub. Evidently a theory assuming a constant head for all radii does not hold at capacities less than normal, and some different assumption is required.

3. Since the tangential components vary inversely as the radius at the best efficiency point, the angular velocity of the absolute flow will vary inversely as the square of radius, as the following relationships show. From equation 4.22

$$\omega_h = c_{u2h}/r_h = C/r_h^2$$

and

$$\omega_o = c_{u2o}/r_o = C/r_o^2 \qquad (4.23)$$

Such an angular velocity distribution is not easy to visualize in view of the constant angular velocity of the impeller which is responsible for all changes in velocities.

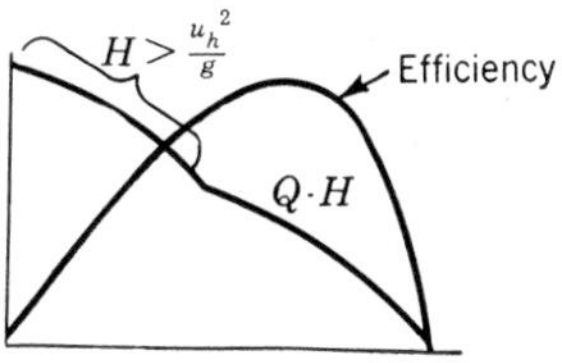

Fig. 4.12. Axial flow fan characteristics.

4. The advocates of the free vortex pattern of flow for axial flow impellers usually resort to selection of impeller vane sections from airfoil test data. This procedure is not applicable to extreme mixed flow impellers or straight radial flow impellers. Thus the designer is left to his own resources in filling the gap between the straight radial and straight axial impeller types.

The forced vortex reasoning of impeller action is free from these drawbacks because:

1. It applies equally well to straight centrifugal, mixed flow, and straight axial flow blowers.

2. With axial flow impellers the forced vortex regime is maintained for the whole head-capacity range. Zero-head and zero-capacity points occur at the same time at the hub and periphery of the impeller.

3. A constant absolute angular velocity is maintained at all capacities ahead, through, and, beyond the impeller, this velocity increasing as the capacity decreases.

4. Head generated at different radii of the impeller expressed as a fraction of the maximum head at zero capacity is constant:

$$\psi_e = \frac{H_e}{u_2{}^2/g} = \frac{c_{u2}}{u_2} = \text{Constant}$$

where ψ_e, the head coefficient defined by equation 3.17, is constant for all radii and at all capacities. Thus, at each radius the impeller vane elements transmit the same amount of energy (Hg) per foot of peripheral velocity or, stated differently, the "dimensionless head" ψ_e produced at different radii is constant at all capacities.

5. Using a forced vortex pattern of flow leads to a geometrical procedure of impeller vane layout which is valid for straight axial flow impellers as well as for mixed flow impellers of any profile.

REFERENCES

1. Schmidt, "Some Screw Propeller Experiments with Particular Reference to Pumps and Blowers," *J. Am. Soc. Naval Engrs.*, Vol. 40, No. 1, Feb., 1928, p. 15.
2. Wislicenus, "A Study of the Theory of Axial-Flow Pumps," *Trans. A.S.M.E.*, Vol. 67, No. 6, Aug., 1945, p. 451.

CHAPTER 5

General Characteristics
of Turbomachinery—
Incompressible Fluid

5.1 DIMENSIONLESS CHARACTERISTICS OF TURBOMACHINERY

There are six independent variables that affect the generation of head by the impeller of a turbomachine.

Q capacity, volume per unit time l^3/t
n speed, revolutions per sec. $1/t$
D impeller diameter, representing the blower size for a series of similar blowers l
ρ fluid mass density, mass per unit volume m/l^3
μ absolute viscosity m/lt
E energy applied to the fluid per unit mass $E = gH$ l^2/t^2

Energy per unit mass $E = gH$ will be used for the purpose of this article rather than head H in feet (which is energy per pound of fluid), because of its more general character and because it includes the effect of the acceleration due to gravity. By application of dimensional analysis to the problem of head generation by an impeller, it can be shown that the relation among the above six quantities, necessary to describe the operation of a turbomachine, can be reduced to a functional equation of the form[*]

$$f(\Pi_1, \Pi_2, \Pi_3) = 0 \tag{5.1}$$

where Π_1, Π_2 and Π_3 represent dimensionless products as follows:

$$\Pi_1 = D(gH)^{\frac{1}{2}}/\nu \tag{5.2}$$

$$\Pi_2 = Q/(gH)^{\frac{1}{2}}D^2 \tag{5.3}$$

$$\Pi_3 = nD/(gH)^{\frac{1}{2}} \tag{5.4}$$

In equation 5.2, $\nu = \mu/\rho$ is the kinematic viscosity of the pumped fluid.

---

[*] For development see reference 1.

According to dimensional analysis, the relationship between Π_1, Π_2, and Π_3 can be established only experimentally. The Π products remain constant for similar impellers and dynamically similar conditions, irrespective of the rotative speed or size of the impellers; they are "criteria" of the flow. For practical purposes these expressions will be transformed by making use of the fact that if any of the Π functions are constant for similar impellers their products, or any power, also will remain constant and also will be "criteria" of operation of the impeller. Thus,

$$\Pi_4 = \Pi_1\Pi_2 = (D/\nu)(Q/D^2) = Q/\nu D \tag{5.5}$$

$$\Pi_5 = \Pi_2{}^{1/2}\Pi_3 = nQ^{1/2}/(gH)^{3/4} \tag{5.6}$$

$$\Pi_6 = \Pi_2/\Pi_3 = Q/nD^3 \tag{5.7}$$

The expressions Π_4, Π_5, and Π_6 are a new set of independent dimensionless criteria describing the operation of an impeller. To this will be added one more,

$$\Pi_7 = 1/\Pi_3{}^2 = gH/(n^2D^2) \tag{5.8}$$

This can be used alternately for Π_5 or Π_6. It is not an independent as

$$\Pi_6{}^{1/2}/\Pi_7{}^{3/4} = \Pi_5 = nQ^{1/2}/(gH)^{3/4} \tag{5.9}$$

Obviously an infinite number of dimensionless criteria can be obtained in a similar manner, but only three of them will be independent. The form of Π_4, Π_5, Π_6, and Π_7 was selected because these terms were already in use in dimensional form (mostly in the water turbine and centrifugal pump fields) long before they were developed by the use of the dimensional analysis.

(a) **Reynolds Number.** The expression 5.5 is a form of Reynolds number, in which the impeller diameter D represents the size of the machine and Q/D^2 the velocity, as for similar pumps Q/D^2 is proportional to the velocities at the corresponding point of channels comprising impeller and casing of the turbomachine. It is important to realize that Reynolds number (equation 5.5 or any other of several Reynolds numbers possible for several sections of the channels comprising a blower) does not posses the properties of a criterion of flow through the turbomachine such as are usually associated with Reynolds number for pipe flow. Thus the same Reynolds number does not assure the same pattern of velocity distribution or the same regime, viscous or turbulent. The change from one regime to the other may take place at different rates of flow in different parts of the machine. Besides, very little is known about the significance of the Reynolds number of the flow through curvilinear and convergent or divergent channels where some of the channels are in rotary motion with energy added or taken away from the flow. For that reason all attempts in the past to calculate the hydraulic friction losses through turbomachines by applying the methods and data (correlated on the basis of Reynolds number) for flow in pipes never served any useful purpose. Moreover, in a turbomachine, the skin friction loss becomes secondary to eddy losses caused by a lack of streamlining and diffused flow prevailing in the impeller and casing. Note also that identical Reynolds numbers can be obtained with blowers of different physical configurations, or different specific speeds.

For a great majority of blower applications, speed and viscosity are not great enough to show any appreciable effect of Reynolds number on the blower efficiency. However, when applied to the whole field of the turbomachinery, and particularly to centrifugal pumps pumping viscous petroleum products, the variation of Reynolds number covers a range from 10 to 10^6. Efficiency variation from 90 per cent (water) to 10 per cent have been established within this range of Reynolds numbers (references 1 and 2). In blower practice the minor effect of speed and size variation on the blower efficiency is estimated from past experience.

(*b*) **Specific Speed.** The expression for II_5, equation 5.6, is a dimensionless expression for specific speed first mentioned in Art. 2.5

$$\text{II}_5 = nQ^{\frac{1}{2}}/(gH)^{\frac{3}{4}} \tag{5.6}$$

To be dimensionless all terms have to be expressed in fundamental units; i.e., n, in revolutions per second; Q, in cubic feet per second; H, in feet; and g, in feet per second squared. However, for practical uses the specific speed expression is used in the form as given by equation 2.17. The physical meaning of specific speed is revolutions per minute (r.p.m.) to produce 1 c.f.m. at 1 ft. of head with a similar impeller reduced in size. However, the physical meaning of specific speed has no application in practice, and specific speed is used only as a type number for the best efficiency point (b.e.p.) of all similar impellers irrespective of their size or rotative speed.

(*c*) **Specific Capacity.** The expression for II_6 is called "specific capacity"

$$\text{II}_6 = q_s = Q/nD^3 \tag{5.10}$$

This is also dimensionless if Q, n, and D are measured in fundamental units. The physical meaning of the specific capacity q_s is volume of fluid per 1 r.p.s. with an impeller of 1 ft. diameter. The specific capacity remains constant for all similar impellers. The affinity laws follow from this property. Thus for a given blower ($D =$ Constant) Q varies directly as n to maintain q_s constant. Also, for similar blowers, if n is constant, Q varies directly as cube of the impeller diameter ratio. If both n and D are varied, both rules are applied simultaneously. Specific capacity q_s is used occasionally for plotting the blower performance in dimensionless form.

(d) **Specific Head and Head Coefficient.** The expression 5.8 is a dimensionless expression for head and may be termed "specific head"

$$\Pi_7 = h_s = gH/n^2D^2 \tag{5.11}$$

As it appears in this equation, specific head means input energy per unit mass per revolution and with an impeller of 1-ft. diameter. It remains constant for all similar impellers. Affinity laws follow from this property of the specific head: for a given D, head varies directly as square of the speed to satisfy the above condition; also, if n is kept constant then head H varies directly as the square of the impeller diameters.

As a dimensionless characteristic the specific head expression is slightly modified and is known as the "head coefficient"; it is denoted by ψ (Greek letter psi) †

$$\psi = \frac{H}{u_2{}^2/g} = \frac{gH}{\pi^2n^2D^2} = \frac{h_s}{\pi^2} \tag{5.12}$$

The head coefficient ψ expresses the head in feet as a fraction of the maximum theoretical head at zero capacity for meridional inlet (no prerotation) $u_2{}^2/g$.

For the flow to be dynamically similar while speed, size, and viscosity are varied, it is necessary that all three criteria remain constant. In a practical sense it is impossible to comply with this requirement, for, if the viscosity is kept constant and only speed and size are varied, the Reynolds number will vary while Π_2 and Π_3 remain constant. However, since Reynolds number affects similarity of flow only so far as hydraulic skin friction losses and velocity distribution are concerned, its effect is very small on the over-all performance of the impeller because in a good turbomachine hydraulic losses are of the order of 5 per cent. The affinity laws hold true with an accuracy sufficient for practical purposes throughout a wide range of speeds and sizes and represent the basis of the design procedure of all turbomachinery.

† Following Rateau, a Greek letter μ (mu) is used to some extent for the head coefficient.

5.2 DESIGN PROCEDURE

The design of a blower impeller involves the following steps (the casing design procedure is discussed in Chapter 9):

(*a*) **Selection of Speed.** To meet given c.f.m. and head conditions the rotative speed is selected first. This establishes the specific speed or type of the impeller. Selection of the speed is governed by a number of considerations:

1. Type of driver contemplated for the unit.

2. Higher specific speed results in a smaller blower and cheaper drivers.

3. Optimum hydraulic (and total) efficiency possible with each type varies with the specific speed. This relationship has not

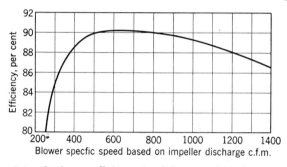

Fig. 5.1.   Optimum efficiency for different specific speeds.

been established accurately for blowers. However, in the centrifugal pump field (including axial flow pumps) the optimum efficiency possible with each specific speed is definitely known to the whole industry. Figure 5.1 shows a typical curve representing such relationships.

4. If the total required head cannot be produced in one stage, owing to limitation of maximum permissible impeller peripheral velocity, it is divided between two or more stages. The head per stage also affects the final specific speed and, hence, the expected efficiency of the blower.

Having established the specific speed of the proposed impellers, the designer looks for a suitable "model" from existing impellers of the same specific speed which have satisfactory hydraulic performance, i.e., suitable slope of the head-capacity curve and acceptable efficiency. Besides the required specific speed the model should be of the same class of blower and be of suitable mechanical type. For instance, an impeller of a multistage blower (large shaft and impeller hub) would

not be a suitable model for single-stage overhung construction with an
end inlet. The reduction factor or multiplier to be applied to the
existing model is found by the use of affinity laws. Design of an
impeller for which no existing type is available is made from basic
design constants discussed later in this chapter.

(b) **Reduction Factor or Multiplier.** If an impeller which is selected
for a model is rated Q_1 c.f.m. at H_1-ft. head at n_1 r.p.m. and its impeller
diameter is D_1 and the new impeller is required to produce Q_2 c.f.m.
H_2-ft. head at n_2 r.p.m., with an impeller diameter D_2, the specific
speed of both should be the same,

$$n_1 Q_1^{1/2}/H_1^{3/4} = n_2 Q_2^{1/2}/H_2^{3/4} \tag{5.13}$$

In addition, the following relationships between model and the new
capacities and heads can be written:

$$Q_2 = Q_1 f^3 (n_2/n_1) \tag{5.14}$$

$$H_2 = H_1 f^2 (n_2/n_1)^2 \tag{5.15}$$

where $f = D_2/D_1$ is the reduction factor or multiplier.

From equation 5.15 the following formula for the reduction factor
f is obtained:

$$f = \frac{n_1/\sqrt{H_1}}{n_2/\sqrt{H_2}} = \frac{n_1}{n_2}\left(\frac{H_2}{H_1}\right)^{1/2} \tag{5.16}$$

Expression $n/\sqrt{H}$ is referred to as "unit speed," meaning r.p.m.,
needed to produce 1 ft. of head by a given impeller. It is also possible to express the factor f in terms of capacities and speed from
equation 5.14

$$f^3 = \frac{Q_2/n_2}{Q_1/n_1} = \frac{n_1}{n_2}\frac{Q_2}{Q_1} \tag{5.17}$$

Q/n is referred to as unit capacity and represents c.f.m. per revolution
for a given impeller. Formula 5.16 is better suited for slide rule
calculations.

(c) **New Impeller Design.** To design a new impeller for which no
model is available designers use "design factors" established experimentally from successful designs that give direct relationships between
the impeller total head and capacity at the design point and several
elements of Euler's velocity triangles. These are dimensionless
velocity ratios, independent of the impeller size and speed, which are
correlated on the basis of specific speed for different impeller discharge

angles.   In addition a number of ratios of important linear dimensions, not directly related to velocities, are found helpful in perfecting hydraulic design of impellers.   These ratios, too, are entirely experimental and do not lend themselves to theoretical treatment.   The degree of perfection of a design is measured by the value of the blower hydraulic efficiency.

The impeller profile and vane layout is possible if the following elements are known:

1. Meridional velocities at inlet and outlet.
2. Impeller outside diameter.
3. Impeller vane inlet and outlet angles.

These same quantities determine both Euler's entrance and discharge triangles.   For straight radial vanes, all particles of fluid enter and leave the impeller at the same diameter, and the vane is "plain" or of single curvature.   Thus only one entrance and one discharge triangle determines the impeller design.   For mixed flow and axial flow impellers, velocity triangles are drawn for several streamlines.   Three streamlines usually suffice for average mixed flow and axial flow impellers.   Variation of vane angles along the radius determines the vane curvature and "twist."   The graphical problems connected with an impeller layout are presented in detail in Chapter 16.   This article will deal with the selection of the impeller design elements listed above. They are chosen for the design point only.   The head-capacity curve is estimated from previous experience and based on typical curves for different specific speeds.

(*d*) **Impeller Vane Discharge Angle.**   This is the most important single design element.   It has been shown that theoretical characteristics are determined by the vane angle alone.   In actual turbomachinery β_2 is still the deciding factor in design.   *All the design constants and proportions depend on the value of β_2.*   Therefore a choice of β_2 is the first step in selecting impeller design constants.   This selection is based on consideration of the desired steepness of the head-capacity curve, operating range (pumping), and whether or not a maximum output is desired from the impeller for a given diameter at the selected speed.   Both head and capacity increase with the angle β_2.   For that reason, for aircraft use where size and weight are highly evaluated, centrifugal superchargers use $\beta_2 = 90°$.   This also permits a maximum peripheral speed not possible with lower values of β_2 where mechanical strength is a factor.   However, reduction in size of blowers is accomplished at the expense of efficiency.   Both impeller and casing efficiency falls off appreciably with increasing values of β_2. The difference in the blower efficiency may be of the order of five to ten points for $\beta_2 = 25°$ and $\beta_2 = 90°$, or about 1 point for each 5°. This can be easily understood in view of the fact that the flow through the impeller and casing is decelerating, and higher impeller discharge angles lead to a rapidly divergent channel, requiring a great number of vanes. Velocities leaving the impeller are higher for higher values of β_2 (higher percentage of kinetic energy), and conversion of velocity into pressure in the casing incurs losses which are difficult to control. In the centrifugal pump industry, it has been well established that the optimum performance is realized with impeller angles of about 25° for all specific speeds. Experience with blowers follows the same trend. Whenever possible, lower values of β_2 are chosen, and higher values are employed only to obtain maximum head for a given maximum selected value of the peripheral velocity as determined from considerations of strength.

(e) **The Head Coefficient.** Determination of the impeller outside diameter D_2 is the next step in the impeller design. This is done by selecting a suitable "head factor" or "speed constant." These are dimensionless ratios connecting the head in feet with the peripheral velocity of the impeller, established experimentally for several values of the impeller discharge angle. For a continuous row of blowers of consistent design, such constants, when plotted against specific speed for each value of β_2, form a continuous function. The same is true of all design constants or ratios of important impeller or casing linear dimensions. Also, there should be a continuity in the variation of several constants for a constant specific speed and variable values of β_2. The above requirements are really definitions of a continuous row of consistent blower designs. Such design constants are not necessarily the same for different designers as the locations of the best efficiency point on the head-capacity curve is affected by the type of blower casing.

There are several "head-speed constants" in use by the designers of turbomachines. For the blowers, the use of a "head coefficient" has decided advantages over any others for the reasons which will become apparent from later discussions. The head coefficient ψ is defined as:

$$\psi = \frac{H}{u_2{}^2/g} \qquad \text{or} \qquad H = \psi \frac{u_2{}^2}{g} \qquad (5.18)$$

For the same specific speed, the value of the head coefficient increases with the value of the discharge angle β_2, which means a smaller impeller (u_2) is required to produce the same head. For the same β_2, ψ decreases for higher specific speeds and a larger impeller is required for the same head. Experimental determination of ψ to cover the whole range of specific speeds and β_2 would require a great number of consistent designs and tests, which hardly could be accumulated from any one source. Fortunately an analysis of available test data disclosed a certain regularity, or law, in the arrangement of ψ plots versus specific speed and discharge angle β_2 (Figs. 6.10 and 6.12). These relationships will be discussed in detail in Chapter 6.

(f) **Mean Effective Impeller Diameters.** The correlation and plot of several design constants covering a complete range of impellers from straight radial to axial flow types becomes particularly simple if

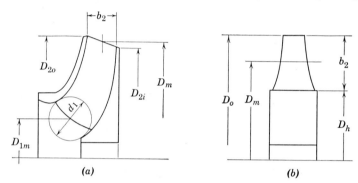

Fig. 5.2.   Mean effective diameter.

peripheral velocity at the impeller discharge is based on the "mean effective" impeller diameter defined as follows (Fig. 5.2):

$$D_m{}^2 = (D_{2o}{}^2 + D_{2i}{}^2)/2 \qquad (5.19)$$

For axial flow impellers this reduces to:

$$D_m{}^2 = D_o{}^2(1 + \nu^2)/2 \qquad (5.20)$$

where $\nu = D_h/D_o$ is the hub ratio (ν is Greek letter nu).

It can be shown that for mixed and axial flow impellers the mean effective diameter divides the flow through the impeller into two equal parts. It may be of interest to point out that, based on the mean effective diameter, the head coefficient for zero flow is the same ($\psi_o = 0.585$) irrespective of the angle β_2 or specific speed.

(g) **The Capacity Coefficient.** This is used as a capacity design constant and is defined as:

$$\phi = c_{m2}/u_2 \qquad (5.21)$$

where c_{m2} is the meridional velocity at impeller discharge, for the best efficiency point, based on the net discharge area (excluding vanes) and disregarding the leakage. After the pressure coefficient is selected and u_2 is established, c_{m2} can be calculated. The capacity coefficient increases for higher specific speeds at constant values of β_2. Also, ϕ increases with the angle β_2 for a constant specific speed (Fig. 6.12). In Chapter 3, it has been shown that when the capacity and head coefficients are used for plotting the Euler's and input head-capacity characteristics the same diagrams will also serve as Euler's and input discharge velocity triangles. The head and capacity coefficients for the best efficiency point (based on actual head and capacity), if plotted on the same coordinates, will determine the "actual velocity triangle," thus establishing the value and direction of the absolute velocity leaving the impeller. These coefficients are the most important ele-

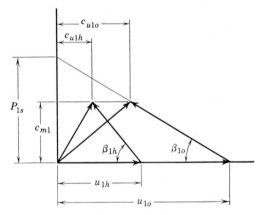

Fig. 5.3.   Inlet velocity triangle.

ments in the casing design (given on the Chart, Fig. 6.11). It becomes evident now that this chart would be impossible with any other type of design constants.

(h) **Entrance Velocity Triangle.** The meridional velocity at impeller inlet c_{m1} is, as a rule, higher than that at impeller discharge. The ratio c_{m1}/c_{m2} for low specific speed impellers ($n_s = 400$) is about 1.3 for single-stage overhung impellers and may be as high as 1.625 for multistage impellers with large shafts through the impeller eye. This ratio decreases as specific speed increases and approaches unity for axial flow impellers, or $n_s = 2500$. Within these limits c_{m1} is varied to obtain a satisfactory velocity triangle, which is controlled by the following considerations:

The vane entrance angle and velocity c_{m1} are selected so that some "nominal" prerotation is allowed. This will locate the "shockless" capacity slightly to the right of the b.e.p. (Fig. 5.3). The entrance angles can be prescribed by specifying the ratio of the pitch-per-second P_{1s} to the meridional velocity c_{m1}. A forced vortex pattern of flow is assumed in the impeller approach. This ratio varies within narrow limits,

$$R_1 = P_{1s}/c_{m1} = 1.15 \text{ to } 1.25$$

for blowers with straight end intake nozzle. For horizontally split casings, where some prerotation is induced by the shape of the inlet nozzle, higher values of R_1 are allowed

$$R_1 = 1.25 \text{ to } 1.35$$

Higher values of R_1 lead to higher entrance angles β_1 and result in a lower blower total efficiency (a point or two) as has been amply demonstrated in the centrifugal pump field.

The meridional velocity c_{m1} is based on the total area of approach disregarding the vane thickness, and omitting leakage (Fig. 5.2), so that

$$c_{m1} = Q/\pi D_{1m} d_1 \qquad (5.22)$$

In actual impellers, vane tips are tapered off at the entrance; thus, disregarding the vane thickness does not introduce appreciable error in the value of β_1. In any case it can be considered that the velocity triangle will be satisfied just ahead of the vane tips. The velocity through the impeller eye is selected equal to c_{m1} or slightly lower.

In multistage blowers the area of impeller approach should be such that the meridional flow toward the impeller vanes is steadily accelerated. This tends to equalize the velocity of approach, a condition necessary for efficient impeller performance.

From the observation of the entrance velocity triangle (Fig. 5.3) it is evident that R_1 is the ratio of the shockless capacity to the normal or rated capacity. However, allowing for vane thickness, the true ratio is somewhat lower. On the other hand, conditions at the impeller discharge are just as important, if not more, in locating the shockless or the best efficiency capacity.

In high speed blowers, for reasons of mechanical strength, it is sometimes desirable to make the impeller eye diameter as small as possible. Thus it may be necessary to exceed the normal ratios of inlet velocities suggested above. Further limitations may be set with respect to the adverse effects of a high Mach number, for high meridional velocities lead to high relative velocities. It is not recommended that c_m/a exceed 0.5; thus

$$c_{m1}/a \leq \tfrac{1}{2}$$

where a is the acoustic velocity at the inlet conditions (reference 3). Since the critical Mach number is determined by the relative velocity at entrance, a certain degree of prerotation may be necessary to reduce the relative velocity. According to Pfleiderer (reference 4), an inlet angle β_1 of 32 to 35° is most favorable from the point of view of reducing the effects of high Mach number.

For the average blower the volume increase at the impeller approach, due to velocity head pressure drop, can be neglected. However, for high speed and high pressure blowers (superchargers), the increase in volume of flow and drop of temperature through the impeller eye may be such as to make the effect of Mach number observable when not anticipated. The method of calculation of the actual volume of flow through the impeller eye is discussed in the article 7.3d.

5.3 DIMENSIONLESS SPECIFIC SPEED

For analysing blower performance and correlating the experimental design constants (pressure and capacity coefficients), the expression for specific speed (equation 5.6) can be transformed to include the dimensionless capacity ϕ and dimensionless head ψ rather than the measured c.f.m. and head in feet.

Make the following substitutions into equation 5.6.

$$Q = \text{c.f.m.} = (c_{m2}b_2\pi D_{\text{ave}})/60 \tag{5.23}$$

$$n = 60u_2/\pi D_m \tag{5.24}$$

$$H = \psi u_2{}^2/g \tag{5.25}$$

$$\phi = c_{m2}/u_2 \tag{5.26}$$

and segregating all constants into one, we obtain

$$\frac{(\text{r.p.m.})\ \sqrt{\text{c.f.m.}}}{H_{\text{ft.}}{}^{3/4}} = n_s = 3530 \left(\frac{b_2}{D_m}\right)^{1/2}\left(\frac{D_{\text{ave}}}{D_m}\right)^{1/2}\frac{\phi^{1/2}}{\psi^{3/4}} \tag{5.27}$$

where b_2 is impeller width at discharge.

D_m is mean effective diameter.

D_{ave} is an average of the two impeller shroud diameters at discharge $(D_{2o} + D_{2i})/2$.

The ratio D_{ave}/D_m is equal to unity for centrifugal impellers and is only slightly more than one for high specific speed axial flow impellers, for instance

$$(D_{\text{ave}}/D_m)^{1/2} = 0.965 \qquad \text{for} \qquad n_s = 4500$$

Since for all similar impellers the ratio b_2/D_m is constant, the ratio

$$\omega_s = \phi^{1/2}/\psi^{3/4} \tag{5.28}$$

can be used as a type number or another form of dimensionless specific speed.

In Fig. 6.10, lines of constant ω_s can be calculated for any desired value of ω_s by assuming ψ and calculating ϕ. Thus lines of constant ω_s are part of the network, having an absolute scale not depending upon any test points. It will be observed from equation 5.27 that for a given b_2/D_m, which fixes the impeller profile, lines of constant ω_s are lines of constant specific speed n_s.

Also note that by using different impeller discharge angles β_2 the same performance specific speed n_s (in terms of r.p.m., c.f.m., and head in feet) can be obtained with impellers of different ω_s, but the impeller profile b_2/D_m will be different for the two cases.

It can be shown that the following relationship is true

$$\phi \frac{b_2}{D_m} = \frac{Q}{D_2{}^3 n} \frac{1}{\pi^2} = \frac{q_s}{\pi^2} \tag{5.29}$$

and the equation (5.27) can be transformed to

$$n_s = 1124(q_s{}^{1/2}/\psi^{3/4}) \tag{5.30}$$

Obviously $q_s{}^{1/2}/\psi^{3/4}$ is another form of the dimensionless specific speed *independent of the actual impeller profile*. For that reason both expressions (equations 5.29 and 5.30) were particularly useful in correlating the design data of different sources in developing the chart (Fig. 6.10) in Chapter 6.

5.4 REDUCTION OF IMPELLER DIAMETER

In order to reduce the head and the capacity of a given centrifugal blower, the impeller diameter is generally reduced. Rules for estimating the performance for a given reduction in impeller diameter are closely associated with the affinity laws but are not entirely accurate. The error becomes greater the more the impeller diameter is reduced.

(*a*) **Centrifugal Impellers.** When the impeller diameter is cut in a centrifugal blower a new but similar Euler's velocity triangle is obtained at the discharge and is constructed on a reduced peripheral velocity vector u_2' (Fig. 5.4). All velocities of this new diagram are reduced in the ratio of the impeller diameters D_2'/D_2. If the subtractive term in Euler's equation ($u_1 c_{u1}/g$) is omitted, the following rules for predicting performance are obtained: the head varies directly as the square of the diameter ratio; capacity varies directly as diameter ratio; and brake horsepower varies directly as the cube of the impeller diameter ratio. However, as the impeller diameter is reduced the rules become approximate only, because: (1) the hydraulic efficiency decreases with cut impellers (appearing as a loss in head) instead of

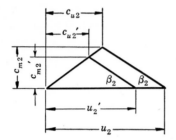

Fig. 5.4. The discharge velocity triangles for full and reduced impeller diameters.

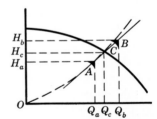

Fig. 5.5. Inlet velocity triangles for full and reduced impeller diameters.

remaining constant as assumed in the above rules; and (2) the subtractive term in Euler's equation is seldom if ever zero, and, when the impeller diameter is reduced, c_{u1} increases to c_{u1}' (Fig. 5.5), and the subtractive term $u_1 c_{u1}/g$ becomes greater. The reduction in gross efficiency due to reduced impeller diameters is caused by several factors.

1. Cutting impellers with streamlined tapered vanes results in blunt vane tips, which cause more disturbance in the volute. This effect

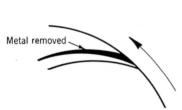

Fig. 5.6. Impeller vane overfiling.

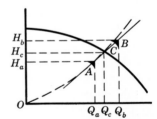

Fig. 5.7. Determination of impeller diameter cut.

may be partly or entirely eliminated by again tapering the vanes, after cutting, by "overfiling" or removing the metal on the leading face of the vane (Fig. 5.6).

2. A reduced impeller diameter results in a longer path for the liquid to travel in the volute casing before reaching the discharge nozzle.

3. In general, for exaggerated entrance vane angles, cutting the impellers moves the best efficiency point away from the "shockless" entrance conditions.

4. A reduction in mechanical efficiency occurs with cut impellers because the mechanical losses remain the same while the power output drops as the cube of impeller diameters.

The following procedure eliminates trial and error methods in calculating the impeller diameter required for a given head-capacity point. In Fig. 5.7, the specified point A is below the head-capacity curve $Q\text{-}H$. Take an arbitrary capacity Q_b, higher than the given

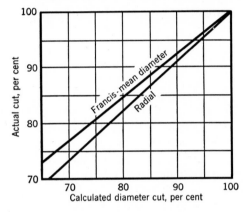

Fig. 5.8.   Correction for calculated impeller diameter cut.

capacity Q_a, and calculate the head H_b by applying the affinity laws.

$$H_b = H_a(Q_b{}^2/Q_a{}^2)$$

Connect points B and A to obtain the point of intersection C on the $Q\text{-}H$ curve. The required impeller diameter ratio is Q_a/Q_c. The line AB is a part of a parabola connecting corresponding points or points of the same specific speed. The efficiency at point A will be approximately the same as that at point C.

The calculated impeller diameter ratio Q_a/Q_c should be increased somewhat to compensate for the inaccuracy of the above established rules. Figure 5.8 gives the actual impeller diameter ratio in per cent plotted against calculated impeller diameter ratios. This correction again is approximate only, the accuracy decreasing with increased specific speed.

(b) **Axial Flow Impellers.** Reducing the outside diameter of an axial flow impeller would require a new casing or a liner to accommodate the reduced diameter. For that reason it is rarely used in practice. Referring to the preceding chapter and Fig. 4.6, the variation of the head and the capacity with cut impellers can be established: (1) the capacity varies directly as the new area swept by the impeller vane, the axial velocity remaining the same; (2) the head at the outside diameter will be reduced directly as the square of the diameters. The integrated head H' will be equal to the average of the head at the hub H_h (unchanged), and the new reduced head at the outside diameter $= H_o(D_o'/D_o)^2$.

$$2H' = H_h + H_o(D_o'/D_o)^2 \qquad (5.28)$$

Axial flow impellers designed for a constant head at all radii at the design point will produce the same head as the full diameter impellers if cut.

It should be noted that when the impeller diameter is reduced its specific speed is increased approximately inversely as the impeller diameter. Conversely by extending the impeller diameter its specific speed is reduced in the inverse ratio of impeller diameters. This can be made use of (when exact model is not available) for estimating dimensions of a new impeller. But in no case should cut impellers be used for actual multiplication because impeller optimum performance (including casing) is impaired when its diameter is cut. In a new design all elements, impeller entrance, and casing proportions are selected for the optimum efficiency.

Note that with a reduced impeller diameter the head coefficient is decreased. This follows from the fact that the actual impeller diameter is greater than that required by affinity laws to produce the required head. The reduction of the head coefficient is directly proportional to the square of the ratio calculated/actual impeller diameters as given on Fig. 5.8. This is in agreement with the general trend of variation of the head coefficient, i.e., higher specific speed impellers require a lower head coefficient as shown in Fig. 6.12.

When the head coefficient is plotted versus inlet volume Q, or inlet volume per revolution Q/n, the decrease of head coefficient appears even more than indicated above for compressible fluids. This is so because the affinity laws apply to the volumes at impeller discharge, and volume with cut impeller will not reexpand to the inlet pressure to the same degree as with full impeller diameter. This question is further elaborated in Chapter 8 where affinity laws are reviewed for compressible fluids.

5.5 COMPRESSIBLE FLUIDS

1. The discussion of the characteristics of the turboblowers in this chapter is developed as it applies to incompressible fluids. For com-

pressible fluids the actual volume of gas at the impeller discharge should be used for the specific speed calculation. Inlet c.f.m. can be used only for rough estimates. *The affinity laws hold only for the volumes at the impeller discharge.*

Presentation of the method of establishing the volume of flow as it progresses through a blower is given in the later chapters.

2. *Mach Numbers.* Introduction of the velocity of sound (a) as another independent variable to describe the characteristics of turbo-blowers would result in an additional dimensionless criterion $c/a = M$, known as Mach number, where c is the maximum local velocity of the fluid (the relative velocity at entrance is taken for the critical Mach number calculations). All the general relationships developed in this chapter cease to hold when the Mach number approaches unity (over 0.75). The effect of a high Mach number on the blower characteristics (head, capacity, and efficiency) is very similar to the effect of cavitation in centrifugal pumps, i.e., the head capacity and efficiency drop. Above the critical value of Mach number, the same Mach number does not assure a similarity of flow or hydraulic performance.

Remarks. In connection with the design procedure outlined in this chapter it should be noted that if all new impellers were built by multiplication of existing types there would be no progress in performance of turbomachines. Designing new impellers from basic design elements always involves some degree of experimentation. It depends upon the skill of the designer to sort out values leading to the optimum efficiency.

REFERENCES

1. Stepanoff, *Centrifugal and Axial Flow Pumps*, Wiley, 1948, pp. 76, 310.
2. Ippen, "The Influence of Viscosity on Centrifugal Pump Performance," *Trans. A.S.M.E.*, Vol. 68, No. 8, 1946, p. 823.
3. Eckert, *Ladeeinrichtungen*, Franckh, Stuttgart, 1952, p. 27.
4. Pfleiderer, *Strömungsmaschinen*, Springer, Berlin, 1952, p. 90.

CHAPTER 6

Hydraulic Performance
of Centrifugal Blowers

A study of losses in centrifugal blowers may be undertaken for one of the following reasons: (1) information about the nature and magnitude of losses may indicate the way to reduce these losses; (2) if the losses are known, it is possible to predetermine the head-capacity curve of a new machine by first assuming, or establishing in some other manner, the head-capacity curve of an idealized blower; (3) since the Q-H curve of an idealized blower is a straight line, the shape of the head-capacity curve of an actual blower is determined by the hydraulic losses. Thus it would seem possible, when something is known about the losses, to change the shape of the head-capacity curve to suit some special requirement.

Considering the high degree of perfection of modern turbomachinery as demonstrated by gross efficiencies of over 90 per cent, it is remarkable that so little exact knowledge is available on the losses of centrifugal blowers. None of the three above objectives has been achieved to any appreciable degree because of the present lack of knowledge of losses.

The progress in design has been accomplished mostly in an experimental way, the gross efficiency being the only criterion of improvement in performance. In this book all losses are grouped under the headings: hydraulic, leakage, mechanical, and disk friction losses. Only hydraulic losses will be discussed in this chapter.

6.1 HYDRAULIC LOSSES

These are the least known of all the losses in turbomachines, and at the same time they are the most essential ones to consider in attaining the three objectives set forth above. The reason for this is that there are so many factors contributing to hydraulic losses. Even the combined effect of these factors cannot be ascertained accurately. In general it can be said that hydraulic losses are caused by: (1) skin friction and (2) eddy and separation losses due to changes in direction

76

and magnitude of the velocity of flow.   The latter group includes the so-called shock loss and diffusion loss.

In the channels from the inlet to the discharge nozzle, there is not a single stretch of the path where either the direction of flow or the area and shape of the channel is constant; besides, part of the channel is rotating, thus upsetting the velocity distribution and further complicating the study of hydraulic losses.   Under such conditions it is impossible to calculate the friction loss through the machine with a degree of accuracy sufficient to serve any useful purpose.

In the following discussion no attempt will be made to give formulas or methods for calculating hydraulic losses in various parts of blowers. The need for prediction of head-capacity characteristics of a blower has long passed because, when new types are contemplated, sufficient data are available for designers to estimate the characteristics from existing types.

(*a*) **Friction and Diffusion Losses.**   The general formula for friction loss is

$$h_f = f \frac{L}{4m} \frac{v^2}{2g} \tag{6.1}$$

where f is a friction coefficient.

L is the length of the channel.

m is the hydraulic radius of the channel section.

v is the velocity at the section with the hydraulic radius m.

This formula could be applied to the several parts of the total path; the suction nozzle, impeller channel, volute, and discharge nozzle.   However, actual measurements of the length L and the hydraulic radius m may present difficulty in many cases (extreme mixed flow impeller or inlet nozzle of a double inlet machine, for instance).   The selection of a suitable friction coefficient is a problem in itself.   For these reasons several investigators combine all the friction losses in one term, expressing it by a simplified formula:

$$h_f = K_1(v_1{}^2/2g) = K_1Q^2 \tag{6.2}$$

where K_1 is a constant for a given type of machine and includes all lengths, areas and area ratios, and friction coefficients.   Thus K_1 covers all the unknown factors and also any errors caused by the inability to find a better expression for the several items contributing to the friction losses.   Similarly an expression can be set up for the diffusion loss in the impeller channel or discharge nozzle and stated by

$$h_d = f_2(v_2{}^2/2g) \tag{6.3}$$

Again, selection of the coefficient f_2 for the impeller channel presents difficulty. Therefore, for simplicity it is customary to express all diffusion losses by a formula

$$h_d = K_2(v_2{}^2/2g) = K_2Q^2 \tag{6.4}$$

where K_2 is a constant for a given type of machine.

Since the losses expressed by equations 6.2 and 6.4 both vary as the square of the capacity, they can be combined into one formula:

$$h_{fd} = h_f + h_d = K_3Q^2 \tag{6.5}$$

which is a square parabola with its axis on the axis of heads (Fig. 6.1).

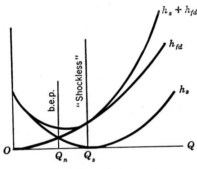

Fig. 6.1. Hydraulic losses.

(b) **Eddy and Separation Losses.** Losses at the impeller entrance and exit are usually called shock losses. The author accepts this term very reluctantly because in mechanics "shock" or impact does not necessarily mean a loss and in hydraulics, if impact is in the direction of flow, most of the energy of impact is recoverable (impulse action). Fluid flow in a blower tends to avoid shock by acquiring prerotation at the impeller inlet and by establishing a velocity gradient in the volute casing at the impeller discharge, thus cushioning the shock. The nature of the hydraulic loss at the impeller entrance, when fluid

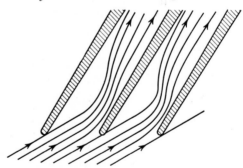

Fig. 6.2. Shock loss is a diffusion loss.

approaches at a high angle of attack, is that due to a sudden expansion or diffusion after separation (Fig. 6.2). At the impeller discharge the loss is mostly caused by a high rate of shear due to a low average velocity in the casing and high velocity at the impeller discharge. It should be noted that even at the b.e.p. the average volute velocity is considerably lower than the tangential component of the absolute velocity at the impeller discharge (c_{u2}'), and since this is the optimum condition it cannot be improved by changing the volute area. Besides, there is a shock loss at the volute casing tongue and at the entrance of diffusion vanes when a diffusion vane casing is used. These losses are of the same nature as shock loss at the entrance to the impeller; that is they are diffusion losses.

If we assume that the impeller design is such that at a capacity Q_s (shockless) the direction of flow agrees with the vane angles at both entrance and discharge, thus incurring no additional losses at these points, then at capacities above and below Q_s there will be a sudden

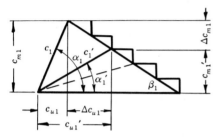

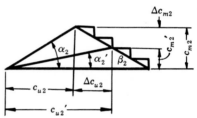

Fig. 6.3. Shock component of peripheral velocity at entrance to impeller.

Fig. 6.4. Shock component of velocities at discharge.

change in the direction and magnitude of the velocity of flow. This change results in losses which can be expressed as

$$h_{s1} = K_4(\Delta c_{u1}{}^2/2g) \tag{6.6}$$

for the entrance, and

$$h_{s2} = K_5(\Delta c_{u2}{}^2/2g) \tag{6.7}$$

for the exit of the impeller.

In Fig. 6.3, at capacity Q_s, the meridional velocity at impeller entrance is c_{m1}, and the flow is approaching the impeller under an angle α_1 with a tangential component of the absolute velocity c_{u1}. When the capacity is reduced ($c_{m1}' < c_{m1}$) the fluid should have a tangential component c_{u1}' to enter the vanes at an angle β_1, and

$$\Delta c_{u1} = c_{u1}' - c_{u1}$$

Similarly, at the discharge (Fig. 6.4) at capacity Q_s, the meridional velocity is c_{m2}, and the tangential component of the absolute velocity is c_{u2}. At a reduced capacity, the tangential component will increase to c_{u2}', and the increment of the tangential component is the difference between the two: $\Delta c_{u2} = c_{u2}' - c_{u2}$. At capacities greater than Q_s, both Δc_{u1} and Δc_{u2} are negative. Note that, in Figs. 6.3 and 6.4, for equal increments of c_{m1} or capacity, Δc_{u1} increases the same amount. Similarly, for the same steps in c_{m2}, the value of Δc_{u2} increases by an equal amount. Thus both items increase on both sides of Q_s as the square of the capacity increments. In this way it is possible to combine both equations 6.6 and 6.7 into one expression, or

$$h_s = K_6(Q - Q_s)^2 \qquad (6.8)$$

This represents a square parabola with its apex at Q_s (Fig. 6.1).

6.2   TOTAL HEAD-CAPACITY CURVE

(a) **The Head-Capacity Curve Equation.** The head-capacity curve of an idealized blower is a straight line. For a given discharge vane angle, a single line will represent the characteristics of machines of all specific speeds when plotted to dimensionless scales. When the essential design elements are selected, the location of the best efficiency point, and hence the specific speed, is fixed. Hydraulic losses for the selected proportions of essential passages will determine the head-capacity curve of the actual blower. In general, for a constant speed, the head-capacity curve can be obtained by subtracting losses from the input head of an idealized machine. For a given capacity the actual head may be expressed by

$$H = H_i - K_3 Q^2 - K_6(Q - Q_s)^2 \qquad (6.9)$$

To draw the H_i line knowledge of one point only on this line is necessary since, at zero head, H_i and H_e lines intersect at a capacity given by $\phi = c_{m2}/u_2 = \tan \beta_2$. Such a point is shown in Fig. 6.10 (point B) and is discussed later.

Constants K_3 and K_6 are determined from an actual Q-H curve by selecting several points on the head-capacity curve, substituting the values of Q and H into equation 6.9 and obtaining any desired number of simultaneous equations which can be solved for K_3 and K_6. As should be expected, the value of the constants thus found are different from blower to blower and are inconsistent along the same curve. For that reason there has been no serious attempt to establish such constants. Graphically, the total head-capacity is obtained by subtracting the friction and shock losses, as shown in Fig. 6.1 from the H_i curve (Fig. 6.5). By referring to Fig. 6.1 it will be noticed that the b.e.p. will always occur at a capacity lower than the shockless capacity Q_s because the sum of the friction and shock losses determines the location of the peak efficiency. The impeller vane entrance angle at the b.e.p. is exaggerated or laid out for a meridional inlet (without prerotation) for a capacity greater than the normal capacity; this means that at the b.e.p. prerotation is allowed.

The Q-H curve on Fig. 6.5 is a parabola with its apex displaced to the right of the axis of heads. Such curves are approached on low and medium specific speed blowers.

(b) **General Blower Characteristics.** By expressing the constants K_3 and K_6 of equation 6.9 in terms of the blower physical dimensions (ratios) and angles, it is possible to transform equation 6.9 to the form

$$H = An^2 + BnQ + CQ^2 \qquad (6.10)$$

where A, B, and C are constants depending on the blower design. For a constant speed n, this is an equation of the head-capacity curve.

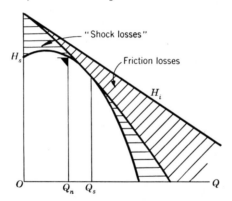

Fig. 6.5. Q-H curve is obtained by subtraction of hydraulic losses from input head.

Since equation 6.10 has no practical application and its development does not reveal anything new or instructive, it is omitted from this discussion.[*]

6.3 HYDRAULIC EFFICIENCY

(a) **Hydraulic Efficiency at Zero Capacity.** In Chapter 5 it was shown that the shut-off head of actual blowers, expressed in dimensionless coordinates, is essentially constant for all specific speeds. This is expressed by the fact that ψ_s, the head coefficient at shut-off, is constant for all specific speeds (point D, Fig. 6.8). This in turn means that the hydraulic efficiency at shut-off is constant for all specific speeds and all angles β_2.

$$H_s = 0.585 u_2{}^2/g \quad \text{and} \quad e_{hs} = H_s/H_i$$

[*] The development of equation 6.10 is given by Pfleiderer (reference 1), Spannhake (reference 2), LeConte (reference 3), and others.

From Fig. 6.10

$$e_{hs} = DO/BO = 0.585/0.725 = 0.808 = \text{Constant} \qquad (6.11)$$

(*b*) **Hydraulic Efficiency versus Specific Speed.** On Fig. 6.6 *BE* is the input head line; *DGHJK* is the actual total head-capacity curve; and *NMLK* is the hydraulic efficiency curve. If a line *PE* is drawn

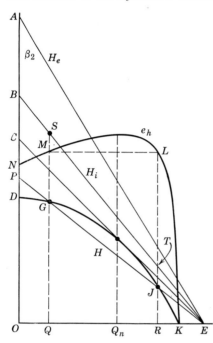

through *E* intersecting the total head-capacity curve at two points, *G* and *J*, these points will be found to be points of equal hydraulic efficiency since

$$GQ/SQ = JR/TR$$

This follows from the relation of the two sets of similar triangles, *EGQ* and *EJR* and *ESQ* and *ETR*. As line *PE* is moved toward line *CE*, it will always cut the total head-capacity curve at two points of equal hydraulic efficiency, and, in the limiting case, line *PE* will become tangent to the total head-capacity curve at the point of maximum hydraulic efficiency.[†]

If several total head-capacity curves for blowers of different specific speeds are intersected by a line *PE* (Fig. 6.7) all the points

Fig. 6.6.   Hydraulic efficiency.

of intersection, *Q*, *R*, *S*, *T*, *U*, and *V*, will be points of the same hydraulic efficiency. Now, if line *PE* is moved toward line *BE* it will become tangent to the several total head-capacity curves at the points of best hydraulic efficiency *K*, *L*, and *M*.

Experimental evidence with centrifugal pumps indicates that all head-capacity curves for a continuous row of pumps within the useful range of specific speeds will have a common tangent *CE* at the point of best hydraulic efficiency.

In Fig. 6.8 are plotted several head-capacity points representing the best efficiency points of pumps of different specific speeds. These

[†] Lichtenstein (reference 4) has proved analytically that a tangent to the total head-capacity curve at the point of best hydraulic efficiency will pass through the point *E*, intersection of the input head line with the axis of capacities.

pumps are of consistent design, the same impeller discharge angle, about $22\frac{1}{2}°$, being used. The points show a definite trend to align themselves along the line passing through the point of zero input head $(c_{m2}/u_2 = \tan 22\frac{1}{2}°)$. Now, if it is assumed that all total head-capacity curves have a common tangent, *the optimum peak hydraulic efficiency is the same for pumps or blowers of all specific speeds.* Such a conclusion can be justified by the following reasoning and qualifications.

1. It is assumed that all machines are of such sizes that the scale effect can be disregarded.

2. For a continuous and consistent row of machines of different specific speeds it will be assumed that the hydraulic losses are divided

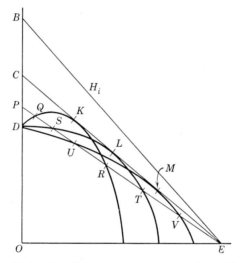

Fig. 6.7. Hydraulic efficiency is the same for all specific speeds.

between the impeller and casing in the same ratio. Then, confining discussion to the impeller only, it can be stated with more confidence that the impeller hydraulic efficiency is the same for all specific speeds. At the b.e.p. hydraulic losses are almost entirely friction losses. These losses are proportional to the number of impeller channels and their lengths, but the head produced also increases with the number of channels and length. If both maintain the same ratio, the optimum hydraulic efficiency of the impeller will remain constant for all specific speeds. At zero capacity, hydraulic friction losses are zero and the hydraulic efficiency is determined by the shock losses only. These losses bear a constant ratio to the total head for several specific speeds, and a constant hydraulic efficiency at shut-off results. This has been proved experimentally.

3. *For axial flow and mixed flow blowers, angle β_2 is taken at the mean effective diameter $D_m = \sqrt{(D_{2o}{}^2 + D_{2i}{}^2)/2}$. The peripheral velocity u_2 for the dimensionless head and capacity coefficients is based on the mean effective diameter. For straight axial flow blowers β_2 is the discharge angle of the mean line and not a chord angle.*

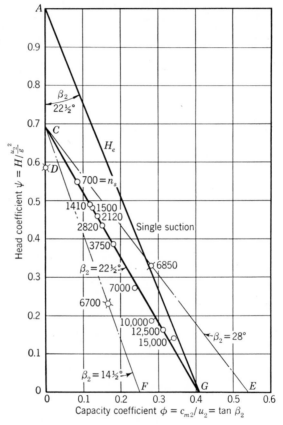

Fig. 6.8.   Pump specific speed based on gallons per minute equals blower specific speed based on c.f.m. multiplied by 2.74.

(c) **Effect of Discharge Angle β_2 on Impeller Hydraulic Efficiency.** Figure 6.9 shows Euler's head H_e and input head H_i, lines AE and BE, respectively, for a given discharge angle β_2. Line CE is the locus of the best hydraulic efficiency points of actual total head curves for all specific speeds. The point D, the actual shut-off head, is common for all total head capacity curves. Location of the maximum capacity point E is fixed by the angle β_2 as $OE = \tan \beta_2$. The optimum hydraulic efficiency of the impellers of all specific speeds is CO/BO.

If the impeller discharge angle is changed from β_2 to β_{21} the maximum capacity point F will be given by the relationship $OF = \tan \beta_{21}$. Points A, B, C, and D remain the same, and H_e, H_i, and H lines can be drawn as shown by dotted lines. The line CF now becomes the locus of heads for the optimum hydraulic efficiency of the impeller. The hydraulic efficiency itself stays unchanged and is still equal to CO/BO. Thus the optimum impeller hydraulic efficiency is constant for all specific speeds and does not depend on the discharge vane angle β_2. There is sufficient experimental evidence to corroborate this conclusion in the field of centrifugal pumps.

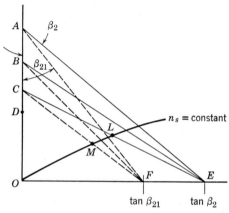

Fig. 6.9. Hydraulic and vane efficiency are independent of discharge angle β_2.

Referring to Fig. 6.9 it will be noticed that the vane efficiency, $e_{va} = BO/AO$, being constant for impellers of all specific speeds and at all capacities, does not change when the discharge angle β_2 is varied. It has been found that when the discharge angle is varied the head and capacity change in such a way that the specific speed remains constant.

$$\omega_s = \phi^{1/2}/\psi^{3/4} = \text{Constant} \tag{6.12}$$

It follows also from the equation 5.27, for a constant impeller profile b_2/D_2, that specific speed n_s remains constant for different values of β_2.

6.4 AUTHOR'S DIAGRAM OF BLOWER CHARACTERISTICS

(a) **Construction of Diagram.** In Fig. 6.10 the author has prepared a master diagram covering essential design and performance features of impellers of all specific speeds and impeller discharge angles β_2, for the optimum best efficiency points. The fact that the points line-up along a straight line on Fig. 6.8 for one value of $\beta_2 = 22\frac{1}{2}°$, which

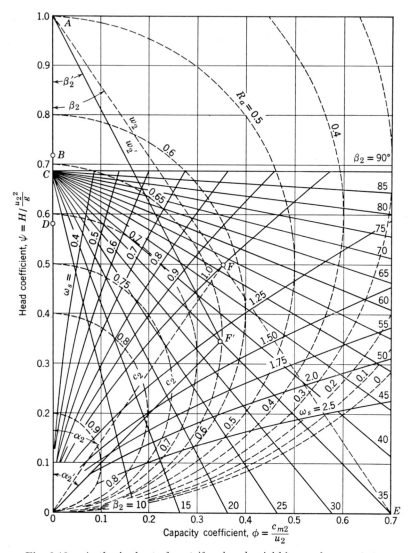

Fig. 6.10. Author's chart of centrifugal and axial blower characteristics.

intersects the axis of ϕ at a point where $\phi = \tan 22\frac{1}{2}°$, strongly suggested to the author that for any other values of β_2 the values of ϕ
and ψ for the b.e.p. will also arrange themselves on the lines connecting
point C with points of $\phi = \tan \beta_2$ on the axis of ϕ. This was sub-
stantiated by the test values of ϕ and ψ, covering a complete range of
specific speeds and values of β_2 by centrifugal and axial flow pumps and
blowers.

Point B on the diagram was obtained by calculating the hydraulic efficiency CO/BO at b.e.p. of a representative centrifugal pump, as discussed in detail in reference 5. Point D represents the shut-off value of ψ_s which as stated earlier, is common for all machines.

(b) **Properties of the Diagram.** 1. Lines radiating from point C are loci of the best efficiency head-capacity points (b.e.p.) for different impeller discharge angles and specific speeds, the latter increasing from top to bottom of the chart. Since the shut-off (point D) is common to all angles and specific speeds, location of the b.e.p. fixes the slope of the head-capacity curve.

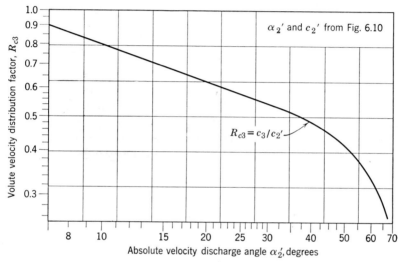

Fig. 6.11. Volute velocity distribution factor.

2. By connecting any point on the chart, say F', with points O and A, the *actual* velocity triangle is obtained with angles and velocities approximately (but very closely) equal to those at the impeller discharge. Any inaccuracy results from the effects of the hydraulic losses in the casing.

3. The Euler's velocity triangle AFO is obtained by connecting point A with E to obtain F at a given capacity ϕ.

4. The chart gives the basic impeller design data—impeller diameter, width, and discharge angle; also the casing velocity (volute or diffusion vanes) and volute or discharge diffusion casing vane angle α_2'. To obtain the average casing velocity, the value of the absolute velocity c_2', as given by the input (actual) velocity triangle, is multiplied by a velocity distribution factor given in Fig. 6.11 which is plotted as a function of the discharge angle α_2'.

5. The functional relationship of controlling design elements is clearly shown on the diagram. (a) When impeller discharge angle β_2 is changed without changing the impeller profile, the operating point moves along the constant specific speed curve. (b) If the operating point is moved along the constant head line (ψ = Constant) the chart will give variation of the meridional velocity c_{m2}, for different β_2 and hence the impeller width, to meet a given capacity. (c) If, for a given impeller, the casing area (volute) is changed, the operating point moves along the constant β_2 line until the impeller capacity ($A_2 \times c_{m2}$) is equal to the volute capacity ($A_v \times c_2' \times R_{c3}$); where A_v is the volute throat area and $c_2' \times R_{c3}$ is the average casing velocity c_3. (d) For a given blower casing and fixed impeller profile, variation of the impeller discharge angle moves the b.e.p. along the line of constant absolute velocity angle α_2'. (e) The ratio $OE/\phi = \tan \beta_2/\phi$ is the "impelling ratio," defined by equation 4.20, which is an important factor for the determination of vane discharge angles for several streamlines when that for the mean effective diameter is selected (axial and mixed flow impellers).

6. The chart in Fig. 6.10 gives only essential elements of the discharge velocity triangles for a continuous row of hydraulic types. In addition to those represented on the chart, there are a number of design elements, such as the impeller hub ratio, number of vanes, and casing design, which have a bearing upon the blower performance. If these secondary design elements deviate considerably from the normal average values, the points of ψ and ϕ will not fall in their proper places on the chart. It is the designer's problem to recognize such deviations from normal designs and anticipate their effect on the blower performance.

7. Figure 6.10 is prepared for blowers having no means to produce or prevent prerotation at the impeller inlets. When prerotation is allowed, Fig. 6.10 can be used, but the actual head (specified) should be either reduced or increased by the value $c_{u1}'u_1/g$. The value of c_{u1}' is obtained by multiplying the value of c_{u1}, as given on the Euler's entrance triangle drawn on the entrance guide vane angle α_1, by a factor $0.691 = CO/AO$ in Fig. 6.10 thus allowing the same vane effectiveness of the guide vanes as was established experimentally for the impeller vanes.

8. The input head lines can be drawn by connecting points for different discharge angles β_2 ($\phi = \tan \beta_2$ on the axis of ϕ) with point B, instead of C. This is determined by $CO/BO = e_h$, where e_h is the hydraulic efficiency. Once determined for one value of the discharge angle and specific speed, e_h remains the same for the whole chart for

blowers approaching optimum performance, for which $e_h = 0.95$ has been found experimentally. However, the input head is of academic interest only—the value of Fig. 6.10 is that it contains actual head, capacity, velocities and angles.

9. A number of half-circles in Fig. 6.10 marked $R = 0.1, 0.2 \cdot \cdot \cdot 0.9$ represent the degree of reaction or fraction of the total pressure measured at the impeller discharge. Obviously $(1 - R)$ will represent the kinetic energy as a fraction of the total head generated by the impeller. Degree of reaction is discussed in Art. 14.1; where it is used to designate the degree of prerotation allowed ahead of an axial impeller. It has no particular use for centrifugal impellers.

(c) **Use of Fig. 6.10.** To use Fig. 6.10 for selection of the values of the head and capacity coefficients to meet a given set of c.f.m. and head requirements, the dimensionless specific speed ω_s should be known. Then, entering the chart following ω_s, values of ψ and ϕ are read off for a selected impeller discharge angle β_2. The performance specific speed n_s can be calculated as soon as the rotational speed is chosen. To calculate the dimensionless specific speed ω_s for a known dimensional specific speed n_s through use of equation 5.27, the ratio b_2/D_m should be known. (The ratio D_{ave}/D_m is assumed to be equal to unity.) An experimental determination of the relationship between b_2/D_m and n_s for different values of the impeller discharge angle β_2 was not satisfactory because data obtained from several sources would not plot consistently. The reason for this lies in the fact that there was no continuity in design; the effect of blower casing design was particularly prominent.

To overcome this difficulty the specific capacity (defined by equation 5.29)

$$q_s = (b_2/D_m)\pi^2 \tag{6.13}$$

was plotted against specific speed n_s for several values of β_2 with good results. Having that, the value of the head coefficient ψ could be calculated for any desired values of n_s and β_2 from the equation 5.30.

$$n_s = 1124(q_s^{1/2}/\psi^{3/4}) \tag{6.14}$$

These values are plotted on the upper part of the chart (Fig. 6.12). Now it is possible to enter the chart (Fig. 6.10) and read off values of ϕ for any set of n_s and ψ or n_s and β_2 values. These values are plotted on the lower part of chart (Fig. 6.12).

Using information from the chart (Fig. 6.12), it is possible to calculate ω_s as a function of n_s, or, using equation 5.27, one can draw another chart representing b_2/D_m for various values of n_s and β_2. However, such plots would have no advantages over the chart (Fig. 6.12), which gives ψ and ϕ directly and which permits entering the chart (Fig. 6.10) for selection of the values of the velocity c_2' and angle α_2', which are the controlling factors for the casing design.

Note that, based on the experimental plot of the specific capacity q_s, the values of ψ (and ϕ) are uniquely defined by equation 6.14. The values of ψ and ϕ on the chart (Fig. 6.12) agree satisfactorily with test data of blowers covering a wide range of specific speeds and β_2

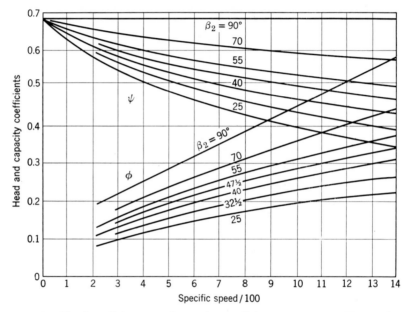

Fig. 6.12. Head coefficient ψ and capacity coefficient ϕ versus specific speed n_s, based on impeller discharge c.f.m.

and with volute and vaned diffuser casings. A study of the performance of a number of blowers having vaneless diffusers (width equal to b_2) and $\beta_2 = 55$ to $60°$ disclosed that values of ϕ were from 1.10 to 1.25 times higher than those on the chart (Fig. 6.12) whereas values of the specific capacity q_s were essentially consistent with the rest of the data derived from volute and vaned diffuser blowers. This merely means that the vaneless diffuser presents less restriction to the flow than the volute or vaned diffuser, thus inducing higher velocities and narrower impellers to produce the same specific capacity. The values of ψ for units with vaneless diffusers plot satisfactorily on the chart (Fig. 6.12).

Location of point C on the chart (Fig. 6.10) is based on data from single-stage units having total efficiencies of from 85 to 90 per cent (centrifugal pumps). However, the values of ψ and ϕ are expected to be accurate for total blower efficiencies (polytropic) of 80 per cent; the possible deviation is partly compensated by the fact that single-stage blowers, as a rule, have straight end inlet nozzles while the chart was originally developed for single-stage double-suction centrifugal pumps where some prerotation was induced by the shape of the suction nozzle. When a lower efficiency is expected (low n_s, small unit, multistage blower) the value of ψ as read off the chart should be reduced approximately in proportion to the expected total efficiency.

(*d*) **Number of Vanes.** At the best efficiency point, hydraulic losses are almost entirely friction losses. These friction losses are pro-

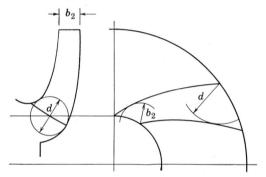

Fig. 6.13.   Number of vanes for centrifugal impellers.

portional to the number of channels and their length, but the head produced also increases with the number of channels and their length. If losses and head maintain the same ratio, the optimum hydraulic efficiency of the impeller will remain constant for all specific speeds. From a study of successful designs the following formula was arrived at, connecting the number of impeller vanes with the pressure coefficient which holds through a wide range of specific speeds

$$l/t = 4.75\psi \tag{6.15}$$

where l = the vane true length.

$t = \pi D_m/z$.

z = the number of vanes.

In a well-proportioned impeller, the average width of the impeller channel at discharge on the plan view is approximately equal to the average channel width at the inlet on the profile view (d in Fig. 6.13), and the width of the channel at inlet on the plan view is equal to the width of the channel at impeller discharge (b_2 in Fig. 6.13). Obviously with such proportions the impeller channel cross section in the middle portion approaches a square, which is the best compromise that it is possible to accomplish hydraulically.   Note that the proportions of the impeller channel as given by Fig. 6.13 lead to the condition that relative velocity at entrance is equal to that at discharge (disregarding compression).   Although this is true approximately in practice, the relative velocity is not a controlling factor in the impeller design.   If values of β_2 and c_{m2} are selected, the relative velocity is fixed.

Both of the above rules are approximate only.   But variation of vane numbers ± 1 has no appreciable effect on the blower performance. From a great number of successful designs of centrifugal blowers it has been found that the number of vanes is accurately given by the rule $z = \beta_2°/3$.   For small impellers the number of vanes should be reduced.

6.5   SUPPLEMENTARY REMARKS ON THE CHART (FIG. 6.10)

The properties of the chart, and the manner in which it was developed, being known, it becomes clear that a selection of coordinates or proper expressions for the dimensionless head and capacity and introduction of the mean effective impeller diameter were the most important means to achieve the results as they appear on the chart (Fig. 6.10).

In Chapter 12 on centrifugal flow fans a procedure is outlined on how to modify the chart (Fig. 6.12) for designs that differ materially in some respect from the optimum normal design and for which the b.e.p. values of the head and capacity coefficients will not fall on their proper lines on the chart.   Such a procedure may be employed when simplified hydraulic forms are used as in the case of fans or when the effects of Reynolds number cannot be neglected as in small slow speed blowers or in pumping viscous fluids (e.g., centrifugal pumps pumping petroleum products).

(*a*) **Other Forms of Head and Capacity Coefficients.**   There are a number of other expressions for the dimensionless head or pressure coefficients in use, with which the reader should be familiar.   One of them has the form

$$\psi_1 = \frac{H}{u_2{}^2/2g} = 2Hg/u_2{}^2 = 2\psi \tag{6.16}$$

For centrifugal impellers this is twice the value of the head coefficient used on the chart (Fig. 6.10).   Still another form is found occasionally in the older literature on axial flow compressors:

$$\psi_2 = 2\Delta p/\rho_1 u_2{}^2 \tag{6.17}$$

where Δp is the stage pressure rise.

ρ_1 is the mass density at inlet.

It can be shown $\psi_2 > \psi_1$ and not equivalent to it.

$$\frac{\psi_1}{\psi_2} = \frac{k p_1}{(k-1)\Delta p}\left[\left(\frac{p_2}{p_1}\right)^{\frac{k-1}{k}} - 1\right] \qquad (6.18)$$

Examples: At $u_2 = 1000$ ft. per sec., $\psi_1 = 0.46; \psi_2 = 0.50$.

At $u_2 = 500$ ft. per sec., $\psi_1 = 0.49; \psi_2 = 0.50$.

The head coefficient ψ (and ψ_1) remains constant only if head in feet is used as a function of the impeller size (u_2). Variation of ψ_2 as compared with ψ shows the effect of density on Δp, while the head in feet remains the same. For incompressible fluids $\psi_2 = \psi_1$.

The head coefficient ψ_1 defined by equation 6.16 is usually based on the peripheral velocity u_2 at impeller outside diameter and not on the mean effective diameter as defined by equation 5.19. In converting ψ_1 to ψ, equation 6.16 is applicable only to centrifugal impellers. For axial and mixed flow impellers the following relationship holds to convert ψ_1 to head coefficient ψ as used in this book and in Fig. 6.10. From equation 6.16 we can write

$$\psi_1/\psi = 2u_m{}^2/u_o{}^2 = 2D_m{}^2/D_2{}^2 \qquad (6.19)$$

where ψ_1 is based on the outside impeller diameter D_2; and ψ is based on the mean effective diameter D_m, defined by equations 5.19 and 5.20.

A capacity coefficient or flow coefficient, used to some extent, was introduced by Rateau.

$$\delta_r = \frac{Q}{R_2{}^2}\frac{1}{u_2} \qquad (6.20)$$

Where R_2 is the impeller outside radius. This is connected with ϕ as follows:

$$\delta_r = \phi(b_2/D_2)4\pi = (4/\pi)q_s \qquad (6.21)$$

Note that δ_r differs from the specific capacity by a constant $4/\pi$ and is a measure of the through-flow ability of the turbomachine. For that reason δ_r cannot be used as a capacity constant to determine the impeller width b_2. A modified expression for the flow coefficient is also in use to a limited extent.

$$\delta = \frac{4Q}{\pi D_2{}^2}\frac{1}{u_2} = \frac{\delta_r}{\pi} = \frac{4q_s}{\pi^2} \qquad (6.22)$$

Note that the head coefficient ψ_1 and ψ_2 and capacity coefficients δ and δ_r do not possess the same properties as ψ and ϕ as used in this chapter and would not permit the construction of the chart (Fig. 6.10).

It should be pointed out that axial flow impeller test data to be plotted on Fig. 6.10 is referred to the discharge angle β_2 (not the chord angle) at the mean effective diameter and not at the outside impeller diameter.

(*b*) **The Dimensionless Blower Casing Criterion.** By simple algebraic substitutions it can be shown that head coefficient ψ, capacity coefficient ϕ, and dimensionless specific speed ω_s are functions of the

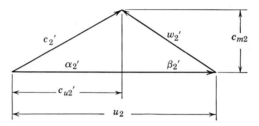

Fig. 6.14.   Discharge velocity triangle.

impeller discharge angle β_2' and the absolute velocity at discharge angle α_2' only.   Thus, by referring to Fig. 6.14, it can be written

$$\psi = \frac{c_{u2}'}{u_2} = \frac{c_2' \cos \alpha_2'}{u_2} = \frac{\sin \beta_2' \cos \alpha_2'}{\sin (\alpha_2' + \beta_2')}$$

or,

$$\psi = \frac{1}{1 + \tan \alpha_2' \cot \beta_2'} \tag{6.23}$$

and

$$\phi = \frac{c_{m2}}{u_2} = \frac{c_2' \sin \alpha_2'}{u_2} = \frac{1}{\cot \alpha_2' + \cot \beta_2'} \tag{6.24}$$

Hence,

$$\omega_s = f(\alpha_2', \beta_2') = \phi^{1/2}/\psi^{3/4} \tag{6.25}$$

The importance of the impeller discharge angle β_2 as a single controlling design element has been emphasized aready.   Attention is called to the fact that the absolute velocity angle at impeller discharge α_2' represents the casing criterion in the above relationships.

The affinity laws and several criteria of performance of turbomachines established in Chapter 5 really apply to the impeller only. Blower casing design deals with two variables: velocity of flow from the impeller and its direction.   Since velocity varies with the speed, the angle α_2' is the only criterion which can be used as an independent variable to correlate the casing design data for blowers of different specific speed. Figure 6.11 shows the casing "velocity distribution factor" plotted against the angle α_2', and not against specific speed.

(c) **Specific Capacity and Through-Flow Ability of a Blower.** It is important to grasp the physical meaning of specific capacity q_s defined by equations 5.10, 5.29, and 5.30 and referred to the b.e.p. It represents the "through-flow ability"‡ of a complete blower. It has been shown in Chapter 4 that the flow through a blower is produced by the energy gradient, the value of which is determined by the impeller discharge angle. The location of the b.e.p. and hence of q_s is determined by the combined restrictive action of the impeller and casing, which in turn jointly locate the point of minimum combined losses of the system. The restrictive action of the blower passages may be differently divided between the impeller and casing, i.e., a tight (narrow) impeller and a rather liberal casing, or vice versa. Finding the optimum flow condition of a blower is the objective of every designer. The restrictive action of the blower passages should not be connected in any way with the combined resistance to the flow which results in a loss of head but should be thought of as an efficient nozzle that determines the rate of flow. Thus, two blowers of different specific speed may be equally efficient, but their specific capacity q_s may be greatly different. Any changes in the casing such as reduction of the volute area, reduction of the diffuser casing vane angle, or increase in number of vanes above normal will reduce the specific capacity. But, since head is produced by the impeller alone, it will not change near the b.e.p., but the b.e.p. will move to a lower capacity and higher head. Or, if impeller width is increased, the specific capacity will increase but not in proportion to the impeller outlet area increase because impeller passages are only one link in a series of passages from the inlet to the outlet. In normal designs a higher specific capacity (which means also a higher specific speed) leads to lower hydraulic friction losses and a better gross efficiency.

(d) **Absolute Velocity at Impeller Discharge.** The values of the head coefficient ψ and capacity coefficient ϕ on the chart (Fig. 6.10) are based on the measured head and capacity. The capacity of the impeller is higher than the measured capacity by the amount of leakage. Also, the tangential component of the absolute velocity (c_{u2}') is higher at impeller discharge than that corresponding to ψ by the amount of hydraulic losses beyond the impeller discharge. The true value of the absolute angle at the impeller discharge (α_2') differs little

‡ A translation of German word "Durchschluckfähigkeit."

from that given by the chart. The value of the average volute velocity $c_3 = R_{c3} \times c_2'$ is corrected by the experimental factor R_{c3} based on the actual volute areas.

Thus, although the chart (Fig. 6.10) involves several minor approximations, the values contained in the chart can be used with confidence for design of impellers and volute and vaned diffuser casings as long as the hydraulic design does not deviate appreciably from the continuous types on which the chart is based. The vaneless diffuser casing requires a special correction as outlined previously in this chapter.

REFERENCES

1. Pfleiderer, *Die Kreiselpumpen*, Springer, Berlin, 1949, p. 251.
2. Spannhake, *Centrifugal Pumps*, M.I.T., Cambridge, Mass., 1934, p. 152 (translation).
3. LeConte, *Hydraulics*, McGraw-Hill, 1926, p. 314.
4. Lichtenstein, "Method of Analyzing of Performance Curves of Centrifugal Pumps," *Trans. A.S.M.E.*, Vol. 50, No. 3, 1928, p. 3.
5. Stepanoff, *Centrifugal and Axial Flow Pumps*, Wiley, p. 101.

CHAPTER 7

Thermodynamics of Turboblowers

In Chapters 3 and 4, it was shown that the generation of pressure
or head by an impeller is accomplished entirely by dynamic means
through the application of mechanical work. *The nature of the fluid,
or its thermodynamic properties, has no effect on the amount of work in
foot-pounds per pound of fluid that an impeller can apply or the fluid can
absorb.* To state it differently: the head produced by an impeller is
independent of the nature of the gas or any of its properties. However, as fluid progresses through the impeller and casing, its pressure
and temperature increase and its specific volume decreases. Therefore, to establish the controlling dimensions of the impeller and casing
passages, the volume of flow per second, or specific volume of the fluid,
should be known at those points. The fluid velocities being known
from the dynamics of the impeller, it is possible to determine the
thermodynamic properties of the fluid at any point of its path by using
relationships established in thermodynamics. *Addition or subtraction
of heat from the fluid as it travels through the impeller has no effect on the
impeller performance; i.e., on the head generated or hydraulic efficiency.*
Change in specific volume and fluid density is the only effect of the
heat flow to or from the fluid. Again, thermodynamics enables one to
establish the fluid properties at the required points. Thus it is evident that neither the design nor application of blowers is possible without knowledge of thermodynamics. However, it should be borne in
mind that the subject of thermodynamics deals with properties of the
fluid only irrespective of the means used to cause changes of these properties. At the same time dynamics determine completely the properties
of the machine, its ability to produce head and its degree of perfection,
irrespective of the fluid pumped or heat flow to or out of the system.

Since the proof of thermodynamic laws and doctrines is based on the
appeal to reason, and because no two minds reason in the same manner,
there is a considerable variation in presentation of the subject in
various treatises on thermodynamics.

It is the author's firm conviction that thermodynamic processes in turboblowers cannot be properly described without the use of the available energy function. This is not treated adequately in textbooks on the *thermodynamics for mechanical engineers*, although all textbooks on thermodynamics for chemical engineers allow a prominent part to the available energy function under the name of "free energy" as applied to "batch" processes.

However, these books do not cover in sufficient detail the mechanical processes (changes in pressure, volume, and temperature) in which mechanical engineers are primarily interested. Thermodynamic processes in chemical engineering are primarily of the "batch" type and most frequently are conducted at constant pressure and temperature and hence at constant volume, thus mechanical effects are deliberately excluded. Therefore, there is not much in the textbooks on thermodynamics for chemical engineers which mechanical engineers can immediately apply to solution of the problems arising in the design and application of turbomachines.

7.1 AVAILABLE ENERGY FUNCTION

Introduction. Although the concept of available energy was introduced by Maxwell (reference 10) and also used by Kelvin and Gibbs, over 75 years ago, its utility is hardly recognized by mechanical engineers. Recently a number of articles appeared abroad (references 4, 5, and 6) showing application of the available energy function to the energy balance of power plants and presenting a rational definition of thermal efficiency of turbomachines. In this article the available energy concept is used to solve several problems in connection with the operation of turbomachines which cannot be solved with the aid of enthalpy and internal energy functions alone. The available energy function supplements (not supersedes) the enthalpy and internal energy functions.

(*a*) **Available Energy.** Available energy denotes the maximum useful work that a system of known initial state can develop rejecting heat at the temperature of the surroundings T_0. The latter may be the temperature of the ambient atmosphere or of a special sink of unlimited heat capacity, a steam condenser for instance. This maximum of useful work is attainable by a perfect heat engine operating on a reversible cycle, the system after having completed its work being at rest and in equilibrium with its surroundings as regards temperature and pressure (reference 1). The available energy in this case, representing a change of state ("batch process"), is equal to the decrease from the initial to the final state of the quantity

$$b = u - T_0 s \tag{7.1}$$

where u is the internal energy of the system.

s is the entropy of the system.

T_0 is the absolute temperature of the sink.

For a steady flow process the available energy is represented by the change of the quantity

$$b = h - T_0 s = u + pv - T_0 s \tag{7.2}$$

where h is the enthalpy of the system.

p is pressure.

v is specific volume.

The available energy, like enthalpy and internal energy, is a property of state and has no absolute value. When given in the form of equations 7.1 and 7.2 it represents values measured from a given state or an arbitrary datum in which all these properties are assumed to be zero, usually absolute zero temperature. All problems dealing with available energy are concerned with changes rather than absolute values of this function.

(b) **Energy Equations.** Energy equations in thermodynamics represent the first law of thermodynamics or law of "conservation of energy." This is differently stated. The expression in terms of enthalpy, or what was known until recently as "total heat content," was formulated at times when heat was considered as a weightless fluid "calorific," thus this law appeared as a form of the principle of conservation of matter, generally accepted then. *A statement that "energy cannot be created or destroyed" dates to those times and applies to enthalpy, which is a particular form of energy, part of which is unavailable. This is applied to theoretical reversible and irreversible actual processes.* Energy losses mean degradation or dissipation of available energy which becomes unavailable for doing work in a given cycle or steady flow process, the enthalpy remaining constant.

Later formulations of the first law when applied to reversible cycles or steady flow processes state that the work delivery by a system is proportional to the heat taken in by the system (reference 7). This deals with available energy only and asserts the equivalence of heat (available part of enthalpy) and work.

Expressed in terms of enthalpy, the energy equation

$$h_2 - h_1 = Q - w = c_p(T_2 - T_1) \tag{7.3}$$

does not disclose how much of the total enthalpy change was added as heat and how much of it was furnished as work; both are fused into one "enthalpy" which does not reveal how much of the energy is available for doing work.

Thus, if the whole amount of $h_2 - h_1$ was delivered to the system as heat $c_p(T_2 - T_1)$, the part of it, $T_0(s_2 - s_1)$, is unavailable energy. On the other hand, if the whole amount of $h_2 - h_1$ was supplied as work (isentropic compression) the whole amount is available energy. Note that in equation 7.3 quantities q and w, representing the amount of heat and work added, exist only in transit.*

If we accept a definition of energy as *"capacity for performing work or producing an effect"* (references 2, 3, and 10)† the unavailable energy can hardly be called energy as it can produce no effect. At the same time enthalpy is a particular kind of energy, part of which is not available. *The equation of conservation of energy in terms of enthalpy will be referred to as an equation of conservation of enthalpy*, rather than energy, to distinguish it from the equations of available and unavailable energy introduced below.

In a cyclic or steady flow process, since the system cannot accumulate or be depleted of energy, the energy flow into the system should be equal to the energy flow out of the system. Expressed in terms of enthalpy it can be stated that

$$\text{Enthalpy input} = \text{Enthalpy output} \tag{7.4}$$

This relationship holds for both reversible theoretical or irreversible actual processes.

For reversible processes, since there is no degradation of energy, the portion of enthalpy which enters the system as available energy also leaves it as available energy, hence

$$\text{Available energy input} = \text{Available energy output} \tag{7.5}$$

Obviously by subtraction we obtain for reversible processes

$$\text{Unavailable energy input} = \text{Unavailable energy output} \tag{7.6}$$

---

* The vast amounts of energy used by the industries are transformed into electric energy for convenience of transportation and distribution. However, electric energy as such exists in transit only, as there are no means to store any appreciable amounts of electric energy. In a storage battery energy is transformed into chemical energy to be stored.

† This definition of energy has been generally accepted in physics and mechanics from times before thermodynamics became a science.

The energy equilibrium equations 7.4, 7.5, and 7.6, when modified to account for amounts of energy degraded as a result of the irreversibility of processes, permit us to keep a separate account of the available and unavailable energy in the actual steady flow processes.

(c) **Unavailable Energy.** The object of a cycle or steady flow process is the transformation of energy. All forms of energy, except heat, are theoretically *completely* interchangeable and are available energy in full. On the other hand, to convert heat to work, a part of the heat energy must be rejected at a lower temperature. This constitutes the Carnot principle. The amount of rejected heat $T_0(s_2 - s_1)$ becomes unavailable energy. Here T_0 is the temperature of the surroundings or sink, corresponding to the cold body in Carnot cycle. Since the temperature of the cold body is fixed for a given system and process, the unavailable energy is determined by the increase of entropy.

In real cyclic or steady flow processes there are inevitable internal losses caused by mechanical and hydrodynamic friction which result in the irreversible conversion of work energy into heat. This is accompanied by an increase of entropy or unavailable energy to be ultimately rejected to the sink. This is of great practical importance, as conservation of the available energy is our main object, whereas the unavailable energy is free in unlimited quantities and sometimes is removed from a system at a great expense (by condensers).

Transfer of heat from one part of the system to another through a finite temperature difference reduces the possibility of heat conversion into work and is also accompanied by an increase of entropy thus adding to the amount of unavailable energy to be rejected to the surroundings. The increase of the unavailable energy due to the last two causes is at the expense of the available energy of the system and constitutes degradation or dissipation of energy (enthalpy remaining constant). The degraded energy is also referred to as "waste" or "loss," which terms are used synonymously with the "unavailable energy" term. *Equation 7.2 can be used for calculation of the change of the available energy for actual steady flow irreversible processes if s_1 and s_2 represent the initial and final entropies of the working substance irrespective of the actual path of the changes of states (references 4, 5, and 6).*

(d) **Energy Datum.** The physical meaning of available energy can be visualized as that of "total heat content" or enthalpy if the ambient atmospheric or sink temperature is selected as the datum for measuring heat. Then all enthalpy would be available energy and there would be no energy to reject. Heat would be completely convertible to work.

The Carnot principle would lose its significance, or rather it would become a part of the definition of the available energy. The unavailable energy would be rejected (algebraically) before and not after the process.

It may be pointed out, for example, that pressures of fluids up to the present day are measured above the atmosphere, even though the atmosphere varies with time and location.

Perhaps an analogy from hydraulics will serve to illustrate the significance of the selection of the datum. Thus if water levels for hydroelectric plants were always measured from sea level there would be some energy rejected in the process of conversion of hydraulic into electric energy; namely that equal to the weight of flow times the tail race head above the sea level. However, hydraulic engineers are accustomed to think in terms of the "net total head," i.e., head above the level of the sink, and this makes all hydraulic energy available energy completely convertible to work.

Taking a broader point of view, it will be found that all forms of energy are measured, and are available energy, only above a certain level fixed for any given system or process. *The flow of energy is proportional to the difference in potential of the system with respect to the other system. Potential is "the driving force" that causes the energy flow. The amount of the energy transferred is proportional to the product of the potential drop and a quantity factor, representing a rate of flow of energy.* The accompanying tabulation gives these relations for several forms of energy.

Form of Energy	Potential	Quantity Factor	Amount of Energy
Hydraulic	Head H	Weight of flow W	HW
Gravity	Elevation H	Weight W	HW
Elastic	Pressure p	Volume v	pv
Electric	Voltage E	Current I	EI
Work	Force F	Distance L	FL
Work	Torque T	Angular velocity ω	$T\omega$
Heat	Temperature T	Entropy s	Ts

The practical datum levels for measuring the several forms of energy, except heat, were so selected that they are theoretically interchangeable and completely convertible to work.

It should be pointed out, however, that measuring enthalpy above the sink temperature would not put heat on an equal basis with the other forms of energy because in irreversible processes any form of energy is "degraded" into heat. Thus there always will be unavailable energy represented by $T_0 \Delta s$ irrespective of its origin, to be rejected to the sink.

7.2 APPLICATION OF AVAILABLE ENERGY FUNCTION

(*a*) **Adiabatic Compression.** Since all turbomachines in practice work essentially on the adiabatic steady flow process, use of enthalpy for the energy equation did not incur any difficulties or serious numerical errors, as the unavailable energy term $T_0 \Delta s$ was either small or zero. In this case the enthalpy function becomes identical with the available energy function. However, if a process deviates appreciably from the adiabatic (heat due to losses added, or external cooling), the enthalpy function fails to correctly represent the change in available energy of the system (the only part engineers are interested in) and a correct answer is obtained only by the use of the available energy function.‡

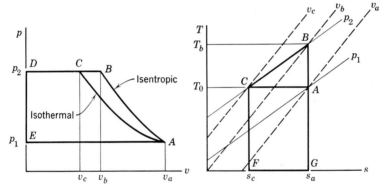

Fig. 7.1.   Isothermal and isentropic compression *pv* and *Ts* diagrams.

The use of the enthalpy function for the energy equation, for processes where change in entropy occurs, leads not only to a different numerical result but also to a different interpretation of the physical aspects of the process, as is shown in the following example.

Suppose a gas, say air, is compressed isentropically in a steady flow process from a state *A* (shown on *pv* and *Ts* diagrams on Fig. 7.1) to a state *B*. The work of compression, which is the input to the compressor, is equal to

$$\text{Work input } w_{\text{in}} = \frac{RT_0}{(k-1)/k}\left[\left(\frac{p_2}{p_1}\right)^{(k-1)/k} - 1\right] \qquad (7.7)$$

‡ Keenan uses a term "availability" for available energy (reference 7) for brevity, although the saving is only 3 letters. Gibbs and Maxwell's term is "available energy." The French use "available energy" (reference 8). The Russian and German term is "ability to do work"—translated literally from German "Arbeitsfähigkeit" (references 5, 6). Under the circumstances the advisability of a new term for available energy is questioned.

This is numerically equal to the change of enthalpy or, the process being isentropic, also equal to the change of the available energy.

$$h_2 - h_1 = c_p(T_b - T_0) = b_2 - b_1 \qquad (7.8)$$

Now if the air is cooled at constant pressure p_2 to the original temperature $T_a = T_0$ the amount of heat removed by cooling is equal numerically to the entire input w_{in},

$$q = c_p(T_b - T_0) = h_2 - h_1 \qquad (7.9)$$

However, the system is not restored to its original state at A, but has changed to a state C. The pressure still remains at p_2, and the entropy decreased from s_a to s_c. The system obviously is capable of doing work by expansion, for instance, in pneumatic tools. This is so because, out of the total amount of heat (q) removed by cooling as given by the equation 7.9, the amount $T_0\Delta s$ is unavailable energy and could not come from the system where the entire input was the available energy. Therefore the available energy of the system was reduced only by the amount.

$$c_p(T_b - T_0) - T_0\Delta s \qquad (7.10)$$

This means that the system still possesses available energy numerically equal to $T_0\Delta s$. The unavailable part of the heat removed by cooling equal to $T_0\Delta s$ was furnished by the atmosphere with the inlet air.

By application of the available energy equation the energy removed from the system by cooling is equal to the change in the available energy when going from the point B to C.

$$b_c - b_b = (h_1 - T_0 s_c) - (h_2 - T_0 s_a) \qquad (7.11)$$

$$= T_0(s_a - s_c) - (h_2 - h_1)$$

$$= T_0(s_a - s_c) - c_p(T_b - T_0)$$

which is the same value as given by equation 7.10, the negative sign meaning heat removed from the system.

The process as described is followed very closely by compressed air supply installations. The compression of air is very nearly adiabatic, and air in the receiver is cooled approximately to the temperature of the atmospheric air.

In Fig. 7.1, for a steady flow process, the work of compression is represented by the area $ABDE$ on the pv diagram and $BCFG$ on the Ts diagram. Heat removed by cooling is equivalent to the area

$BCFG$. The unavailable part of it, furnished by the atmosphere, corresponds to the area $ACFG$ on the Ts diagram, and the part of the available energy removed from the system as heat by cooling is equal to the area ABC on both diagrams. The energy retained by the system is equal to the area $ACDE$ on the pv diagram and $ACFG$ on the Ts diagram. This energy is equal to the work of isothermal compression from the pressure p_1 to p_2 discussed in the next article.

(*b*) **Isothermal Compression.** Isothermal compression may be thought of as an adiabatic compression done in a great number of infinitesimal steps with cooling after each step. Suppose on Fig. 7.2 we are compressing atmospheric air isothermally in a steady flow reversible process from the atmospheric pressure p_1 to a pressure p_2.

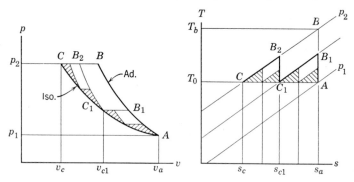

Fig. 7.2. Isothermal compression by steps.

The power input w_{in} and the energy change (there being no losses in a reversible process) is equal to

$$\text{Input} = w_{\mathrm{in}} = p_1 v_a \log_e (p_2/p_1) = \text{Output} \qquad (7.12)$$

which is the same as the work of compression from a state A to a state C on Fig. 7.2 (batch process) because $p_1 v_a = p_2 v_c$.

The amount of heat removed by cooling can be arrived at by following the method presented in the preceding article. By performing compression in two steps the amount of the available energy removed from the system by cooling is represented on the pv and Ts diagrams by two triangles AB_1C_1 and C_1B_2C, which is approximately one-half the amount if compression and cooling are made in one step. The amount of the unavailable energy removed by cooling in two steps is the same as on Fig. 7.1 and is represented by the area ACs_cs_a on Ts diagram. The four cross-hatched triangles in Fig. 7.2 represent the amount of available energy removed by cooling if the process is accomplished in four steps. The amount of unavailable energy removed in this four-step process is the same as in both previous cases. It becomes evident that as the number of steps is increased and the compression becomes isothermal the amount of available energy removed from the system by cooling is approaching zero. The amount of unavailable energy rejected to cooling is equal to

$$q_{\text{out}} = T_a \Delta s \qquad (7.13)$$

The same result can be obtained by reversing the procedure, i.e., first precooling air sufficiently, then compressing it adiabatically to restore the original inlet temperature (Fig. 7.2a). If this amount of unavailable energy is actually carried away by the cooling means (say water at the temperature T_0) it is furnished by the surrounding

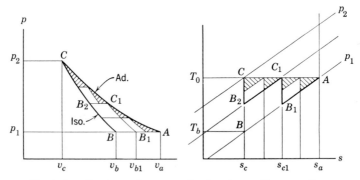

Fig. 7.2a.   Isothermal compression by steps with precooling.

atmosphere with the inlet air. If cooling is done by the ambient atmosphere then the unavailable heat transfer from and to the system becomes imaginary, as the whole reversible isothermal process in reality is. In every case the amount of heat $T_0 \Delta s$ is brought into the system by the inlet air, and an equal amount is removed by the surrounding atmosphere at a constant temperature T_0 at an infinitely slow rate. This process is a hypothesis devised for treatment of reversible processes in thermodynamics.

By applying the available energy equation 7.5 to the process of isothermal compression we obtain

$$b_c - b_a = h_c - h_a - T_0(s_c - s_a) = p_1 v_a \log_e (p_2/p_1) = w_{\text{in}}$$

or since $pv = $ Constant for an isothermal process

$$u_c - u_a - T_0(s_c - s_a) = w_{\text{in}}$$

$$T_0 \Delta s = w_{\text{in}} \qquad (7.14)$$

since $u_c = u_a$ for an isothermal process.

Thus the work of isothermal compression w_{in} *appears as an increase in the available energy of the system.* The system possesses a definite driving force or potential (pressure) and a definite tendency for a spontaneous change of state which is a sign of stored energy in the system. If allowed to expand at a constant temperature the same amount of work can be derived from the system at the expense of the available energy content of the system.

Although the *internal energy of the gas or substance is the same at the end of the isothermal compression, the available energy of the system is increased by virtue of its elastic properties.* The equation of state $pv = RT$ shows that the pressure varies inversely as the volume thus making the system a perfect spring. It is known in mechanics that metal springs can store energy due to their elastic properties as a result of the molecular displacement of the metal. The energy stored in the compressed gas at the ambient temperature is available for doing work and actually does work in the case of compressed air tools. The term *"stored energy" is used here to apply only to available energy.*

The total energy possessed by a system, available and unavailable, will be referred to as "enthalpy content" or "total enthalpy content" corresponding to the "heat content" and "total heat content" used in the recent past and still used widely in Europe. The unavailable energy cannot be stored in a system in thermal equilibrium with the surroundings, nor can a system be depleted of its unavailable energy. Obviously, there is no point in storing unavailable energy. We store something to be available on demand. *When energy is stored the system pressure and/or temperature are increased.*

The above changes of energy, available and unavailable, in a reversible steady flow isothermal process could not be established from the enthalpy or internal energy consideration. The equation representing the first law requires that

$$u_2 - u_1 = q - w_{in}$$

and since $u_2 = u_1$ for an isothermal process

$$q = w_{in} \qquad (7.14a)$$

This has been frequently interpreted to mean that the *power input actually goes to the cooling water and the energy of the system remains unchanged. For an isothermal expansion it has been stated that the work done is wholly supplied by the heat absorbed from the surroundings.* This contravenes the second law.§

§ A further discussion of the subject is given in Art. 7.5.

(*c*) **General Case of Polytropic Compression.** For the case of a steady flow irreversible compression process with cooling the following three energy equilibrium equations can be set up (Fig. 7.3).

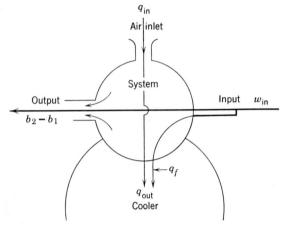

Fig. 7.3. Diagram of polytropic compression; heavy lines = available energy; light lines = unavailable energy.

1. The conservation of enthalpy requires that

$$h_2 - h_1 = c_p(T_2 - T_1) = w_{in} - q_{out} \qquad (7.15)$$

hence

$$w_{in} = c_p(T_2 - T_1) + q_{out}$$

2. The equilibrium of available energy can be given the form

$$w_{in} - q_f = b_2 - b_1 = h_2 - h_1 - T_1(s_2 - s_1) \qquad (7.16)$$

where q_f is the part of the input energy converted irreversibly into heat through all internal losses.

3. The unavailable energy balance is maintained by

$$q_{out} = q_{in} + q_f \qquad (7.17)$$

The amount of heat q_{in} brought into the system from the surrounding atmosphere, all of which is unavailable energy, can be determined from the above equations,

$$q_{in} = q_{out} - q_f$$

$$q_{in} = w_{in} - c_p(T_2 - T_1) - q_f = b_2 - b_1 - c_p(T_2 - T_1) \qquad (7.18)$$

$$q_{in} = h_2 - h_1 - T_1(s_2 - s_1) - c_p(T_2 - T_1) = +T_1(s_1 - s_2) \qquad (7.19)$$

It will be noticed that the amount of heat brought into the system is the heat content of the inlet fluid. Also *from equation 7.17 it follows that no part of the power input, except that equivalent of the internal losses, is removed by cooling.*‖

The thermal efficiency of the polytropic process is equal to the ratio of the increase of the available energy of the flow from inlet to outlet to the power input.

$$\text{Thermal efficiency} = \frac{b_2 - b_1}{w_{in}} = \frac{c_p(T_2 - T_1) - T_1(s_2 - s_1)}{c_p(T_2 - T_1) + q_{out}} \quad (7.20)$$

All values entering equation 7.20 are either directly observed on test or taken from the gas tables for the measured pressures and temperatures. *No assumptions as to the exact path followed by the process are necessary in the above definition of the thermal efficiency.* A more detailed discussion of the thermal efficiency is given in the Art. 7.4.

(*d*) **Joule's Law and Throttling.** The following statement, sometimes referred to as Joule's law, is frequently quoted. "The intrinsic energy of a perfect gas depends upon the temperature and is independent of volume." Joule ran elaborate tests to prove this statement experimentally. He took two containers, one filled with air at 22 atm. pressure, the other under vacuum. Both were enclosed within a bath of water. Through a restriction, air was admitted from the high pressure container to the one under vacuum. After the equilibrium was reached no temperature change was observed in the gas or the water bath.

It is apparent that Joule's law applies to the "substance" or gas only and refers to that part of the energy which is a function of temperature only. However, in the process of throttling, the "system" has suffered a loss of the available energy at the rate of $(T\Delta s)$ *which is equal to the amount of work necessary to bring the system to the original state.*

(*e*) **Second Law.** Using the concept of available energy, it is possible to state the second law of thermodynamics as follows: the available energy of a real system in a steady flow or cyclic process tends to decrease. This statement conveys the same idea as Clausius' well-known formulation: "The entropy of the universe tends toward a maximum," but is more realistic and easier to grasp.

7.3 HEAD GENERATION, THERMODYNAMIC RELATIONSHIPS

(*a*) **Impeller Total Head, Adiabatic Compression.** In the preceding chapters, the process of head generation, or pressure rise by an impeller, was examined, and constants connecting the physical impeller dimen-

‖ Note that all the above deductions hold if we assume that the system in Fig. 7.3 includes a reciprocating compressor instead of a turbocompressor.

sions with performance (head capacity) were introduced for incompressible fluids. These fluids could be gases where change of gas density as a result of compression could be disregarded (as it can be for fans) or incompressible fluids or liquids, water being the most common of the liquids. The simple relationships between pressure rise and head in feet existing for liquids

$$(p_2 - p_1)/\gamma = H$$

hold only in differential form as applied to every increment of pressure rise along the path of the fluid through the impeller.

$$dp = \gamma dh \tag{7.21}$$

To determine the total head produced by the impeller, equation 7.21 can be integrated, utilizing the relationships between the specific weight γ (or specific volume v) and pressure p established in thermodynamics for perfect gases. It will not be necessary to go through this procedure later if we take advantage of the fact that: total head in feet (length) is equal numerically to the work of compression in foot-pounds per pound of fluid. For the work of compression we can use the formulas known in thermodynamics. Thus, for adiabatic and isentropic steady flow compression, the work of compression is given by the "adiabatic" formula

$$H_{ad} = \frac{RT_1}{(k-1)/k} \left[\left(\frac{p_2}{p_1} \right)^{(k-1)/k} - 1 \right] \tag{7.22}$$

where H_{ad} is total head in feet equal to the work of compression in foot-pounds per pound.

R is the gas constant.

k is the ratio of specific heats c_p/c_v.

p_2 and p_1 are the discharge and inlet pressures.

T_1 is the inlet temperature °R.

Equation 7.22 also represents the work of compression per pound of fluid by a reciprocating compressor going through the following steps: intake (along EA, Fig. 7.1), compression from p_1 to p_2 (along AB), and discharge into a receiver (along BD), after which the cylinder is open for a new intake with pressure dropping from p_2 to p_1 (along DE). On the $T's$ diagram the same work is represented by the area below BC or area $BCFG$.

In Chapter 1 it has been shown that the same formula 7.22 can be obtained by calculating the height H of a gas column to which gas would rise after compression if permitted to expand freely at the top of the column to its inlet pressure p_1 and temperature T_1. This means that the work of compression per pound under the above-stated conditions is equal to the work of straight lifting of 1 pound of gas to a height H.

Note that in the development of the expression for the head H in Chapter 3, no distinction is made between the velocity head and pressure head; this is true for any point along the path of the fluid through the blowers. On the other hand, in thermodynamics, the basic relationships for reversible processes are established with changes of state taking place at infinitely slow rate.

A study of equation 7.22 reveals the connection between the gas properties (R, T, and k) and the pressure ratio realized by a given impeller at a selected speed. *Since the head produced remains constant irrespective of the nature of gas and whether it is cooled or not, several important conclusions follow from the observation of the equation 7.22.* Usually the bracketed term is designated by a letter X, thus

$$H_{ad} = \frac{RT_1}{(k-1)/k} \cdot X \tag{7.23}$$

and, utilizing the relationship $pv = RT$,

$$H_{ad} = \frac{p_1 v_1}{(k-1)/k} \cdot X = \frac{p_1}{\gamma_1} \cdot \frac{k}{(k-1)} \cdot X \tag{7.24}$$

The values of X for air and all diatomic gases with $(k-1)/k = 0.283$ are given in tables found in reference books for convenience.

1. For a given blower at a selected speed, H being fixed, it follows that a higher inlet temperature results in a lower compression ratio because

$$T_1 \times X = \text{Constant} \tag{7.25}$$

and a higher T_1 means a lower value of X and a lower compression ratio.

2. If the inlet pressure is reduced by throttling, temperature remaining constant, the compression ratio remains the same, and the discharge pressure is reduced in the same ratio.

$$p_2'/p_1' = p_2/p_1 \tag{7.26}$$

3. When pumping different gases the compression ratio is lower for gases having higher gas constant R. Assuming that k is the same, then

$$RX = \text{Constant} \tag{7.27}$$

The gas constant R in the formula 7.23 represents the effect of the gas density, as the value of the gas constant R is inversely proportional to the gas density. This follows from the formula known from thermodynamics

$$R = 1545/M \tag{7.28}$$

where M is the molecular weight of gas. But, since according to Avogadro's law equal volumes of all gases contain an equal number of molecules at the same pressure and temperature, the density of gases is proportional to their molecular weights. Occasionally gas density is expressed as specific gravity G with respect to air ($G = 1.0$) under the same pressure and temperature. Then the gas constant R can be found also from

$$R = 53.34/G$$

where 53.34 is the gas constant of dry air.

4. Note that the pressure ratio (or X) does not depend upon the inlet pressure p_1 because RT_1 is independent of the pressure. If pressure is varied volume changes inversely as pressure, and their product $p_1v_1 = RT_1$ remains constant.

Thus, for example, the same impeller at a given speed will raise pressure from 15 to 30 p.s.i.a. or raise pressure from 1000 to 2000 p.s.i.a. Note that it requires the same power per pound of fluid in both of the above cases. What it really means in the above case is that *it takes the same power to raise a pound of fluid to a height H irrespective of whether that pound of gas is initially compressed or not.*

5. An increase of inlet temperature T_1 will require a higher head (and hence a higher speed or larger impeller diameter) to produce the same pressure ratio. The b.hp. for a given weight of flow will increase directly as the head or directly as the inlet temperature.

Using known thermodynamic relationships, equation 7.22 can be algebraically transformed to

$$H_{ad} = h_2 - h_1 = c_p(T_2 - T_1) \tag{7.22a}$$

showing that for a given gas (c_p) the temperature rise is proportional to the adiabatic head. From equations 7.22 and 7.22a we obtain

$$T_2 - T_1 = T_1 X = \frac{H_{ad}(k - 1)}{Rk} \tag{7.29}$$

indicating that *the bracketed factor X really has a physical meaning, namely, that of temperature rise per degree of the inlet temperature.* Note that in equation 7.22a both sides of the equations should be in consistent units, foot-pounds.

From equation 7.29 it also follows that

$$T_2 = T_1(X \times 1) = T_1 \left(\frac{p_2}{p_1}\right)^{(k-1)/k} \tag{7.29a}$$

where T_2 is the discharge temperature, °R. *Since head H_{ad} for a given impeller and a given speed is constant, the temperature rise $(T_2 - T_1)$ is independent of the inlet temperature T_1 (equation 7.29).*

(*b*) **Affinity Laws.** (1) If the speed of a given blower is changed, its head will vary directly as the square of the speed, and its capacity (c.f.m. at impeller discharge) will vary directly as the speed. Cubic feet per minute at inlet will vary approximately as the speed, the exact volume depending upon the compression ratio from the impeller inlet to the impeller discharge.

The exact value of the inlet c.f.m. can be established by application of the method and formulas given later in this chapter. For small speed variation (say not over 2 to 1) the hydraulic efficiency of the blower remains essentially the same. Therefore, the b.hp. requirement varies approximately as cube of the speed. The above rules are represented by the formulas below:

$$\frac{H_1}{H_2} = \frac{n_1{}^2}{n_2{}^2} = \frac{X_1}{X_2} = \frac{(T_2 - T_1)_1}{(T_2 - T_1)_2} \tag{7.30}$$

$$Q_1/Q_2 = n_1/n_2 \tag{7.31}$$

$$\text{b.hp.}_1/\text{b.hp.}_2 = n_1{}^3/n_2{}^3 \tag{7.32}$$

where, n is the speed, Q is capacity c.f.m., subscript 1 refers to the original, and subscript 2 to the new speed.

(2) If two geometrically similar impellers (i.e., of the same specific speed) are operated at the same speed then their heads are in the ratio of their impeller diameter ratio squared; c.f.m. at impeller discharge varies directly as the cube of the impeller diameter ratio, and b.hp. as the fifth power of the same ratio.

$$\frac{H_1}{H_2} = \left(\frac{D_1}{D_2}\right)^2 = \frac{X_1}{X_2} = \frac{(T_2 - T_1)_1}{(T_2 - T_1)_2} \tag{7.33}$$

$$Q_1/Q_2 = (D_1/D_2)^3 \tag{7.34}$$

$$\text{b.hp.}_1/\text{b.hp.}_2 = (D_1/D_2)^5 \tag{7.35}$$

The affinity laws corrected for compressibility of gas (as compared with liquid) form the basis of blower selections and design of new machines for which existing models are available.

(c) **Volume at Impeller Discharge.** For an existing impeller, the values of the head and capacity coefficients ψ and ϕ are known. For a new design these values are selected from the chart in Fig. 6.12. Thus the operating point can be located on the chart in Fig. 6.10 and the dimensionless value of the absolute velocity at impeller discharge c_2'/u_2 can be scaled off from the chart. Knowing c_2', the pressure head at impeller discharge can be calculated from

$$H_d = H - c_2'^2/2g \tag{7.36}$$

The pressure ratio r_d, from the impeller inlet to the discharge, can be obtained from the polytropic formula, discussed later.

$$H_d = \frac{RT_1}{(n-1)/n} [r_d^{(n-1)/n} - 1] \tag{7.37}$$

$$= \frac{RT_1}{(n-1)/n} X_d \tag{7.38}$$

The volume of gas at the impeller discharge $(c.f.m.)_d$ is obtained from inlet c.f.m. by

$$c.f.m._d = \frac{c.f.m. \times (X_d + 1)}{r_d} = \frac{c.f.m.}{r_d} \frac{T_d}{T_1} \tag{7.39}$$

where $X_d + 1$ is the ratio of the gas temperature at impeller discharge to that of the blower inlet, equation 7.29a.

$$T_d = T_1(X_d + 1) \tag{7.40}$$

Equation 7.40 is given in thermodynamics in the form

$$T_1/T_2 = (p_1/p_2)^{(n-1)/n} \tag{7.41}$$

Equation (7.39) is equivalent to

$$c.f.m._d/c.f.m. = (p_1/p_d)^{1/n} = (1/r_d)^{1/n} \tag{7.42}$$

where p_d is the pressure at impeller discharge.

An approximate but very accurate experimental formula for estimating volume of flow at the impeller discharge, for air, is as follows:

$$c.f.m._d = 2c.f.m./(1 + r) \tag{7.43}$$

where r is the blower compression ratio.

Attention is called to the fact that if a blower is tested at a lower speed than the specified field speed, making it necessary to step up the performance to show the head versus inlet volume at the specified higher speed, it is important to step-up the volume at the impeller discharge and then calculate the inlet volume at the higher speed using the polytropic formula. This involves the following steps:

1. Calculate volume at impeller discharge at the lower test speed.
2. Calculate the volume at impeller discharge at the higher speed.
3. Calculate the velocity head at impeller discharge at the higher speed. It varies as square of the speed from the known velocity head at the lower speed.
4. Determine the pressure and temperature ratio at impeller discharge at the higher speed from known (stepped up) head in feet.
5. Reexpand the gas back to the inlet pressure to determine the inlet volume at the higher speed.

When test results of a blower are represented in the form ψ versus c.f.m./n where ψ is the head coefficient, c.f.m. is inlet volume, and n is r.p.m., a separate curve is obtained at each speed. This is because when speed is varied the volumetric capacity at impeller discharge follows the affinity law. However, due to a higher compression ratio at the higher speed, gas density is increasing, therefore the weight of flow is increasing more than directly as the speed. For that reason at a higher speed a given value of the head coefficient is obtained at a higher value of c.f.m./n, the inlet c.f.m. being proportional to the weight of flow. Figure 7.4 illustrates the above statement.

The effect of speed on the ψ versus c.f.m./n characteristics is more evident with impellers having low impeller discharge angles, because the head-capacity curve is steeper. Note that when test results are represented as ψ versus ϕ, where ϕ is the capacity coefficient $\phi = c_{m2}/u_2$, all points at several speeds fall on the same curve, because both c_{m2} and u_2 vary directly as the speed.

(*d*) **Volume at the Impeller Inlet.** The actual volume of gas approaching the impeller inlet vane tips is higher than the specified c.f.m. of the machine because of the pressure drop caused by the velocity of approach. For a high speed, high head blower operating at an impeller peripheral velocity of 935 ft. per sec. the increase in volume is about 5 per cent. This increase in volume should be included when constructing the inlet velocity triangle. The actual volume of gas at impeller inlet is calculated following the procedure:

1. Determine the inlet meridional velocity c_{m1} based on the specified c.f.m.
2. Calculate the velocity head corresponding to this velocity; which is the head equivalent of the pressure drop at the impeller vanes.
3. Find the expansion ratio (r_e) and temperature drop ($T_1 - T_e$) corresponding to the above velocity head, using the adiabatic formula.

4. The volume at the impeller vanes is given by the relationship

$$c.f.m._e = c.f.m. \times r_e \times T_e/T_1 \qquad (7.44)$$

The above procedure is essentially the same as that for determining the actual volume of flow at the impeller discharge given above.

(e) **Polytropic Adiabatic Compression.** The discussion and formulas used in the preceeding article are based on the adiabatic isen-

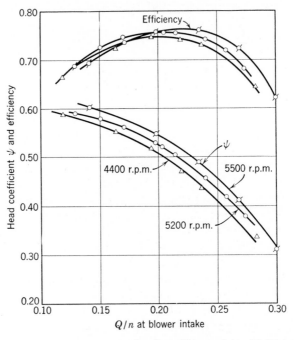

Fig. 7.4. Effect of capacity scale on head coefficient plot. Multistage compressor, inlet $n_s = 435$, Fig. 15.35.

tropic compression. This neglects addition of heat to the pumped fluid due to internal losses including the disk friction. The heat exchange with the surroundings in actual blowers is very small in comparison with power input to the fluid, and the process can be considered as adiabatic; but it is not isentropic because entropy of the fluid increases as it progresses through the machine. To simplify the theoretical treatment of the problem, a "polytropic" compression is assumed in which gas follows the law $pv^n = $ Constant, where $n > k$ and is constant along the compression path. On the pv and Ts diagrams (Fig. 7.5) the process of compression is represented by a line

AB, the path of the process shifting toward higher volume and temperature.

The area ABC on both the pv and Ts diagrams represents the additional work per pound of gas required to compress gas to the same final pressure p_2. This also represents the increase in head in feet over the adiabatic head to reach the same pressure p_2. On the Ts diagram, area $ABKH$ represents heat added to the fluid as a result of internal losses. The part of it represented by the area $AHKL$ is unavailable; the part corresponding to the area ABL is available by virtue of the increase of the discharge temperature. Whether or not this part of the heat is utilized depends on the nature of the particular application of the process. On the Ts diagram the area $ABFGH$

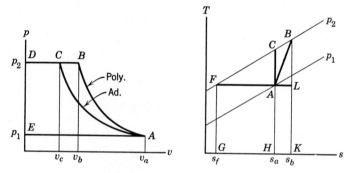

Fig. 7.5. Polytropic compression.

represents the heat equivalent to the polytropic compression work, and the area $BFGK$ gives the heat equivalent of the entire power input excluding external mechanical losses. Note that the path AB is assumed, the actual path is never known. Both diagrams serve only as an illustration of several steps involved rather than the actual values of energy transmitted to the fluid. The amount of the energy degraded, however, is given exactly, as $T_0\Delta s$, which makes the net thermal output a measurable quantity (equation 7.20).

When heat due to internal losses is added to the gas as the flow progresses through the blower passages the energy content of the gas per pound, or enthalpy, is increased. However, the head to produce a given pressure rise is increased at the same rate. Thus the increase of enthalpy in this case comes from the input shaft work. Addition of heat due to losses to the gas appears on the Ts diagram as an increase of the enthalpy rise between two pressure lines, causing the divergence of the pressure lines in the direction of the entropy increase. Higher head to produce the same pressure is a result of the reduction of gas density. Since gas is free to expand at any point along its path, addition of heat takes place at constant pressure, the pressure rise along the path being accomplished entirely by dynamic means.

In a steady flow compression process the work of compression of 1 lb. of fluid is represented by a formula similar to the adiabatic formula 7.22, with k being replaced by n

$$H_p = \frac{RT_1}{(n-1)/n} \left[\left(\frac{p_2}{p_1} \right)^{(n-1)/n} - 1 \right] \tag{7.45}$$

To produce a given pressure p_2, the polytropic head H_p is higher than the adiabatic, as the density is reduced and temperature and volume are increased. This means that higher power is required to compress a given weight of gas. If the inlet and discharge temperature and pressures are measured on a test, the exponent n can be calculated from the thermodynamic relationship.

$$T_1/T_2 = (p_1/p_2)^{(n-1)/n} \tag{7.46}$$

To calculate the polytropic head for a blower for which the discharge temperature is not known, *n is obtained from a formula established in thermodynamics for the adiabatic process.*

$$(n-1)/n = (k-1)/k \times 1/e_p \tag{7.47}$$

where e_p is the polytropic efficiency of the compressor either known or estimated from previous experience. Polytropic efficiency is defined as the ratio of the polytropic head (H_p) to the power input per pound of the gas pumped b.hp./W.

$$e_p = \frac{H_p W}{\text{b.hp.} \times 550} \tag{7.48}$$

Polytropic efficiency is higher than the isentropic efficiency based on the formula

$$e_{\text{ad}} = \frac{H_{\text{ad}} W}{\text{b.hp.} \times 550} \tag{7.49}$$

because the formula disregards the effect of heat due to losses on the head in feet for a given or observed discharge pressure. If heat is added to a static column of gas its height is increased without increasing the pressure at the bottom of the column, the total weight of the column remaining the same. *Polytropic efficiency is the nearest approach to the true output/input efficiency.* If the mechanical losses (bearings and seals) are subtracted from the b.hp., then polytropic efficiency sometimes is referred to as the internal hydraulic efficiency including the disk friction losses.

The development of equation 7.47 is of interest and is given below. For a polytropic compression, following pv^n = constant, pressures and temperatures are related as follows:

$$T_2/T_1 = (p_2/p_1)^{(n-1)/n} \qquad (7.50)$$

and

$$T_2 - T_1 = T_1[(p_2/p_1)^{(n-1)/n} - 1] = T_1 \times X \qquad (7.51)$$

These are similar in form to those for an adiabatic compression, with n replacing k. The input energy to the fluid, equal to the b.hp. minus mechanical losses, appears as a change of enthalpy.

$$w_{in} = h_2 - h_1 = c_p(T_2 - T_1)$$

$$w_{in} = \frac{Rk}{k-1}(T_2 - T_1) \qquad (7.52)$$

$$= \frac{RT_1 k}{k-1}\left[\left(\frac{p_2}{p_1}\right)^{(n-1)/n} - 1\right]$$

Polytropic efficiency, is defined as

$$e_p = \frac{H_p}{h_2 - h_1} = \frac{RT_1 n(k-1)[(p_2/p_1)^{(n-1)/n} - 1]}{RT_1(n-1)k[(p_2/p_1)^{(n-1)/n} - 1]} \qquad (7.53)$$

$$e_p = \frac{(k-1)/k}{(n-1)/n} \qquad (7.54)$$

which is the same as the equation 7.47. The difference between the adiabatic (conventional) and polytropic (very near true output/input) efficiencies increases as the compression ratio is increased and blower polytropic efficiency is decreased.

The ratio of the polytropic to the adiabatic efficiencies is equal to the ratio of the corresponding heads H_p/H_{ad}, the input (w_{in} = b.hp. − Mechanical losses) remaining the same for both methods of calculation.

$$\frac{e_p}{e_{ad}} = \frac{\dfrac{k-1}{k}(r^{(n-1)/n} - 1)}{\dfrac{n-1}{n}(r^{(k-1)/k} - 1)} = \frac{H_p}{H_{ad}} \qquad (7.55)$$

where r is the compression ratio p_2/p_1. Making use of equation 7.49, we obtain

$$\frac{e_p}{e_{ad}} = e_p \frac{r^{(k-1)/ke_p} - 1}{r^{(k-1)/k} - 1} \qquad (7.56)$$

Equation 7.56 is plotted on Fig. 7.6 for different compression ratios and polytropic efficiencies. *Polytropic efficiency is a true criterion of the perfection of the hydraulic design of a blower. This does not change*

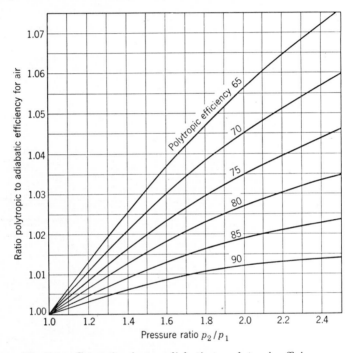

Fig. 7.6. Correction factor adiabatic to polytropic efficiency.

with speed and compression ratio (change of density of gas). Fig. 7.6 permits one to estimate the adiabatic efficiency for a given set of conditions when the polytropic efficiency of a machine is available. Adiabatic efficiency is still used to a limited extent in the industry.

Figure 7.7 shows variation of n in terms of polytropic efficiency. As the efficiency is decreased, the amount of heat added to the fluid is increasing, and the value of n increases until it reaches $+\infty$ at $e_p = 28.3$ per cent. For efficiency $e_p < 28.3$, the value of n becomes negative, the specific volume increasing irrespective of higher final pressure (Fig. 7.8).

Figure 7.9 shows the performance of a single-stage gas booster (Fig. 15.33) indicating both adiabatic and polytropic head, efficiency, and head coefficient. Note the difference in the shape of adiabatic and polytropic head-capacity curves at low rates of flow.¶ Actually the polytropic head is higher than it appears on the curve because there is an appreciable heat radiation loss at the low rates of flow, the temperature rise being in excess of 100°F. This explains why the flow at this point is perfectly stable irrespective of the apparent decrease

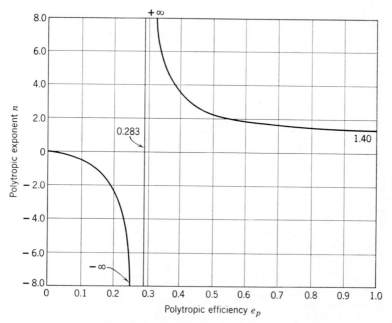

Fig. 7.7.   Polytropic exponent n versus polytropic efficiency e_p.

of head. The value of the polytropic exponent n for the point at 680 c.f.m. is 165.5, whereas the value of the exponent $(n - 1)/n$ is approaching unity.

¶ The effect of heat due to internal hydraulic losses, including disk friction, on the fluid density is observed on high pressure boiler feed pumps. For instance the water temperature rise due to losses in pumping 250°F. water against 1800 p.s.i. pressure is about 50°F., resulting in a reduction of density 2.7 per cent and a reduction of discharge pressure (the head remaining constant) of 50 p.s.i. Thus a pump which has a steadily rising head-capacity curve on cold water will show a drop of pressure near shut-off when pumping hot water if the change in density is disregarded. The head-capacity curve remains rising and perfectly stable under such conditions.

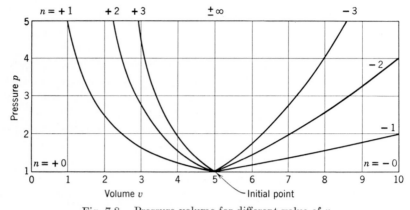

Fig. 7.8.   Pressure-volume for different value of n.

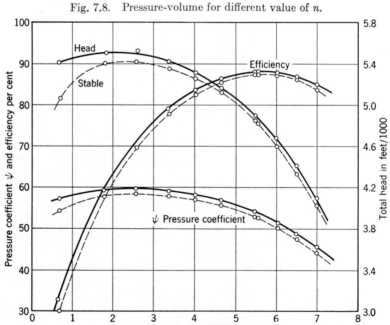

Fig. 7.9.   Polytropic and adiabatic heads. Solid line, polytropic; dotted line, adiabatic; 3500 r.p.m.; $n_s = 465$.

It may be of interest to point out that the head near zero flow produced by a centrifugal pump of the same specific speed is higher than that produced by a blower, the pressure coefficient approaching the value $\psi = 0.585$ suggested by the chart Fig. 6.10, point D. This difference is increasing for higher specific speed impellers and, it is believed, is caused by a greater degree of prerotation at the impeller approach with air, on account of the higher viscosity of air as compared to water.

(f) **Affinity Laws and Polytropic Compression.** In Art. 7.2b variation of the head and capacity were given for changing speed and/or size of the impeller. The affinity laws apply to the true generated head. The actual generated head cannot be directly measured, and polytropic head should be used as the best approximation for refiguring the performance of similar impellers. Use of adiabatic head introduces an error, the absolute value of which is increasing as compression ratio is increased. From the above it follows that *for designing and analysis of the performance data polytropic head should be used and not adiabatic. It is only on the basis of polytropic head that the design constants, such as head coefficient ψ remain constant under all possible conditions, until the effects of Mach and Reynolds numbers appear.*

(g) **Adiabatic Efficiency by Heat Balance.** When the output of a compressor is calculated by the adiabatic formula, and the input by using the enthalpy change of the flow, efficiency is called adiabatic and the method of calculation is referred to as heat balance, a term inherited from the times when the "enthalpy" was not yet introduced. The expression for efficiency is reduced to

$$e_{ad} = \frac{T_2' - T_1}{T_2 - T_1} \qquad (7.57)$$

where $T_2' - T_1$ is the adiabatic temperature rise (calculated). Thus adiabatic efficiency by heat balance is a ratio of the adiabatic temperature rise to the actual temperature rise. The method is equally applicable to cooled machines, in which case equation 7.59 changes to

$$e_{ad} = \frac{c_p(T_2' - T_1)}{c_p(T_2 - T_1) + q_{out}} \qquad (7.58)$$

where q_{out} is the amount of heat removed by cooling per pound of the pumped gas.

With the compressor casing well insulated, the heat balance method of testing for efficiency is expected to be accurate to within a fraction of a point of efficiency, being on the high side. With the casing exposed to the ambient temperature the error may exceed one point depending upon the size of the machine.

It should be pointed out that the A.S.M.E. Test Code PTC10-1949 does not recommend the heat balance method when the vapor superheat is less than 20°F., or when the temperature rise from inlet to the outlet of the compressor is less than 125°. With high moisture content heat may be absorbed from the flow to vaporize any entrained liquid particles thus reducing the temperature rise.

7.4 POLYTROPIC VERSUS THERMAL EFFICIENCY

(a) **Polytropic Efficiency.** We are now in a position to elaborate upon the difference between polytropic and thermal efficiencies. The difference stems from the definition and method of measuring the output of a compressor. Polytropic output is defined as

$$\text{Polytropic output} = (H_p \times W/550) \text{ hp.} \qquad (7.59)$$

where H_p is fluid output in foot-pounds per pound of fluid, or head in feet. The head developed by an impeller, at a given speed, is not affected by the heat flow to the fluid (heat due to hydraulic losses) or from the fluid (cooling). Thus the output is a result of the dynamic action of the impeller and is independent of thermal effect taking place during and after the process of compression. Polytropic efficiency represents the degree of hydrodynamic or, for brevity, hydraulic perfection of the machine. It is a built-in quality of the machine which is fixed and can be changed only by wear, or effects of Mach and Reynolds numbers. Disregarding the latter effects, hydraulic efficiency of a compressor remains the same for any gas, cooled or uncooled, and at any speed. It is of utmost interest to the designer as it is a measure of his skill, if results are not impaired by faulty or careless manufacturing procedure. Polytropic efficiency permits calculation of the power demand for all possible operating conditions. For a cyclic or steady flow process, polytropic output is calculated with formula 7.45, which is approximate but very accurate, involving only one assumption, namely that the polytropic exponent n remains constant during the process of compression. On the pv diagram (Fig. 7.10) the polytropic output is represented by the area $ABMN$. On a Ts diagram the heat equivalent to the polytropic compression work is represented by the area $ABELJ$. On both diagrams the area of the triangle ABC represents the increase of compression work to a given pressure due to heat addition resulting from hydraulic losses. The area $ABHJ$ represents the heat equivalent of all internal losses; the area $BELH$ shows the entire power input, exclusive of external mechanical losses.

(b) **Thermal Efficiency.** The output for the thermal efficiency includes the thermal effects in addition to the elastic work of compression. It is given by the increase of available energy of the system as expressed by the equation 7.20.

$$\text{Thermal output} = h_2 - h_1 - T_1(s_2 - s_1) \qquad (7.60)$$

The difference between the polytropic and the thermal output is better observed on the Ts diagram, Fig. 7.10. Here the area $BELH$ represents $(h_2 - h_1)$ and the area $AGHJ$ is equivalent to $T_1(s_2 - s_1)$. It will be observed that the thermal output is greater than the polytropic output by the area of the triangle ABG. The latter represents a portion of the heat due to hydraulic losses and is manifested by the temperature increase of the discharge fluid above T_c the temperature of adiabatic compression. This part of the output theoretically is

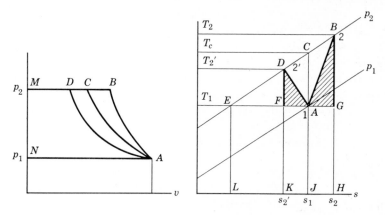

Fig. 7.10.   The difference between polytropic and thermal output, ABG on Ts diagram for uncooled and ADF for cooled machines.

available for doing work, requiring a perfect engine working between the temperature levels T_2 and T_1. In practice this heat may be utilized if the gas has to be heated for a further use, like in a blast furnace or gas turbine application. But this heat is too expensive in comparison with fuel heating to credit this amount of heat to the compressor output.

For uncooled compressors the thermal efficiency is higher than the polytropic efficiency, the difference increasing with the compression ratio. Thermal efficiency does not represent correctly the degree of hydrodynamic perfection of the design, therefore it is of academic interest only.

For a cooled blower the thermal efficiency is lower than the polytropic efficiency, the difference increasing with the compression ratio. On the Ts diagram, Fig. 7.10, the polytropic work of compression is represented by the area $ADELJ$; the area of the triangle ABD represents the reduction of the compression work as a result of cooling.

The area $AFDELJ$ shows the thermal output as it appears in the numerator of equation 7.60, where the first term corresponds to the area $DELK$; and the second term becomes positive and corresponds to the area $AFKJ$. The polytropic output is greater than the thermal by the amount equivalent to the area of the triangle ADF. The area $ABHJ$ shows the heat equivalent of all internal losses. This and the heat represented by the area $ADKJ$ are removed by cooling. The area $ADELHBA$ represents the energy input, which is smaller than the input for adiabatic polytropic compression ($BELH$) by the amount represented by the area ABD.

The difference in the behavior of the steady flow process and batch process should be noted. In a batch process system, which can be thought of as a cylinder and a piston, heat can be added to the system and if the piston is locked the pressure will rise. The system can return elastic work instead of heat but cannot do it continuously. Whereas, in a steady flow process heat is added at a constant pressure, and is carried by the flow as an increase in gas temperature and volume. It can be returned by the system as heat, for instance, as a result of cooling by surroundings, but cannot be completely converted to work continuously.

(c) **Numerical Example.**   (1) The following readings were obtained on a six-stage compressor, with all impeller diameters $17\frac{3}{4}$ inch at 7400 r.p.m., uncooled,

$p_1 = 14.49$ p.s.i.a. $W = 2.595$ lbs./sec.

$T_1 = 542.5°$R. $h_2 - h_1 = 55.98$ B.t.u. from tables

$p_2 = 39.12$ p.s.i.a. $s_2 - s_1 = 0.0177$ B.t.u./lb.-F. from tables

$T_2 = 774.6°$R.

Power input hp. $= 210.7$ by heat balance, excluding bearing losses. The polytropic exponent n is found from

$$T_2/T_1 = (p_2/p_1)^{(n-1)/n}   1.427 = (2.695)^{(n-1)/n}$$

$$(n - 1)/n = 0.357$$

Total head by the polytropic equation

$$H_p = \frac{53.35 \times 542.5}{0.357} (0.427) = 34{,}500 \text{ ft.}$$

Polytropic efficiency

$$e_p = \frac{34{,}500 \times 2.595}{550 \times 210.7} = 0.773$$

Thermal efficiency

$$e_t = \frac{[h_2 - h_1 - T_1(s_2 - s_1)]W}{\text{b.hp.}}$$

$$e_t = \frac{(55.98 - 542.5 \times 0.0177)778 \times 2.595}{550 \times 210.7} \quad (7.61)$$

$$= 0.81$$

If, instead of $T_1(s_2 - s_1)$, we substitute $0.5(T_2 - T_1)(s_2 - s_1)$ in formula 7.62, polytropic efficiency is obtained.

$$e_p = \frac{[(h_2 - h_1) - (T_2 + T_1)(s_2 - s_1)0.5]W}{\text{b.hp.}}$$

$$e_p = \frac{[55.98 - (774.6 + 542.5)0.0177 \times 0.5]778 \times 2.595}{550 \times 210.7} \quad (7.62)$$

$$= 0.772$$

Adiabatic efficiency by the adiabatic formula is

$$e_{\text{ad}} = 0.745$$

Corrected to polytropic efficiency from Fig. 7.6.

$$0.745 \times 1.037 = 0.773$$

(2) The following readings were obtained with the same compressor cooled, at the same speed.

$$p_1 = 14.52 \qquad W = 3.47$$

$$p_2 = 39.82 \qquad h_2 - h_1 = 27.25$$

$$T_1 = 539.4 \qquad s_2 - s_1 = -0.02389$$

$$T_2 = 651.3 \qquad \text{b.hp.} = 264.7$$

$$(n - 1)/n = 0.185$$

Polytropic head = 32,200 ft.
Polytropic efficiency $e_p = 0.772$
Thermal efficiency

$$e_t = \frac{[(h_2 - h_1) - T_1(s_2 - s_1)]W}{\text{b.hp.}}$$

$$e_t = 0.745$$

Polytropic efficiency, by using equation 7.62,

$$e_p = 0.772$$

Adiabatic efficiency for the same point is $e_{ad} = 0.795$ and is obviously too high to be a true efficiency as the actual head is considerably lower than that given by the adiabatic formula. Isothermal efficiency for the same point $e_{iso} = 0.692$. This is a conventional efficiency and is considerably lower than the true output/input efficiency because the outlet temperature is considerably higher than the inlet temperature and hence the true head in feet is higher.

Note that the two above points do not represent the same point on the head-capacity curve, as the rate of flow is different. The best efficiency point is somewhere between the two points.

7.5 REMARKS ON THE AVAILABLE ENERGY

In the following paragraphs we quote, from publications on thermodynamics, a number of statements which are not justified in light of relationships established in this chapter from considerations of the available energy function. Every case is an illustration of the insufficiency of enthalpy and internal energy functions to account for energy flow involving mechanical effects.

(a) **Isothermal Compression and Expansion.** In Art. 7.2b it was stated that equation 7.14a, repeated below

$$q = w_{in} \qquad\qquad 7.14a$$

has been frequently interpreted as meaning that the power input actually goes to the cooling water and the energy of the system remains unchanged. A few examples follow (remarks in brackets are by author of this book). "This relation [an equivalent of equation 7.14a] discloses the unique circumstance that except for that portion of the work input which goes to increasing the kinetic energy of the gas, all energy input as work passes out wholly and concurrently as heat to the cooling medium" [reference 2, p. 467]. "The total work of compression is removed as heat by the cooling water" [reference 11, p. 14]. Again: "The major part of the power input to a centrifugal compressor is removed by cooling" [reference 16, p. 196]. Almost any number of similar quotations can be compiled.

These statements disclose a failure to differentiate between available energy (work input) and unavailable energy (internal energy at atmospheric temperature) and fail to recognize the role and properties of the sink.

If the above statements are reworded to read, the heat removed by the cooling medium is "numerically equal" to the work input, no objections can be raised.   However, this would bring up a question as to where the energy removed by cooling is coming from, which as has been shown in Art. 7.2 cannot be answered without resorting to the concept of available energy.

The following statements deal with isothermal expansion: "In isothermal expansion the work done is wholly supplied by heat absorbed from external source" [reference 12 p. 40].   Here "external source" means "surroundings," or sink; or "In isothermal processes of perfect gases, energy comes in by heat transfer at the same rate that it leaves by work" [reference 13, p. 149].   As they stand, these statements violate the second law as no work can be extracted from the surrounding or sink which can furnish only unavailable energy in any amounts.   They again neglect the fact that for energy to be moved there *must be a difference in potential present*.   There is no difference in temperature to move any heat spontaneously, but there is a pressure differential that is the driving force to cause expansion.   In every case expansion work is done at the expense of the available energy of the system.   Besides, these statements misrepresent the mechanics of the process.   In actual processes expansion of a gas under pressure (say compressed air at 100 p.s.i. and ambient temperature) can proceed doing work (driving pneumatic tools for instance) without waiting for any heat transfer from outside.   In the case of pneumatic tools this actually happens, the exhaust air being at a temperature considerably below the ambient temperature.   To restore air to the original temperature the exhaust air is heated to the ambient temperature, utilizing heat from the surroundings at a temperature of the sink, all of which is unavailable energy.

A need of a potential difference as a "driving force" in any thermodynamic process is not sufficiently stressed in the writings on the subject.

(b) **Expansion Without Doing Work.**   This process is known also as "throttling."   It has been pointed out in Art. 7.2d discussing Joule's experiment that throttling is accompanied by a loss of available energy equal to $(T\Delta s)$, where T is the temperature of the gas and Δs is the increase of entropy as a result of throttling.   To restore the system to its original state requires an amount of work $(T\Delta s)$ to be applied to the system.   In this connection the following statements by Stodola (reference 14, p. 34) are of interest.   "Throttling of any fluid leaves the heat content unchanged."   A few lines below we find "Whatever precautions we may take there is no way of making steam in the throttled condition B, (after throttling) even in an ideal engine, yield the same amount of work as could be obtained from steam in condition A (before throttling).   There will always be a loss at least $Z(= T\Delta s)$

heat units." Now the question arises: where this loss is coming from? This cannot be answered without resorting to the available energy function. In the above quotation "heat content" is an old term for enthalpy. A related question to the one above can be asked. "Is the energy of air at 100 p.s.i. equal to that of air at atmospheric pressure and the same temperature?" This question cannot be answered by using the concepts of internal energy and enthalpy alone.

There was no agreement among the authorities of the highest rank of the recent past on the significance of the available energy function, as is evidenced by the following quotations from Stodola (reference 14, p. 1320) who cites M. Planck: "If a gas expands without doing work, its energy remains, notwithstanding its increase of entropy, unchanged. Where is there then a dissipation of energy? It is quite possible, as Rayleigh and Helmholtz have done, to introduce the ideas of 'available' or 'free' energy; except that the law that applies to these is valid only for isothermal processes."

Stodola, p. 1275, removes the limitation imposed by Planck by the last sentence of the use of free energy function (a term used to designate available energy in batch processes) for isothermal processes, by stating: "The free energy is of very general importance and does not come into consideration only for isothermal changes of state as Planck was inclined to assume."

The above statement by Planck was reprinted by Stodola from polemics carried on in *The Electrician* in 1903, dealing with the concept of "entropy."

(c) **Recovery of Heat Due to Friction.** A failure to distinguish between the adiabatic (isentropic) efficiency and the true thermal output/input efficiency as applied to steam turbines led to the impression that heat due to internal losses in a stage is "utilized in the following stage" and that "This recovery has the remarkable effect that a turbine, the stages of which are all designed for the same efficiency, will have a higher total efficiency than the individual stages" [Stodola, reference 14, p. 243].

If steam turbine efficiency is calculated on the basis of the input taken as a decrease of the available energy of the flow rather than the isentropic drop of enthalpy across the stage, the multistage turbine would not show any gain in efficiency over the individual stage efficiencies. A statement to this effect is found in Keenan's book (reference 7, p. 303): "The over-all effectiveness of a turbine in which all stages have the same effectiveness is identical with the effectiveness of the individual stages." Here the term "effectiveness" designates the true output/input thermal efficiency.

It should be pointed out that when heat due to losses travels, say, from the first stage to the second in a steam turbine, the damage has already been done and the loss is equal to the amount of power which this amount of heat failed to produce in the first stage. Although this particular portion of heat may do some expansion work in the second stage there will be another equal amount of heat which will not, but will slip without working to the next stage. Thus the same amount of heat may be thought of as traveling from stage to stage without doing useful work, the loss in per cent remaining the same for a complete unit as it is for the individual stages if efficiency of the several stages remain essentially the same. What is not realized is that, when considering the first stage alone, the second stage serves as a sink (or another system) and the energy received by the second stage is already in a degraded state (reduced pressure and temperature), the process in the first stage being completed. And so it is in every succeeding stage.

The secondary effect of heat due to losses on the output of the following stage (increase in volume or reduction of density) is taken care of automatically by the definition of the available energy. To state it differently: the part of heat due to internal losses which is claimed as "recovered" due to reheat effect actually was not lost.

The following statement by Keenan is of interest in this connection. "The effectiveness (true output/input efficiency) exceeds the efficiency (adiabatic), because the effectiveness includes the so-called reheat effect" (reference 7, p. 302).

The input to the steam turbine based on the decrease of the available energy of the flow is always smaller than the isentropic enthalpy change by $T_0 \Delta s$. Thus the true stage efficiency is always higher than the adiabatic stage efficiency. In practice to account for this difference in efficiencies a multiplier known as "reheat factor," greater than unity, was introduced to bring the measured turbine output to a closer agreement with the calculated output based on the known adiabatic stage efficiency. By its nature the reheat factor is a "correction" for the stage efficiency rather than an index of the "beneficial" effect of the reheat or improvement of the stage efficiency.

Joseph Kaye and K. R. Wadleigh in a recent article on the subject make a definite statement on this point: "The authors agree that the phrases 'gain in energy due to reheat' and 'recovery of heat due to hydraulic losses' are completely misleading and should never be used" (reference 15). For a more detailed presentation of the application of the available energy function to the energy balance of power plants and evaluation of efficiency of steam turbines see references 1, 4, 5, and 6.

(*d*) *Ts* and *pv* Diagrams. The object of steady flow processes, as applied to turbomachines, is a transformation and transfer of energy. Energy can leave one system (source) and enter the other (acceptor of energy) only in the form of work and heat. Therefore a study of such processes is most conveniently done with the aid of *pv* and *Ts* diagrams. On the first, work appears as an area enclosed by the lines representing the path of equivalent cyclic changes of state of the working substance. On the *Ts* diagram, areas represent amounts of heat involved in the process as has been illustrated on several figures in this chapter. Although quantitative calculations of energy changes can be made with the aid of *pv* and *Ts* diagrams drawn to scale, their value lies in the qualitative illustration of the energy changes as an aid in the visualization of the process. In practice *Ts* diagrams reveal more information than *pv* diagrams, because in addition to the temperature and entropy they show also pressures and specific volume. The properties and use of *Ts* diagrams are not as widely known in this country as they are in Europe, where college textbooks put special emphasis on this subject. The utility of *Ts* diagram was fully demonstrated in the presentation and use of the available energy function for the analysis of the steady flow processes given in this chapter.

REFERENCES

1. Darrieus, *Eng.*, Sept. 5, 1930, pp. 283–285.
2. Kiefer and Stuart, *Principles of Engineering Thermodynamics*, Wiley, 1930, p. 1.
3. Mackey, *Kent's Handbook*, Wiley, 1950, pp. 3–50.
4. Seippel, "The Energy Economy of Steam Power Plants," *Brown Boveri Rev.*, Oct., 1950, p. 342.
5. Grassmann, "Zur allgemeinen Definition des Wirkungsgrades," *Chem. Ing. Tech.*, Feb., 28, 1950, pp. 77–80.
6. Hochstein, "Meaning of the Increase of Entropy in the Analysis of Heat Processes," *J. Tech. Phys. (U.S.S.R.)*, Vol. 21, No. 9, 1951, pp. 1121–1136, (in Russian).
7. Keenan, *Thermodynamics*, Wiley, 1941, p. 289.
8. Jouguet, "Remarques sur la thermodynamique des machines motrices," *Rev. Mecanique*, 1906, Vol. 19, p. 41; also, 1907, Vol. 20, p. 213; also, Mar., 1917.
9. Weber, *Thermodynamics for Chemical Engineers*, Wiley, 1939, pp. 108, 109.
10. Maxwell, *Theory of Heat*, Longmans, London, 1891, p. 187.
11. Pfleiderer, *Die Kreiselpumpen*, Springer, Berlin, 1949, p. 14.
12. Goodenough, *Principles of Thermodynamics*, Henry Holt, 1920, 3rd ed., p. 40.
13. Fernald, *Elements of Thermodynamics*, McGraw-Hill, 1938, p. 149.
14. Stodola, *Steam and Gas Turbines*, McGraw-Hill, 1927, p. 34.
15. Kaye and Wadleigh, "A New Method of Calculation of Reheat Factors for Turbines and Compressors," *J. Appl. Mechanics*, Dec., 1951; Discussion, June issue, 1952, p. 231.
16. Kluge, *Kreiselgebläse und Kreiselverdichter Radialer Bauart*, Springer, Berlin, 1953, p. 196.

CHAPTER 8

Special Problems, Thermodynamic and Hydrodynamic

8.1 PROPERTIES OF GAS MIXTURE

The thermodynamic properties of a mechanical gas mixture can be determined if the composition of the mixture by volume or weight is known together with the properties of the components.

Use is made of the following laws:

1. Avogadro's law states: All perfect gases at a given pressure and temperature have the same number of molecules in a given volume.

2. Dalton's law states: Each constituent of a gas mixture behaves as if it occupied the given volume alone. The total gas pressure is the sum of the partial pressures which each gas would exert were it to occupy the volume alone.

To each gas property (M, R, c_p, c_v) of a mixture each component contributes a share of its own property in proportion to its fraction of the total weight. Thus, if R is the gas constant of a mixture and R_1, R_2, and R_3 are the gas constants of gases 1, 2, and 3 and w_1, w_2, w_3 are their weights per pound of mixture, then

$$R = w_1 R_1 + w_2 R_2 + w_3 R_3 \qquad (8.1)$$

Note that w_1, w_2, and w_3 are fractions and $w_1 + w_2 + w_3 = 1$.

Similarly,

$$c_p = w_1 c_{p1} + w_2 c_{p2} + w_3 c_{p3} \qquad (8.2)$$

and

$$c_v = w_1 c_{v1} + w_2 c_{v2} + w_3 c_{v3} \qquad (8.3)$$

and

$$M = w_1 M_1 + w_2 M_2 + w_3 M_3 \qquad (8.4)$$

The composition of a mixture may be given by volumetric analysis by expressing the volume each constituent gas would occupy, as a fraction (or percentage) of the total volume, if all constituents were at the given pressure and temperature. To calculate the gas properties of a mixture in terms of those of the several constituents, volumetric fractions should be converted into the fractions by weight.

133

Suppose the composition of a mixture of three gases by volumetric analysis is v_1, v_2, and v_3, so that

$$v_1 + v_2 + v_3 = 1$$

If γ_1, γ_2, and γ_3 are specific weights in pounds per cubic foot of gases 1, 2, and 3, the weight of each constituent is equal to

$$W_1 = v_1\gamma_1 \qquad W_2 = v_2\gamma_2 \qquad W_3 = v_3\gamma_3 \qquad (8.5)$$

The specific weight of the mixture (pounds per cubic foot) obviously is

$$\gamma = W_1 + W_2 + W_3$$

Then the weight proportion of each gas is

$$w_1 = \frac{v_1\gamma_1}{\gamma} \qquad w_2 = \frac{v_2\gamma_2}{\gamma} \qquad w_3 = \frac{v_3\gamma_3}{\gamma} \qquad (8.6)$$

or, since specific weights of gases are proportional to their molecular weights,

$$w_1 = \frac{v_1 M_1}{M} \qquad w_2 = \frac{v_2 M_2}{M} \qquad w_3 = \frac{v_3 M_3}{M} \qquad (8.7)$$

The specific weight of each component can be found from the equation of state

$$pv = RT = p/\gamma \qquad (8.8)$$

using gas constants R_1, R_2, R_3 of the constituents and p and T of the mixture (when enclosed into separate compartments, each gas is under the same pressure and temperature as the mixture).

Following Dalton's law the internal energy and the entropy of a mixture are respectively equal to the sums of the internal energies and the entropies of its components at their respective partial pressures at the temperature of the mixture.

8.2 COMPRESSIBILITY

The term "compressibility" (sometimes called "supercompressibility") is used in connection with blower applications with reference to the conditions of gas when the latter ceases to follow the state equation for a perfect gas

$$pv = RT \qquad (8.9)$$

A compressibility factor Z is introduced into the state equation to express the relationship between the pressure, volume, and temperature of the gas so that:

$$pv = ZRT \qquad p(v/Z) = RT$$

or

$$p/\gamma Z = RT \tag{8.10}$$

Since R is fixed by the molecular weight of gas only, and p and T are measurable quantities, the compressibility factor Z really shows the deviation of the volume from that expressed by the perfect gas law.

The compressibility factor Z depends upon the nature of the gas and its pressure and temperature. However, if expressed in terms of "reduced" pressure and temperature, the factor Z remains very nearly the same for all gases.

$$\text{Reduced pressure } p_R = p/p_c \tag{8.11}$$

$$\text{Reduced temperature } T_R = T/T_c \tag{8.12}$$

where p_c and T_c are the critical pressure and temperature of the gas, and p and T are the operating pressure and temperature.

Values of the compressibility factor have been calculated and presented in the form of charts (references 1, 10, and 11) or tables (references 2 and 3) for a wide range of reduced pressures and temperatures based on available test data (reference 4). For a mixture of gases not combined chemically, the critical pressure and temperature are calculated on the assumption that each gas contributes to the mixture critical pressure and temperature in proportion to its fraction by volume (not by weight!).

$$p_c = p_{c1}v_1 + p_{c2}v_2 + p_{c3}v_3 \tag{8.13}$$

$$T_c = T_{c1}v_1 + T_{c2}v_2 + T_{c3}v_3 \tag{8.14}$$

where, p_c and T_c are critical pressure and temperature of the mixture and with subscripts 1, 2, and 3 indicate critical pressure and temperature for gases 1, 2, and 3. v_1, v_2, and v_3 are volumes of each gas per cubic foot of mixture, so that

$$v_1 + v_2 + v_3 = 1 \tag{8.15}$$

It should be noted that this method is generally applicable only for conditions not too close to the critical.

Figure 8.1 is a chart of compressibility factors for a wide range of reduced pressures and temperatures and shows the general trend of factor variation. In the region where the compressibility factor is $Z > 1$, the actual volume is greater than that of a perfect gas, indicating that the actual volume occupied by the molecules is not negligible in comparison with the total volume of the gas. On the other hand, when $Z < 1$, the actual gas occupies a smaller volume than indicated by the perfect gas law because at the existing pressures and temperatures the force of attraction between the molecules is the predominating factor (reference 4).

Figure 8.2 shows an enlarged part of Fig. 8.1 where $Z < 1$, which is the case for high pressure natural gas pipe lines and oil field repressuring installations.

Since the compressibility factor will be different for the inlet and discharge conditions of a blower, an average value should be used

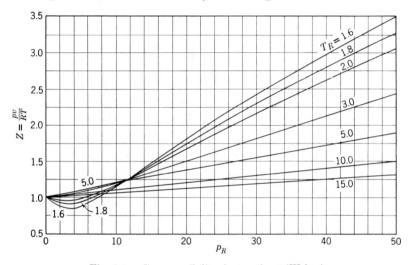

Fig. 8.1. Compressibility factor chart (Weber).

for head calculations using adiabatic or polytropic formulas. For high pressure multistage compressors such average values of the compressibility factor should be applied to each stage in the head calculations. For that reason the blower designer should be familiar with the use of charts and tables of compressibility factors.

Example. A natural gas transmission line station is to handle 756 MMSCFD (millions standard cubic feet per day) and produce a pressure ratio of 1.46, using three gas turbines of 5000 hp. each at 5000 r.p.m. All station discharge pressure is limited to 770 p.s.i.g. Inlet gas temperature is 70°F., specific gravity of gas is 0.60 (air = 1.0); ratio of specific heats, $k = 1.30$; $(k - 1)/k = 0.231$.

Find the size and type of the booster blower; inlet c.f.m., head in feet, and specific speed.

The flow rate of gas pipe lines is usually given in MMSCFD at 14.7 p.s.i.a. pressure and 60°F.

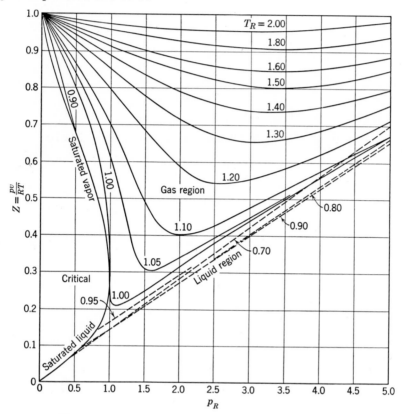

Fig. 8.2.   Detail of compressibility factor chart (Weber).

1. Inlet pressure p_1,

$$p_1 = (770 + 14.7)/1.46 = 537 \text{ p.s.i.a.}$$

2. Specific volume v_0 at 14.7 p.s.i.a. and 60°F,

$$v_0 = \frac{RT_0Z_0}{p_0} = \frac{89.0 \times 520}{14.7 \times 144} = 21.85 \text{ cu. ft./lb.}$$

The gas constant $R = 53.35/0.60 = 89.0$, and compressibility factor $Z_0 = 1$ for standard conditions.

3. Weight of flow W,

$$W = \frac{756 \times 1,000,000}{24 \times 3600 \times 21.85} = 400 \text{ lb./sec.}$$

4. Specific volume v_1 at inlet conditions from

$$p_1 v_1 = Z_1 R \cdot T_1$$

hence

$$v_1 = \frac{89.0 \times 530 \times 0.89}{537 \times 144} = 0.545 \text{ cu. ft./lb.}$$

Here $Z_1 = 0.89$ from tables [note that using Stano chart (reference 3) compressibility factor $Z = 1/(\text{table factors})^2$].

5. Inlet c.f.m.

$$\text{c.f.m.} = v_1 \times W \times 60 = 0.545 \times 400 \times 60 = 13,070$$

6. Total adiabatic head generated by the station

$$H = \frac{R T_1 Z_1}{(k-1)/k} \left[\left(\frac{p_2}{p_1} \right)^{(k-1)/k} - 1 \right]$$

$$= \frac{89.0 \times 530 \times 0.89}{0.231} [(1.46)^{0.231} - 1] = 16,650 \text{ ft.}$$

Head per unit $H = 16,650/3 = 5550$ ft.

7. b.hp. required, assuming 83 per cent adiabatic efficiency.

$$\text{b.hp.} = \frac{WH}{550 \times 0.83} = \frac{400 \times 5550}{550 \times 0.83} = 4870$$

8. Specific speed based on inlet volume

$$n_s = \frac{\text{r.p.m. (c.f.m.)}^{1/2}}{H^{3/4}} = \frac{5000 \times (13,070)^{1/2}}{(5550)^{3/4}} = 890$$

Remarks. (1) As a type number specific speed based on the station inlet volume is used only for rough approximation. Since three units will operate in series, inlet c.f.m. of the second and third stages will be lower, owing to compression in the preceeding stage, and their specific speed will be lower. Selection of the design specific speed is based on the impeller discharge volume to meet the requirements of all three stages.

(2) Pipe line operators are more familiar with the adiabatic head. However for design purposes all heads should be polytropic heads.

(3) The total station head was tentatively divided equally among the three units. In practice variation of capacity from stage to stage is best met by a slight speed variation. With motor drive different heads can be assigned to each unit to locate the operating points on the constant head-capacity characteristics to use identical impellers.

The load on the motors will be in proportion to the head as the weight of flow is constant for the stations.

Compression of Saturated Vapor.   It has been pointed out earlier in this article that compressibility factor accounts for the deviation of the gas or vapor volume from that expressed by the perfect gas law. If the actual specific volume of gas is known at the inlet and discharge conditions, the total head required to produce a given pressure ratio can be calculated without the use of compressibility factors.

Use is made of the steady flow polytropic equation in the form

$$H_p = \frac{n}{n-1} \, (p_2 v_2 - p_1 v_1) \tag{8.16}$$

The polytropic exponent $(n-1)/n$ can be eliminated by substituting its value from

$$\left(\frac{p_2}{p_1}\right)^{(n-1)/n} = \frac{p_2 v_2}{p_1 v_1} = \frac{T_2}{T_1}$$

$$\frac{n-1}{n} = \frac{\log_e \, (p_2 v_2 / p_1 v_1)}{\log_e \, (p_2 / p_1)} \tag{8.17}$$

then

$$H_p = \frac{p_2 v_2 - p_1 v_1}{\log_e \, (p_2 v_2 / p_1 v_1)} \log_e \left(\frac{p_2}{p_1}\right) \tag{8.18}$$

Note that equation 7.47 cannot be used for the determination of the polytropic exponent as it applies to gases following the perfect gas law.

The initial pressure p_1, temperature T_1, and the discharge pressure p_2 are usually specified.   The inlet specific volume v_1 can be found from the Mollier (or pressure-enthalpy) chart.   To find the discharge specific volume v_2, proceed as follows: (1) Locate the inlet point on the chart and read off the enthalpy h_1.   (2) Follow the constant entropy line to intersect p_2 line and read the enthalpy of this point h_2.   (3) The difference $(h_2 - h_1)$ represents the isentropic enthalpy rise.   To find the polytropic enthalpy rise, divide $(h_2 - h_1)$ by the estimated or known polytropic efficiency of the stage or the complete unit.

$$(\Delta h)_p = (h_2 - h_1)/e_p \tag{8.19}$$

The discharge point is placed where the enthalpy equal to

$$h_{2p} = h_1 + (\Delta h)_p \tag{8.20}$$

intersects the discharge pressure line p_2, where the discharge volume v_2 and the discharge temperature T_2 are read off the chart.

Equation 8.18 is frequently given the form

$$H_p = \tfrac{1}{2}(p_2 v_2 + p_1 v_1) \log_e (p_2/p_1) \qquad (8.21)$$

by substituting the mean arithmetical value of pv for the first factor, which is known as "log mean" of pv. Within certain limits such substitution results in a minor error.

Considering the advantage derived, the last substitution is hardly worthwhile. Since values of the critical pressures and temperatures, and hence the compressibility factor for all gases and vapors important in practice, are known and furnished to the compressor engineer, there is not much use for the equations 8.18 or 8.21 of this article, as standard polytropic or adiabatic equations, with the proper values of the compressibility factors (average for inlet and discharge), apply. Note that omitting the compressibility factor results in a higher head hence a higher compression ratio.

8.3 EFFECT OF HUMIDITY ON BLOWER PERFORMANCE

Moisture in atmospheric air affects blower performance in several respects, the extent depending upon the relative humidity and temperature and, to a smaller degree, upon the pressure. In the equation connecting the adiabatic head H_{ad} with the pressure ratio $r = p_2/p_1$, repeated below,

$$H_{ad} = \frac{RT_1}{(k-1)/k}\left[\left(\frac{p_2}{p_1}\right)^{(k-1)/k} - 1\right] \qquad (8.22)$$

the moisture content of the air affects the value of the gas constant R and value of k because gas properties of mechanical gas mixtures (not combined chemically) are determined on the basis that each gas contributes to each property in proportion to its fraction of the total weight of the mixture.

It so happens that the effect of k of the first term (outside the brackets) very nearly compensates the effect of k of the second (bracketed) term and therefore can be omitted from consideration. It can be shown that the gas constant R is inversely proportional to the specific gravity of moist air relative to dry air. This follows from equation 7.28

$$R = 1545/M \qquad (8.23)$$

where M is the molecular weight of the mixture. But the specific gravity of gases is proportional to the molecular weights,

$$\text{Specific gravity of gas } G = M/28.97 \qquad (8.24)$$

where 28.97 is the molecular weight of dry air. Substituting M from equation 8.24 into equation 8.23, we obtain

$$R = 1545/28.97G = 53.34/G \qquad (8.25)$$

where 53.34 is the gas constant R for dry air.

Figure 8.3 shows the specific gravity of moist air in terms of relative moisture and temperature.

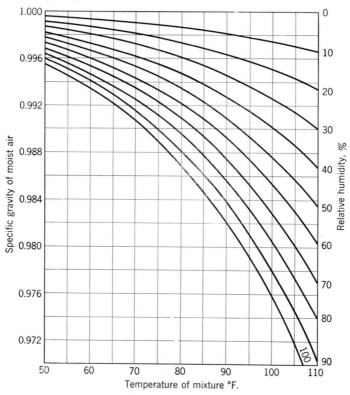

Fig. 8.3.   Specific gravity of moist air.

Since the head H_{ad} of a blower at a given speed is constant, an increase of moisture content in the air will increase the value of the gas constant R and hence reduce the pressure ratio p_2/p_1. Or, conversely, for a fixed pressure ratio p_2/p_1 (observed on test) correction for humidity will result in a higher calculated adiabatic head and higher efficiency. It follows also that to obtain a given discharge pressure with moist air a higher head in feet is required than with dry air, which becomes obvious when it is realized that increased humidity reduces the specific weight of the mixture.

As the relative humidity is increased, the vapor partial pressure is increased and the dry air partial inlet pressure and density are reduced, therefore the weight of dry air delivered by the blower is reduced.

With high pressure blowers that use intercoolers to keep the air temperature down during compression, the moisture in the air poses a special problem since it condenses out in the intercoolers and must be removed from the air stream to prevent collection of moisture in the machine which may result in damage. In the normal compression process the partial vapor pressure of the water increases in the same proportion as the total pressure. Since the saturation pressure, or dew point pressure, is a function of temperature only, the moisture would condense out, were it not for the fact that the mixture temperature also increases during compression. In the intercoolers, however, the mixture temperature is reduced at constant pressure, often to a point below the saturation temperature of the water vapor, with resulting condensation.

It should be pointed out that the heat balance method of determining power input to the blower is limited to a vapor superheat of not less than 20°. With high moisture content heat may be absorbed from the mixture to vaporize any entrained water particles and thus reduce the temperature rise.

8.4 MACH NUMBER

The affinity laws deduced in Chapters 5 and 6 from dimensional analysis considerations apply without any change to compressible fluids so long as no velocities in the blower channels approach the velocity of sound. It will be recalled that compression waves which produce sound are responsible also for propagation of pressure through the fluid. If the fluid moves away with the velocity of sound there is no mechanism by which pressure can be exerted on the fluid to produce acceleration. Thus a further increase of pressure will not have any effect on the flow. As an example, the flow through an orifice or nozzle can be quoted. This flow reaches its maximum when the velocity through the nozzle is equal to the velocity of sound. Any further pressure decrease beyond the nozzle will have no effect on the flow.

The velocity of sound in a fluid is equal to

$$a = \sqrt{kgRT} \qquad (8.26)$$

where $k = c_p/c_v$.

For a given fluid a varies as $\sqrt{T}$ and is independent of pressure. For air

$$a = 49 \sqrt{T}$$

If, when applying dimensional analysis to the problem of flow in a turbomachine, the velocity of sound a is introduced as an additional variable affecting the operation of the impeller, another dimensionless criterion c/a will be obtained in addition to three dimensionless factors given in Chapter 5, equations 5.2, 5.3, and 5.4. Here c is the local fluid velocity. The effect of this criterion, known as Mach number

$$M = c/a$$

can be learned only experimentally. There is no agreement as to what velocity should be used for Mach number as a criterion of the flow conditions in a turbomachine. The peripheral velocity at the impeller discharge (outside diameter of an axial flow impeller) has been used in the past. This has little justification as there are no particles which move with this velocity, and besides this velocity remains constant for all rates of flow. The relative velocity at entrance to the impeller channel as determined from the input velocity triangle is also used extensively. Local velocities in excess of the average velocity will occur in places of low pressure and temperature. This explains why the effect of Mach number is observed with values over 0.75, based on the average relative velocity, instead of 1.0. However, since at rated flow there is a definite ratio between the average relative velocity and any local velocity, a Mach number based on the above velocities may serve as a criterion of performance at high speeds. Note that the velocity of sound in the critical location is not definitely known because neither velocities nor temperatures are uniform along and across the channel of flow.

In the field of centrifugal blowers the maximum peripheral velocities are determined from the impeller strength consideration (depending on design and material) and the effect of Mach number as well as Reynolds number can be disregarded in a great majority of cases. With axial flow compressors, used for supercharging, and gas turbines, peripheral velocities up to 1600 ft. per sec. are in use. A reduction of size and weight of the unit is the compelling reason for such high velocities.

It is only when pumping heavy gases (low gas constant R) at low temperatures that the critical Mach number may be approached with centrifugal blowers. Usually the impeller peripheral velocity is kept below 0.9 of the acoustic velocity. Under these conditions the effect of Mach number definitely appears as head-capacity and efficiency reduction. The immediate result of Mach number effect is a reduction of the operating range between the pumping limit and maximum capacity to a very narrow belt, the head-capacity curve approaching a straight vertical line (Fig. 14.19). When Mach number effects become apparent, the affinity laws, or laws of similarity of flow pattern, cease to hold.

Those familiar with the operation of centrifugal pumps under cavitation conditions cannot fail to notice the similarity of the effects on performance at the critical Mach number and cavitation. The similarity of effects of the two phenomena can be traced to the similarity of the flow pattern under the prevailing conditions, i.e., the maximum velocity of relative flow is reached at some controlling section of the channel (the same in both cases) limiting the capacity of flow irrespective of increase of speed of rotation (reference 5).

8.5 EFFECT OF COMPRESSION RATIO ON THE BLOWER CHARACTERISTICS

(a) Single Stage. In this article it will be shown that the head-capacity and efficiency curves become steeper as the compression ratio is increased and approaches a vertical line in the extreme case of multistage axial flow compressors. As a basis of comparison, characteristic curves for incompressible fluids will be used, such as the head-capacity and efficiency curves of centrifugal pumps of the same specific speed. Having no suitable characteristics for incompressible fluids, performance of a single-stage blower at a low compression ratio can be used for comparison.

For incompressible fluids, since there is no change in density through the impeller, the head and efficiency curves can be plotted against capacity at impeller inlet or impeller outlet or against the rate of weight flow. *With compressible flow, impeller performance is determined essentially by the impeller discharge.* The effect of impeller inlet or blower casing is minor and will be overlooked in this discussion. If plotted against the impeller discharge volume, the performance of an impeller pumping a compressible fluid will be essentially identical with that for the incompressible fluid. *But, since true velocities and fluid density at impeller discharge cannot be measured directly, the volume at impeller discharge is not measurable, and it is customary to plot the head and efficiencies versus the inlet volume. This is the same as plotting the performance against the weight flow, as inlet density is constant.* This leads to a distortion of the head-capacity curve as compared with the curve for the incompressible fluid and is the cause of the change in slope of head-capacity and efficiency curves as can be seen from the following.

Suppose on Fig. 8.4 the dashed lines show the head-capacity and efficiency of an impeller plotted against the impeller discharge volume (upper scale). All values are expressed in per cent of those at the best efficiency point (b.e.p.), or rated values, to eliminate the effects of scales. The inlet volume for any point on the head-capacity curve can easily be measured and will be greater than the volume at the impeller discharge as a result of compression. Thus the rated point A on the discharge c.f.m. scale will move to B on the inlet c.f.m. scale (full lines on Fig. 8.4). The distance AB represents in c.f.m. the decrease in volume due to compression. This decrease in volume is lower for lower head points and is zero for the point C of zero head. *Thus the physical slope of the head-capacity curve to the right of b.e.p.*

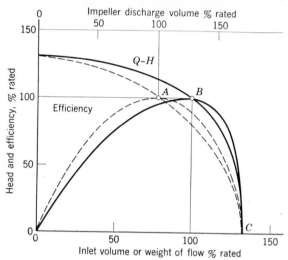

Fig. 8.4.   Effect of capacity scales.

becomes steeper on the inlet c.f.m. or weight flow scale than it is on the incompressible fluid curve.

To the left of the b.e.p. the shifting of the points will be decreasing toward zero capacity where the change in volume is zero because volume is zero. This part of the curve is rarely realized completely on account of "pumping." Besides, this part of the Q-H curve is markedly influenced by the casing, and as a result it differs materially from that for incompressible fluids in that it is flatter and zero head is lower. The efficiency curve will follow a similar shifting owing to selection of inlet c.f.m. for abscissa scale.

If performance is plotted against the dimensionless capacity coefficient $\phi = c_{m2}/u_2$, *where* c_{m2} *is the calculated meridional velocity at impeller discharge, there would be no difference between the performance for the compressible or incompressible fluids.*

However, for practical reasons, inlet c.f.m. or weight of flow are universally used. Obviously the higher the compression ratio the greater the shiftng of the head and efficiency curves on inlet c.f.m. scales. The same reasoning can be applied to a multistage blower when treated as a unit. Being inherently a high compression ratio machine its head-capacity and efficiency characteristics are steeper than the individual stage performance when plotted on the percentage scales. This effect is exaggerated with multistage compressor owing to stage mismatching discussed in the following articles.

(b) **Multistage Blowers, Stage Matching.** In addition to the above effects of fluid compressibility on the performance curves of a multi-stage compressor as plotted on the inlet volume abscissa, multistage performance characteristics are influenced by stage mismatching at conditions other than the design point. To follow up these effects it is sufficient to consider only two stages. The head-capacity curve of a two-stage unit will be thought of as that obtained by the addition of heads for the same weight of flow or the same inlet c.f.m. of the first stage.

To obtain optimum performance from a multistage compressor the design should aim to obtain the peak efficiency of each stage at the rated weight of flow. This means that each stage is designed for different volumetric capacities, allowing for the reduction in volume at impeller discharge as compression progresses from stage to stage. For practical reasons, when possible, it is convenient to make all impellers of the same diameter, thus producing the same heads. For the present discussion it will be assumed that all stages have impellers with the same impeller discharge angle, thus the same basic stage performance can be used for all stages.

By inspection of the polytropic head equation it will be noticed that the optimum conditions, i.e., conditions at which *all stages have peak efficiency at the same rated weight of flow, are maintained only at the design speed, for a given gas only, and at the same inlet temperature.* A change of any of these factors leads to a different compression ratio. A reduction of compression ratio will place the operating point, corresponding to the design inlet volume of the first stage, at a higher capacity, lower head, and efficiency or to the right of the b.e.p. of all subsequent stages. The same is true for all points on the Q-H curve. As a result the total head at the rated weight of flow is reduced, the peak efficiency is impaired, and the head-capacity curve becomes steeper. In other words, impellers are too small for the new conditions. The pumping point is determined by the first stage under such conditions.

A higher compression ratio than that designed for will have the opposite effects but to a smaller degree because shifting of the operating point to left brings a smaller change in the head than in the first case. The peak efficiency is impaired in both cases. For higher compression ratios the design impellers are too wide. When a blower is operated at a higher compression ratio than that for which it was designed, the pumping point is determined by the last stage.

(c) **Effect of Compression Ratio on Stage Matching.** A better insight into the effects of the compression ratio on mismatching of stages at the b.e.p. can be obtained from consideration of dimensionless performance of stages in terms of head and capacity coefficients (reference 9). Suppose Fig. 8.5 represents the dimensionless characteristics of a typical stage applicable to several stages of a multistage compressor, impellers differing only in the width or the outlet impeller areas. The effect of the Reynolds and Mach numbers will be neglected within the range of compression ratios under discussion. Consider two adjacent stages, say, first and second. At the

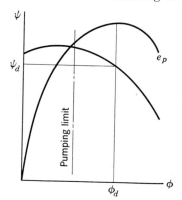

Fig. 8.5. Dimensionless stage characteristics.

design conditions the impeller discharge areas are adjusted to provide for the increase in the gas density (γ) so that

$$A_1/A_2 = (\gamma_2/\gamma_1)_d = r_d^{1/n} \tag{8.27}$$

where r_d is the design compression ratio: ϕ_d and ψ_d are the capacity and head coefficients at the design point for this compression ratio. The area ratio A_1/A_2 is fixed at the design ratio. Suppose the same machine is run at several compression ratios below and above the rated ratio. Let Fig. 8.6 represent its performance in terms of pressure ratios plotted against the weight of flow, which is proportional to the inlet c.f.m. The surge line and the loci of best efficiency points as determined by test are indicated.

From the definition of the capacity coefficient we can write for stages 1 and 2, for the weight of flow W_1 corresponding to the compression ratio r_1 at the best efficiency point,

$$\phi_1 = c_{m2}/u_2 = W_1/\gamma_1 A_1 u_2 \tag{8.28}$$

$$\phi_2 = c_{m2}/u_2 = W_1/\gamma_2 A_2 u_2$$

and, since u_2 and W_1 are the same for both stages,

$$\frac{\phi_2}{\phi_1} = \left(\frac{\gamma_1}{\gamma_2}\right)_1 \frac{A_1}{A_2} = \left(\frac{\gamma_1}{\gamma_2}\right)_1 r_d^{1/n} \qquad (8.29)$$

For the ratio of density at the compression ratio r_1 we can substitute as before

$$(\gamma_1/\gamma_2)_1 = 1/r_1^{1/n} \qquad (8.30)$$

and equation (8.30) will become

$$(\phi_2/\phi_1)^n = r_d/r_1 > 1 \qquad (8.31)$$

Since $r_d > r_1$, the capacity coefficients $\phi_2 > \phi_1$. This means that the operating points of stages 1 and 2 do not come from the best

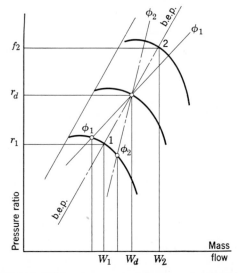

Fig. 8.6.   Effect of pressure ratio on stage matching.

efficiency point ϕ_d on the stage performance but straddle it at any other pressure ratio than the designed one.   For compression ratios lower than the design, the first stage operating point is approaching the surge line, whereas at higher pressure ratios the high pressure stage operating point moves toward the pumping point.   From equation 8.31 it follows that the degree of shifting of the operating points of various stages depends on the ratio r_d/r.   *In every case the peak efficiency is reduced and the surge free operating range is impaired.*

The mass of flow or inlet c.f.m. will be lower than the affinity laws indicate at lower than design compression ratios and will be higher than the affinity laws indicate at higher compression ratios.   The reason of such behavior of multistage compressors lies in the fact that area ratios are fixed and at low compression ratios the density throughout all stages is lower than the design density and volumes are greater. Hence all areas are too small, thus restricting the through-flow ability of the compressor to a lower mass flow. At higher pressure ratios the impeller discharge areas would be too large for the rate of flow given by affinity relations and the best efficiency point will move to a higher capacity (ϕ value) and lower combined head.

Whenever two stages are mismatched the b.e.p. of the combination falls between the b.e.p. of the individual stages.

Use of higher impeller discharge angles (and hence flatter head-capacity characteristics) reduces the shifting of the operating point of the subsequent stages and results in flatter over-all head-capacity and efficiency curves. *Since the head-capacity characteristics of individual stages of axial flow compressors are steep, the combined head-capacity and efficiency curves will exaggerate the above effects, thus reducing the useful range of operation even before the effects of Mach number appear.*

(*d*) **Stage Mismatching at Capacities Greater than Normal.** When a multistage compressor operates at the design conditions the total generated head is equal to the sum of the heads of all the stages at the design rate of weight flow, which, for all stages, coincides with the rated capacity at impeller discharge. At rates of weight flow greater than the design rate, say 120 per cent, the second stage will be operating at higher than 120 per cent of its rated discharge volume, because at the lower head the 120 per cent weight flow will not be compressed to 120 per cent discharge volume. Thus a steeper total head-capacity curve, as plotted against the inlet volume or weight of flow, will result.

The shifting of the operating point on the impeller volumetric capacity to the right at rates of flow higher than normal increases as flow progresses from stage to stage. Thus the greater the number of stages, or the greater the design compression ratio, the steeper the head-capacity curve becomes.

The efficiency curve follows the same trend because for any rates of flow higher than the normal all subsequent stages contribute their reduced head at a lower efficiency, corresponding to a higher impeller volumetric capacity.

At partial rates of flow the shifting of the operating point of the second, third, etc., stages is in the opposite direction. The net result is again a steeper head and efficiency curve. The operating range free from pumping is reduced because the last stage operating point will reach the pumping limit sooner than the first stage as a result of shifting.

(e) **Impeller Selection for Multistage Compressors.** Since any existing multistage compressor cannot meet all possible pumping requirements with optimum efficiency in practice, each size of multistage compressor is generally provided with a greater number of impellers than the maximum number of stages contemplated. Thus a six-stage compressor may have available twelve impellers of different capacities to choose from, to provide for different compressibilities resulting from the variation of speed, gas, inlet temperature, and number of stages. Several impellers may have different discharge angles, as it is advantageous to use lower discharge angles for low capacity impellers to increase the impeller widths. In that case a typical stage performance for each impeller discharge angle should be available.

The procedure of selecting impellers for multistage compressor is essentially the same as designing of new impellers except that instead of making each impeller meet the required discharge capacity, the nearest existing impeller is selected to do the job. Selection is made on the basis of the volume at the impeller discharge.

(f) **Variation of Compression Ratio of Single-Stage Blowers.** If the impeller inlet, impeller outlet, and volute (or diffusion vanes) are at the optimum combination at one speed, at a higher speed the increase in head and capacity will affect different parts of the blower to a different degree. The head and capacity will be determined mostly by the impeller discharge. Reexpanded back to the inlet conditions, the inlet c.f.m. will increase in a higher ratio than the volume at impeller discharge, and the impeller inlet part will work at a capacity higher than the design point. Mismatching of the volute or vaned diffuser will appear in a smaller degree, as the difference in compression from the impeller discharge to the casing passages is small. It will be pointed out in Chapter 9 that at higher speeds efficiency of the velocity conversion in the casing is reduced. The extent of the damage to efficiency at higher speeds due to mismatching of parts is rather difficult to measure because the effect of local Mach number is likely to appear. Again any faults in streamlining of any parts of the passages will be more pronounced at higher speeds. The combined effect of all these factors is a reduction of the peak efficiency of the blower at higher speeds.

8.6   EFFICIENCY OF MULTISTAGE BLOWERS

(a) **Adiabatic versus Polytropic Efficiency.** The true output/input efficiency of a multistage blower is appreciably lower than that of the individual stage efficiency for several reasons. Some of these reasons do not depend on the compressibility of the fluid or thermal effects in process of compression and are common to centrifugal pumps pumping water. To this group belong: (1) additional hydraulic losses connected with the crossover passages from stage to stage, (2) extra leakage from stage to stage and leakage through the axial thrust balancing devices; (3) the adverse effect of the large shaft through the impeller eye, as compared with the performance of the single stage blower of the same specific speed. The first item is by far the most important of the three.

There are a number of causes for multistage efficiency being lower than the individual stage efficiency which stem from the compressibility of the pumped fluid.

1. The A.S.M.E. Test Code PTC10-1949 defines only adiabatic efficiency. This is a conventional (and not real) efficiency based on the theoretical isentropic blower output. The adiabatic efficiency is lower than the true output/input efficiency determined on the basis of the output measured as the change of the available energy or calculated with the polytropic formula. The polytropic formula gives an acceptable approximation to the true output. The *difference between the adiabatic and the true efficiency increases as the compression ratio is increased, as a result of a greater number of stages, higher speed, or higher gas density.* Thus, the adiabatic efficiency will decrease as the compression ratio is increased even when the indiviual stage efficiencies are the same for all stages. However, under these conditions, the true output/input (or polytropic) efficiency remains the same. Figure 7.5 gives the ratio of the polytropic to adiabatic efficiency for different compression ratios.

2. For practical considerations it is customary to make impellers of all stages of the same diameter, thus producing essentially the same head per stage. As the fluid progresses from stage to stage its volume is reduced; thus, the specific speed of individual stages is progressively reduced, resulting in a lower hydraulic efficiency. Blowers have been built with all impellers of the same specific speed, and impeller diameter has been reduced from stage to stage, but the inividual stage efficiencies could not be expected to be the same for all stages, owing to adverse effect of size or Reynolds number.

3. Since multistage blowers are usually designed for the maximum head per stage, they operate at or near the maximum peripheral velocity set by the mechanical considerations of strength of impellers. Single-stage impellers of the same specific speed may not always operate at the maximum head or speed. Higher velocities through the impeller and casing channels require higher degree of streamlining,

which is frequently sacrificed for the sake of strength. Also higher velocities require a lower rate of diffusion through the impeller and diffusion casing channels; this is rarely provided.

4. It has been pointed out in the preceeding article that units are designed with individual stages adjusted so that peak efficiency occurs at the same rate of flow. *At any compression ratio different from the original design compression ratio, stages become "unmatched" and the peak efficiency of the complete unit is reduced.*

(*b*) **Reheat Effect.** Opinions have been expressed that the efficiency of a multistage compressor is reduced below that of the individual stages by the "reheat effect" caused by the heat due to hydraulic losses being retained by the fluid. The effect is opposite to the "reheat factor" in steam turbines where its "beneficial" effects are frequently claimed (references 6, 7, and 8). Obviously the above reasoning fails to differentiate between the adiabatic conventional efficiency and the true output/input efficiency. *If the steam turbine efficiency is calculated on the basis of the input taken as a decrease in the available energy of the flow, the multistage turbine would not show any gain in efficiency over the individual stage efficiencies.*

(*c*) **Commercial Efficiencies.** Adiabatic efficiency and isothermal efficiency, discussed in Chapter 11, are frequently referred to as "commercial" efficiencies to be used in the trade to differentiate it from several others used by designers of turbomachines. In practice the brake horsepower shows the relative merits of several makes of machines offered to meet a given set of conditions; efficiency need not be mentioned. Under such conditions (the same c.f.m. and the same pressure rise), although adiabatic and isothermal efficiencies may be five or ten points below the true output/input efficiency, they will correctly represent the relative merits of blowers of different makes. This is because in the formula for efficiency, since the theoretical output is the same for all makes (numerator), the brake horsepower is inversely proportional to the conventional efficiency.

8.7 ISOTHERMAL VERSUS ADIABATIC COMPRESSION

(*a*) **Batch Process.** If gas is compressed isothermally from pressure p_1 (point A Fig. 8.7) to pressure p_2 (point C) the work of compression is represented by the area under the curve AC or $ACFJ$. If gas is compressed from the same state A to the same pressure p_2, adiabatically along AB, the work of compression is equal to the area $ABGJ$. It can be shown that

$$\text{Area } ACFJ > \text{Area } ABGJ$$

by using the thermodynamic formulas.

$$w_{iso} = p_1 v_1 \log_e (p_2/p_1) > \frac{p_1 v_1}{k-1} \left[\left(\frac{p_2}{p_1} \right)^{(k-1)/k} - 1 \right] = w_{ad} \quad (8.32)$$

The numerical values for the compression ratio $p_2/p_1 = 3$ and atmospheric air are, for example,

$$w_{iso} = 30{,}400 \text{ ft.-lb./lb.} > w_{ad} = 25{,}300 \text{ ft.-lb./lb.}$$

(*b*) **Steady Flow Process.** The common knowledge that it takes less power to compress gas to a given pressure isothermally than adiabatically refers to steady flow processes. This is because it takes more power to discharge gas compressed adiabatically (area $BDRG$)

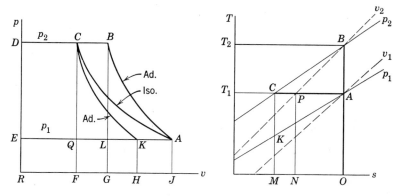

Fig. 8.7.   Batch versus steady flow process.

than isothermally (area $CDRF$). To complete the cycle of adiabatic compression would require some additional work of displacement over that of compression proper equal to $(p_2 v_2 - p_1 v_1) > 0$. The work of displacement in the isothermal cyclic process is equal to zero because $p_2 v_2 = p_1 v_1$. Thus, although the work of compression isothermally is the same for the batch and steady flow processes, the work of a steady flow adiabatic compression is k times that of the batch process. In Fig. 8.7 the work of isothermal compression for a steady flow process is represented by the area $ACDE = ACFJ$. The same for adiabatic compression is equal to the area $ABDE$. The difference between the two is equal to the area ABC.

For the above numerical example

Steady flow isothermal work $= 30{,}400$ ft.-lb./lb.

Steady flow adiabatic work $= 25{,}300 \times 1.393 = 35{,}300$ ft.-lb./lb.

(c) **Precooling.** The object of this article is to show that it is more economical to precool gas and compress it adiabatically to the same final pressure and temperature than to compress it isothermally. Thus, in Fig. 8.7 by cooling gas from A to K (no work applied) and compressing adiabatically along KC, the work of compression for a steady flow process is equivalent to the area $KCDE$ which is less than the work of isothermal compression to the same final state C by the area ACK.

This has a practical significance for the internally cooled multistage compressors discussed in Chapter 11. Since the actual compression occurs in the impellers and there is no way to cool the impellers, the internal cooling really amounts to precooling for the next following stage. Thermodynamically there is no disadvantage in this except that the first stage handles normal inlet gas. However, owing to the low initial temperature, precooling of the first stage would be impractical.

Note that in Fig. 8.7 the line CD does not represent any change of state of the substance, which is merely mechanically removed from the cylinder of a reciprocating compressor. The same applies to the lines BD, AE, and KE. The pv diagram of events as they occur in the cylinder of a reciprocating compressor was used to simplify the presentation of the principle involved. In a steady flow machine, changes of state occur gradually and continuously, and the input work necessary to realize the change of state from inlet to the outlet is exactly equal to that of a reciprocating machine as represented by the area $ABDE$ for adiabatic and $ACDE$ for isothermal compression. The same values can be calculated exactly by the use of known formulas 7.7 and 7.12.

It should be pointed out that the area $ABGJ$ on pv diagram, Fig. 8.7, numerically equal to the work of the adiabatic compression from the state A to the state B in a batch process *has no other physical meaning than the graphical representation of the* $\int pdv$. This diagram cannot be reproduced by any cylinder and piston system in a cyclic process, because a batch process is only one link of a possible cyclic process. If gas in a state B is expanded back to the state A, the same amount of work can be obtained from the process. If gas in a state B is expanded without doing work (throttling) to the state A, all the energy expended on compression (equivalent to the area $ABGJ$ and not the area ABL) will be wasted.

The above remarks apply equally to the area $ACFJ$ representing the work of isothermal compression in a batch process except that this is equal to the area $ACDE$, corresponding to the work of isothermal compression in a steady flow process as stated already.

On Ts diagram (Fig. 8.7) the work of adiabatic compression from state A to state B in a batch process is represented by the area $ABPNOA$ below the constant volume v_2 line between the temperature limits T_2 and T_1 and numerically equal to

$$w_{\text{ad}} = c_v(T_2 - T_1) \qquad \text{batch process} \qquad (8.33)$$

The work of adiabatic compression in a steady flow process for the same pressure and temperature limits is equal to $ABCMOA$ and is numerically equal to

$$w_{\text{ad}} = c_p(T_2 - T_1) \qquad \text{steady flow} \qquad (8.34)$$

For isothermal compression to the same final pressure p_2 the work of compression on Ts diagram is represented by the area $ACMO$ both for

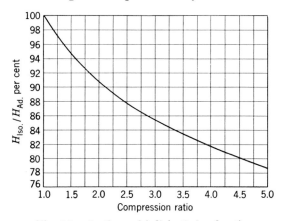

Fig. 8.8.   Isothermal/adiabatic head ratio.

batch and steady flow processes.   This can be easily proved by taking numerical examples and using known thermodynamic formulas.

Figure 8.8 shows ratios of isothermal to adiabatic heads for different compression ratios.   The same ratio shows the power requirement for the isothermal process to produce the same pressure ratio as compared with the adiabatic compression.   However, isothermal compression is rarely approached in practice, as discussed in detail in Chapter 11.

REFERENCES

1. *Worthington Research Bull.* P-7637, 1949.
2. Squier Co., *Supercompressibility Tables*, Dallas, Texas, 1950.
3. Stanolind Oil Co., *Supercompressibility Correction Factor Tables*, Tulsa, Okla., 1949.
4. Dodge, *Chemical Engineering Thermodynamics*, McGraw-Hill, 1944, p. 155.
5. Pfleiderer, "Die Überschallgrenze bei Kreiselverdichtern," *Z.V.D.I.*, Bd., 92, Feb. 21, 1950.

6. Pfleiderer, *Die Kreiselpumpen*, Springer, Berlin, 1949, p. 21.
7. Ponomareff, *A.S.M.E. Trans.*, May, 1948, p. 303.
8. Schultz, *Turbokompressoren und Turbogebläse*, Springer, Berlin, 1931, p. 14.
9. Stephenson, "A Solution of the Surging Problem in Axial Flow Compressors," *J. Aeronaut. Sci.*, Vol. 19, No. 1 Jan., 1952, pp. 67–69.
10. Maxwell, *Data Book on Hydrocarbons*, Van Nostrand, 1950.
11. Nelson and Obert, "Generalized Properties of Gases," *A.S.M.E. Paper* 53-A-194, Generalized Compressibility charts (not a part of the paper) can be obtained from the authors, Northwestern Technological Institute, Evanston, Ill. Also, see *Chem. Eng.*, July, 1954, pp. 203–208.

CHAPTER 9

Blower Casing

The purpose of the blower casing is to guide gas to the impeller, convert into pressure the high velocity kinetic energy of the flow from the impeller discharge, and lead gas away. The casing takes no part in the generation of head, and consequently all theoretical considerations in casing design deal with losses. The theoretical head-capacity characteristic of the impeller is a straight line. The actual shape of blower performance curves is determined by the combined effect of the hydraulic losses of the impeller and the casing. Mechanical losses, including disk friction, remain the same for all capacities, and leakage loss is small and varies slightly with the impeller head. The casing plays an important part in locating the best efficiency point not only by virtue of its hydraulic losses but also by its ability to restrict the flow (against a given head) without incurring any additional losses. Together with the impeller passages the casing fixes the specific capacity $q_s = Q/Dn^3$, discussed in the Arts. 5.3 and 6.5c.

9.1 INLET NOZZLE

Since the fluid path between the casing inlet flange and the impeller eye is short, and velocities in the inlet nozzle are relatively low, the loss of head due to friction in this path is very small. However, the design of the inlet nozzle has an important bearing on the velocity distribution immediately ahead of the impeller which may affect the impeller efficiency. This effect is more pronounced at higher rotative speeds and higher specific speeds.

A straight, tapered axial inlet nozzle, known as "end inlet" nozzle, is the best in every respect for single-inlet impellers. Such a nozzle, the area of which gradually reduces toward the impeller eye, has a definite steadying effect on the flow and assures uniform velocity distribution to the impeller.

A long-radius reducing elbow is next best (Fig. 9.1). For low specific speeds (below 500) the two are equivalent hydraulically. How-

157

ever, at higher specific speeds and maximum rotative speed (maximum head) the optimum efficiency and head will be appreciably reduced with the elbow inlet.

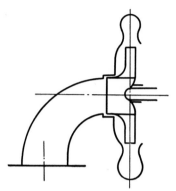

An offset flat elbow inlet, sometimes referred to as a volute inlet, may be used when a horizontal or vertical inlet is wanted. It is almost as efficient as a tapered elbow for low specific speeds, but for high specific speeds the detrimental effects of the sharp 90° turn immediately in front of impeller inlet become most pronounced. In an elbow of this type it is essential to have the flow accelerated gradually in order to suppress the tendency toward velocity distortion due to a double turn just in front of the impeller vanes. To effect a better distribution around the impeller eye, section AF, Fig. 9.2, is given an area some 50 per cent or more greater than that of the impeller eye. At the same time the width of the nozzle at AF is about twice the impeller eye diameter. As a result of the turn, most of the flow shifts

Fig. 9.1. Reducing inlet elbow.

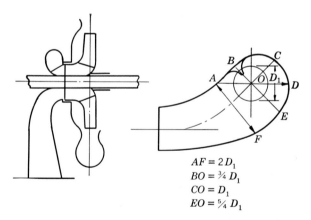

$$AF = 2D_1$$
$$BO = \tfrac{3}{4} D_1$$
$$CO = D_1$$
$$EO = \tfrac{5}{4} D_1$$

Fig. 9.2.   Volute inlet nozzle.

to the outer side; therefore the baffle or stop at B is placed 90° past the middle line of the nozzle OC. Several leading proportions of the volute inlet nozzle are indicated on Fig. 9.2.

Use of guide vanes in the inlet nozzle to control the output of the impeller is discussed in Art. 15.1.

9.2 BLOWER CASINGS—VOLUTE

(*a*) **Introduction.** Volute casings are particularly suited for single-stage blowers. Their main advantage is small size and low cost. There are isolated cases where volute casings have been used for two- and three-stage units, Fig. 9.11, but pattern costs become prohibitive. The use of vaned or vaneless diffuser casings with vaned return channels is practically universal for multistage blowers.

The hydraulic characteristics of volute casings are determined by the following design elements: volute areas A_v, volute angle α_v, volute width b_3, and volute base circle D_3. The selection of these elements is governed by theoretical considerations given below, but their actual values have been established experimentally for best hydraulic performance. Determination of volute areas is based on the average volute velocity c_3 defined as

$$c_3 = Q_v/A_v \tag{9.1}$$

where Q_v is the actual volume of flow through the volute and A_v is the volute throat area. Calculation of the actual volute flow volume should precede the discussion of the volute areas.

(*b*) **Volute Volume Flow.** The volume of flow in the volute is smaller than that at the impeller inlet owing to compression under pressure p_v prevailing in the volute. The pressure p_v, or the compression ratio p_v/p_1 (where p_1 is the inlet pressure) can be calculated from the pressure head H_v existing in the volute. This is obtained from

$$H_v = H - (c_3{}^2/2g) \tag{9.2}$$

where, H is the total head of the impeller, and c_3 is the average volute velocity. This is lower than the absolute velocity at the impeller discharge c_2' and is equal to

$$c_3 = R_{c3}c_2' \tag{9.3}$$

R_{c3} is an experimental factor, less than unity, given in Fig. 6.11 in terms of the absolute discharge angle α_2'. Both c_2' and α_2' are taken from Fig. 6.10 for the selected values of the head coefficient ψ and capacity constant ϕ, or both variables can be calculated from

$$(c_2'/u_2)^2 = \psi^2 + \phi^2 \tag{9.4}$$

and

$$\phi/\psi = \tan \alpha_2' \tag{9.5}$$

The velocity distribution across any volute section is not uniform. This is easy to visualize by having in mind the flow pattern in a pipe

under the most favorable conditions. There the mean velocity of
flow is from 0.78 to 0.92 of the maximum velocity at the center of the
pipe. In a volute the maximum velocity is at the impeller periphery
but it is not uniform across the width of the impeller. Also the
velocity decreases toward the volute walls, owing to frictional drag.
In contrast with pipe flow the high velocity core in the volute is driven
by the impeller and under such circumstances a lower ratio of mean to
the maximum velocity can be expected. The flow pattern is complicated further by the radial outward component of the absolute
velocity which causes a spiral motion along the volute. This motion
is outward in the middle and inward near the walls of the volute (Fig.

9.3). Such a velocity distribution and spiral
motion in the volute were visually observed by
Kranz (reference 1).

The pressure ratio p_v/p_1 is determined from the
adiabatic equation

$$H_v = \frac{RT_1}{(k-1)/k}\left[\left(\frac{p_v}{p_1}\right)^{(k-1)/k} - 1\right] \quad (9.6)$$

The volute volume of flow then is given by

$$Q_v = Q_1(p_1/p_v)^{1/k} \quad (9.7)$$

Fig. 9.3. Spiral   which is the same as
flow in volute cas-
ing. $$Q_v = Q_1(p_1/p_v)(T_v/T_1) = Q_1(p_1/p_v)(X+1) \quad (9.8)$$

where T_v is gas temperature in the volute and X is the bracketed
factor in the equation 9.6.

The effect of leakage loss and hydraulic losses within the impeller
and blower casing are neglected in the above relationships.

(c) **Volute Areas.** Reference to Fig. 9.4 will show that the total
flow of the impeller discharge passes through the volute throat AB,
Section 8; only part of the impeller capacity passes through any other
section, the amount increasing as the flow approaches the volute
tongue. A certain amount of gas is recirculated between the tongue
and the impeller and also between the impeller shrouds and casing
side walls. It has been established experimentally that volutes with
a constant average velocity for all sections result in the best efficiency.
This means that volute areas increase in proportion to their angular
displacement from the tongue where the area is zero (point A).

The average volute velocity is given by equation 9.3 for the best
efficiency point. Considerable deviations from these values are pos-

sible and take place when impeller diameter is cut, or when several impellers are used in the same casing. However, if the volute areas are too small in comparison with the optimum values, the peak efficiency will decrease slightly and move toward a lower capacity. When volute areas are too large the peak efficiency may increase but will move toward a higher capacity. Efficiency at partial capacities will then be lower.

Perhaps *the best proof that a constant velocity volute is the most favorable for efficiency is the fact that at the best efficiency point pressure is*

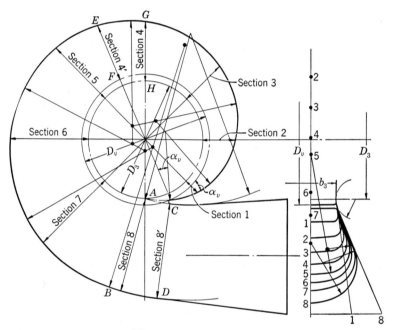

Fig. 9.4. Volute casing.

uniform around the volute. This condition should be considered as the most desirable for the impeller performance. *It will be noticed that the whole recovery of the kinetic energy into pressure takes place in the volute nozzle.* Therefore utmost care should be exercised in laying out the volute nozzle. *It has been established experimentally that for a circular cone an 8° total included angle is the most efficient for velocity conversion. For high velocity gas and disturbed flow the optimum value may be even lower, perhaps 6°.* For practical reasons a 10° total nozzle angle is quite common. Higher diffusion angles adversely affect the efficiency.

The uniform pressure along the volute is maintained only at the best efficiency point. At partial capacities pressure increases toward larger volute sections; at capacities over the rated the trend is reversed. In this manner, a radial force is exerted by the casing (reaction) on the rotating element at all capacities except the rated. However, owing to low gas density, pressure differences do not cause any hardships to the blower. With centrifugal pumps innumerable shaft failures were caused owing to uneven volute pressure distribution when operated at partial capacity.

(d) **Volute Radial Thrust.** With high inlet pressures, such as are encountered in natural gas pipe line booster service (up to 850 p.s.i.a.) owing to high gas density, radial thrust at partial capacities and shut-off may amount to several thousand pounds. Such operating conditions can appear only momentarily during the starting period, and under normal procedure should not cause any difficulties. However, if not attended properly the blower may be subjected to a considerable mechanical strain with a danger of bearing damage.

For estimating the magnitude of the radial thrust, the following formula has been established experimentally with centrifugal pumps by measuring the shaft deflections and calibrating the shaft by dead weights. If P is the radial thrust in pounds it can be expressed by a formula

$$P = K \, \Delta p D_2 B_2 \qquad (9.9)$$

where Δp is the pressure rise in pounds per square inch produced by the blower.

D_2 is the impeller outside diameter in inches.

B_2 is the impeller over-all width at discharge, including shrouds.

K is a numerical constant which varies with capacity and type of the blower.

For medium specific speed impellers of about 600 the following expression has been obtained experimentally for the coefficient K.

$$K = 0.36[1 - (Q/Q_n)^2] \qquad (9.10)$$

where Q is any capacity.

Q_n is the rated capacity at b.e.p.

For lower specific speed impellers higher values of K (up to 0.6) were obtained, and lower values for higher specific speeds can be expected. As a limit for axial flow impellers the radial thrust is zero at any capacity.

The author has shown (reference 5, p. 132) that the pressure distribution in the volute casing, the location of the resultant of all radial forces acting on the impeller, and reversal of its direction can be explained by the energy gradient variation along the fluid path from the impeller to the casing discharge nozzle. For a detailed discussion of the radial thrust the reader is referred to reference 5.

Since the cause of the uneven pressure distribution along the volute path lies in the uneven velocity distribution at capacities other than normal, the radial thrust in the casing with vaned or vaneless diffuser is considerably less or approaching zero owing to greatly reduced velocities in the collecting volute outlet.

(*e*) **Volute Angle.** To avoid shock and separation loss at the volute tongue the volute angle α_v is made to correspond to the direction of the absolute velocity vector at the impeller discharge α_2' is given by Fig. 6.10. Considerable deviation from the angle α_2' is possible in practice without any harmful effects on the efficiency at low and medium specific speeds (below 250). First, it cannot be expected that one vane (volute tongue) can exert much guiding effect on the total flow from the impeller; second, no loss is incurred when the flow enters the vane with a small angle of attack. Usually there is an ample gap provided between the impeller and the volute tongue for the flow to adjust itself for a minimum loss. At higher specific speeds the volute angle α_v and the length and shape of the tongue become more important. Thus, on a mixed flow pump of specific speed 2500, the author has found that removal of a portion of the tongue (high angle part of it) reduced the efficiency from 85 to 81 per cent. Restoring the tongue to the original shape brought the efficiency back to 85 per cent.

It should be realized that at volute sections removed from the volute tongue the flow from the impeller is "bent" or deflected from its direction as it leaves the impeller and near the outer wall the radial component of flow c_{m2} is reversed thus starting a spiral flow along the volute as mentioned above. The radial component is not lost, as the energy corresponding to the $(c_{m2}{}^2/2g)$ is greater than the total combined hydraulic losses of the whole blower.

(*f*) **Base Circle.** The volute base circle is selected so as to provide a clearance between the impeller and the stationary volute tongue necessary for operation without objectionable noise. Usually D_3 falls within the following limits, expressed in terms of the impeller diameter D_2:

$$(D_3 - D_2)/D_2 = 0.10 \text{ to } 0.20$$

The lower figure is used with low specific speeds, the higher with high specific speed impellers. An unnecessarily large base circle incurs additional losses as extra power will be required to circulate gas through the gap between the volute tongue and the impeller. A reduction of the gap below an established limit tends to produce noisy operation. The cause of this lies in the fact that separate streams from the impeller hit the volute tongue before the pressures and velocities are equalized. It is very important, from this point of view, to taper the impeller vanes as much as practicable.

Higher specific speed is characterized by a high absolute velocity angle α_2' at impeller discharge. It has been pointed out that the radial component of the absolute velocity is not destroyed but changes its direction when it reaches the volute wall. To turn velocity with a minimum loss, a higher angle would require more space. For that reason the gap between the impeller and volute tongue is greater for higher specific speed blowers to realize the optimum efficiency.

Volute areas are measured above or outside the base circle. The fact that there is an additional gap between the volute tongue and base circle has no bearing on the method of measuring the volute areas, as the increment of volute area for a given angular displacement remains unchanged and that is the governing consideration.

(g) **Volute Width.** Volute width b_3 (Fig. 9.4) is established from the following considerations:

To satisfy the continuity equation several of the volute elements are connected by the following relationship

$$b_3 D_3 \pi = A_v/\sin \alpha_v \qquad (9.11)$$

$$b_3 \sin \alpha_v = A_v/D_3 \pi$$

Having established the values of A_v and D_3 it is noticed that b_3 is a function of the volute angle α_v, higher volute angles requiring narrower volutes. For known volute section areas narrow volutes mean taller volute section, particularly in the portion adjacent to the volute tongue.

It is definitely established that a volute with width exceeding the impeller width b_2 is more efficient than a volute having a width equal to b_2. Wide volutes also permit use of several impellers, or the same impeller with a reduced diameter, without any appreciable effect on the efficiency. Values of b_3 vary from 1.25 b_2 to 2.0 b_2, the high values applying to low impeller angle and low specific speed narrow impellers.

9.3   VANELESS DIFFUSER

A vaneless diffuser, in a single-stage blower, Fig. 9.5, is used to reduce the impeller discharge velocity before it is collected in a volute casing. Since the volute collecting chamber leads away the discharge from the stationary diffuser, at velocities already reduced, volute areas are made to accommodate the volume discharged from the diffuser. No velocity distribution factor similar to R_{c3} is applied. A further reduction of velocity can be accomplished in the discharge nozzle. Obviously the size of a volute casing with a vaneless diffuser is considerably larger than a volute casing in which all conversion of velocity is performed in the volute nozzle. For that reason, for single-stage blowers, plain volute casings are used in preference to the vaneless diffusers on new designs.

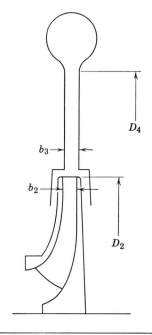

Advantages of the vaneless diffuser are: it gives a flatter efficiency curve; the same diffuser can be used with several impellers using different discharge angles; it has lower pumping limit, or a lower capacity in per cent of the normal capacity at which pumping starts. On the other hand the peak efficiency of blowers with vaneless diffusers (single-stage) is 3 to 4 points lower than that with the vaned diffuser and 1.5 to 2 points lower than that of volute blowers. With vaneless diffusers, cutting of the impeller diameter requires special adapters which are not necessary with volute casings. Cutting impeller vanes only and leaving shrouds full diameter incurs unnecessary disk friction loss.

Fig. 9.5. Vaneless diffuser.

Figure 9.6 shows the relative head-capacity and efficiency curves of the same impeller in vaned and vaneless casings of a 20-in. single-stage blower of 660 specific speed.

Usually a vaneless diffuser is formed by two parallel circular surfaces. There are only two elements of the hydraulic design controlling the performance of the vaneless diffuser; width of the diffuser channel, or the spacing between the disks, and the outside diameter of the diffuser. The ratio of the outside diameter D_4 to the impeller outside diameter D_2, Fig. 9.5, is used as a criterion of the vaneless diffuser. It has been established by tests that nothing is gained (in fact, efficiency may be impaired) by increasing this ratio over 2.0. A ratio $D_4/D_2 = 1.80$ is used on the majority of blowers in operation. Considerably higher ratios were used in past, mostly abroad, for multistage blowers where "inner" cooling was used. A maximum cooling area was attained by increasing the outside diameter of the blower casing. However, in modern multistage compressors, external or "intercooling" is used between several groups of uncooled stages.

There is no good reason for making the diffuser width b_3 different from the impeller width b_2 (Fig. 9.5). A minor reduction of the width down to $b_3/b_2 = 0.8$ results in a steeper head-capacity curve, slightly

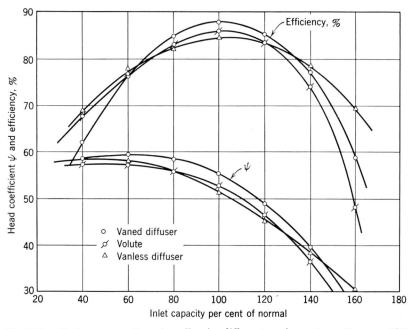

Fig. 9.6. Performance of an impeller in different casings; $\beta_2 = 40$, $n_s = 625$.

lower pumping limit, and a reduction of efficiency to the extent of one or two points.

From the geometry of the vaneless diffuser it could be deduced that both radial and tangential components of the absolute velocity of the impeller discharge are reduced in the inverse ratio of the diffuser diameter. This means that the flow continues, maintaining a constant direction in respect to the radius, thus each particle follows a logarithmic spiral path. This follows from two considerations: (1) continuity for the radial component and (2) conservation of moment of momentum for the tangential component. However, *following Newton's first law each particle leaving the impeller should continue to move on a straight line with a constant velocity. This requirement does not violate the principle of conservation of moment of momentum, but continuity condition cannot be satisfied, meaning that the channel does not run full.*

Owing to effects of viscosity and boundary, such pattern of flow cannot be fully realized in practice.

Continuity as applied to a channel of finite cross-sectional area is "human made" law, based on the hypothetical uniform (average) velocity. This is never realized even in the case of straight pipe flow, whereas Newton's first law is a "law of nature" and has precedence over the continuity relationship. Taking continuity too literally may lead to an entirely erroneous pattern of flow, particularly in a curved or moving channel.

The effects of Newton's law, or deviation from the continuity conditions, were observed in extensive tests by Ingersoll-Rand Company and explain the behavior of the flow as it actually takes place: (1) The velocity distribution leaving the diffuser is less uniform than that leaving the impeller. (2) The peak of velocity distribution shifts from one wall of the diffuser to the other. (5) For the higher velocity portion of the flow the absolute angle of the flow is increasing by 5° or more. Under these circumstances it is easy to visualize that confining the flow between vanes in a vaned diffuser improves diffuser efficiency although additional shock and skin friction losses are introduced.

For the purpose of laying out vanes of the return channel, which leads the gas from the vaneless diffuser to the impeller inlet of the following stage, the vane angle can be assumed as equal to that of the absolute velocity angle at impeller discharge increased by 5°.

The method of layout of the return vanes and profile of the return channels for a multistage blower is the same as that used in connection with the vaned diffuser discussed later in this chapter.

It should be pointed out that several European firms use both vaned and vaneless diffusers utilizing the advantages of each type under the suitable conditions (Fig. 11.8). In this country by far the majority of multistage blowers are built with vaneless diffusers. Because power and fuel costs are more favorable here as compared with those in Europe, the question of blower efficiency is secondary to mechanical simplicity.

9.4 VANED DIFFUSER

(*a*) **Single-Stage Blowers.** Although the peak efficiency of blowers with vaned diffusers is higher, to the extent of 2 points, than that of the blowers with a plain volute and is better to the extent of 4 points, than that of units with vaneless diffuser and volute, there are only few single-stage blowers built with vaned diffusers. Mechanical complications and cost are the main reasons; reduced head-capacity range is a secondary consideration. Hydraulic design of vaned diffuser is guided by the same considerations as that of the volute casing.

The total throat (inlet) area of the diffuser is made equal to that of a volute casing for the same conditions. Although the restrictive action for through flow in the vaned diffuser is greater than that of the volute casing, the flow through the diffuser and in the collecting chamber (volute) is more orderly and the same capacities are realized in both designs for the same total throat area.

The base circle D_3 and the vane entrance angle for the vaned diffuser are established in the same manner as for the volute casing. The diffuser width is made equal to or slightly greater than (1.05 to 1.10) the impeller width, depending on the number of vanes, vane angle, and the throat area (i.e., specific speed).

The number of vanes should be a minimum necessary to realize the required throat area and maintain the shape of the channel between two vanes as discussed below. The outside diameter of the vaned part of the diffuser is not a criterion by itself, but depends on the number of vanes and channel proportions and the gap between the impeller and diffuser vanes. In a well-designed diffuser the outside diameters vary from $1.35D_2$ to $1.6D_2$.

The optimum shape of the channel between two vanes of a diffuser has been established by several investigators here and abroad. This shape should satisfy the following conditions:

1. For a given area, the hydraulic radius of the channel should be a minimum. The best practical approach to this is a square section at or near the entrance to the diffuser. Round sections have proven more efficient, but are difficult to adopt for practical use, except in special designs.

2. The diffuser channel, confined between the two adjacent vanes, should be straight-walled conical.

3. The number of vanes should be a minimum required to form a good channel, the optimum length of the confined channel being fixed in a rather narrow limit.

4. The angle of divergence of the diffuser channel should be equal to or smaller than those established for straight channels with a uniform velocity of approach. For a straight circular conical diffuser an included angle of divergence of 8° was already quoted in connection with volute discharge nozzles. For a square section the optimum divergence angle is about 6°. For a rectangular diffuser section,

formed between two parallel walls, the divergence angle is about 11°
(reference 2). These figures, established experimentally, are not inconsistent if compared on the basis of the rate of area expansion.

5. The correct diffuser entrance angle is secondary to the optimum
diffuser channel proportions. Although, as a starting point, this
angle should be taken from the input discharge velocity triangle.

6. The diffuser depth $(D_4 - D_3)/2$ or the diffuser ratio D_4/D_2 (Fig.
9.7) is not a controlling factor. The number of vanes and D_4 are
adjusted to obtain the desired shape of the diffuser channel.

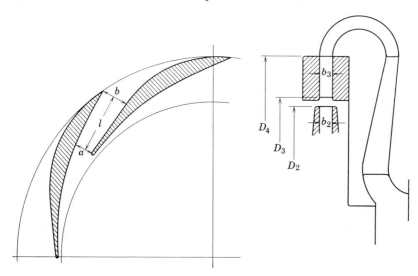

Fig. 9.7.   Diffuser proportions.

Very extensive tests on air, as reported by Smith of the General
Electric Co. (reference 2), fix the length of the confined diffuser passage as four times the opening between the two adjacent inlet vane tips,
or $l = 4a$ (Fig. 9.7).   The preferred area expansion ratio is $b/a = 1.6$.
This corresponds to about $8\frac{1}{2}°$ of divergence for a diffuser with parallel
side walls.   It is interesting to note that the above diffuser proportions were also confirmed by water tests by several independent
investigations.

To extend the length of the channel beyond $l/a > 4$ does not
improve the performance of the diffuser.   Apparently what is gained
by a further velocity recovery is lost in additional diffuser loss and eddy
losses accompanying the joining of two streams from the two adjacent
diffuser channels.

Long and curved diffuser channels cannot perform conversion of

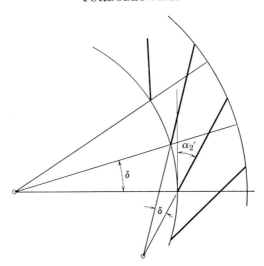

Fig. 9.8.   Flat plate diffuser.

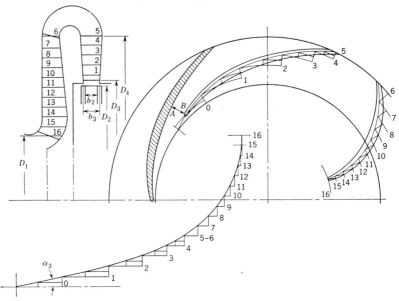

Fig. 9.9.   Diffuser and return channel vanes layout.

velocity into pressure effectively as the flow becomes crowded toward the outer wall of the channel where local high velocities are restored. On one occasion the author observed that increasing the number of diffuser vanes (slightly curved) from 7 to 9, thus increasing the vane overlap, reduced the efficiency of a unit by 3 points.

Using flat straight vanes for the diffuser, the number of vanes is fixed when the diffusion angle of the channel is selected

$$z = 360/\delta \qquad (9.11)$$

where z is number of vanes and δ is the diffusion angle. By referring to Fig. 9.8, this is apparent when the vanes are radial, but the relationship remains when all blades are tilted through the same angle. Having some structural advantages, straight vaned diffusers as a rule have too many vanes, which can cause excessive friction loss.

(b) **Return Channel.** Return channels receive the flow from the diffuser at a reduced velocity, turn it 180° toward the inlet of the next

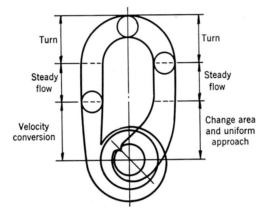

Fig. 9.10.   Diagram of a crossover.

impeller, and take out what is left of the tangential component. To perform this function efficiently, the flow should be gradually accelerated. To arrive at a proper curvature of the return channel vane, it is better to assume the development of a one-piece vane combining the diffuser and return channel vanes (Fig. 9.9) and then transfer one-half of it into the diffuser and the other half into the return channel, using the "error triangle" method presented in detail in the last chapter of this book. The diffuser vanes can be further modified by taking out some of the curvature of the channel and incorporating the favorable proportions discussed above. The number of return channel vanes is established from the same considerations as that of the impeller (Art. 6.4d) and is lower than the latter by two to three vanes.

While experimenting with return channels of different design, the author found a spread of 8.5 points in efficiency between the best and worst channels. Similar results were reported by Lendorf and Meienberg of Escher Wyss concern (references 6 and 7).

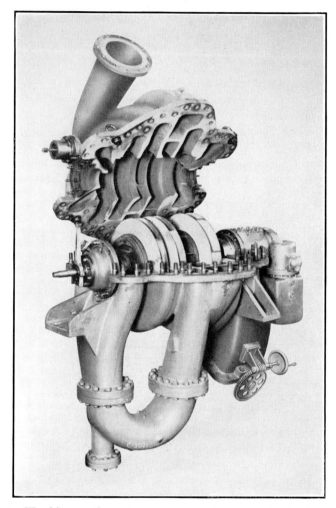

Fig. 9.11.   Worthington three-stage compressor for Freon; inlet c.f.m. = 9,040;
polytropic head, 11,000 ft.; compression ratio, 4.33; gross efficiency, 73.0 per cent;
4,200 r.p.m. (Worthington.)

Utilization of the kinetic energy of the preceding stage in the following stage is the important guiding principle, established experimentally.   The recovery of pressure should proceed not more than
necessary to a slight acceleration in the U turn and next-stage impeller
approach.   A quite common fault of the return channels of the older
design was that the fluid was "dumped" from the diffuser into the
return channel without any attempt to guide the flow or control the
velocities.

(*c*) **Continuous Diffuser Channel.** A comparison of performance of
multistage blowers with that of single-stage blowers (with vaned diffusers) of the same specific speed indicates that there is an excessive
hydraulic loss in the sharp 180° turn between the diffuser and return
channel vanes.   This loss is of the nature of eddy losses due to the
abrupt change in velocity and direction of flow.   Due to the short
passage length the friction loss is insignificant in this part of the flow

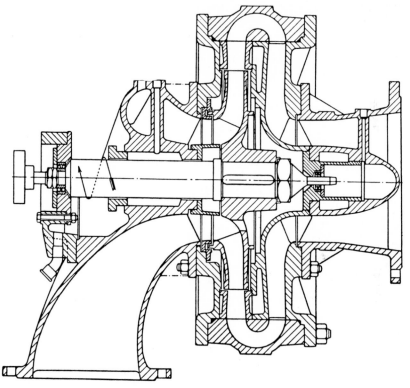

Fig. 9.12.   Sulzer model pump.

passages.   Dividing the channel from stage to stage into a combination
of two vaned parts (diffuser and return channel) and a vaneless U turn
is done for manufacturing reasons both in the blower and centrifugal
pump field at the expense of perhaps 2 to 3 points in efficiency.   Efficiencies of 80 per cent are well established in the centrifugal pump
field on diffuser units for high pressure service such as boiler feed.
However, pumps for petroleum pipe line service of essentially the
same specific speed have shown over 85 per cent using a single passage
from stage to stage, known as "crossover."   Figure 9.10 shows a dia-

gram of a crossover. In this diffusion, 180° turn and distribution of the flow around the eye of the next impeller are performed as separate steps. A short length of the straight part is enclosed between these sections to steady the flow. It is of utmost importance to have the major part of the crossover of a circular section, because, since the channel is not in one plane, a spiral motion is induced which does no particular harm if the channel is round. With square or rectangular cross section considerable eddy loss is produced owing to this tendency

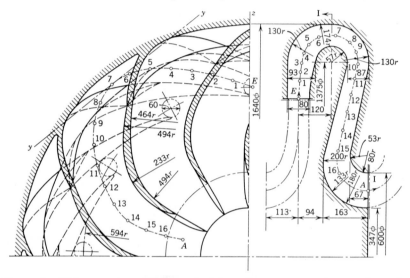

Fig. 9.13. Diffuser and return channel with continuous vanes of pump shown in Fig. 9.12 (Sulzer).

of the flow to whirl. Centrifugal pumps with external crossovers are built up to eight stages.

Use of external crossovers for multistage blowers would lead to major manufacturing complications and high costs. However, a number of three-stage units built for refrigeration service are in successful use. Figure 9.11 shows the Worthington three-stage compressor with external crossover having design very similar to those of good centrifugal pumps.

Experience with centrifugal pumps has established two principles which are basic for a good diffuser and return channel: (1) continuous straight channel and (2) a circular cross section of the channel.

Figure 9.12 shows an assembly of a Sulzer one-stage pump (reference 3) with 21¾ inches impeller diameter which is a model for a five-stage water storage pump for 42,700 g.p.m. (5700 c.f.m.), 1620 ft. head, 500 r.p.m., 20,500 b.hp.; specific speed based on c.f.m. is 495. This includes the return channel, with continuous vanes shown in Fig. 9.13, manufactured in three parts. Tested on water and air this model has shown 85 per cent efficiency (Fig. 9.14). This design is typical of the latest European multistage pumps showing appreciable

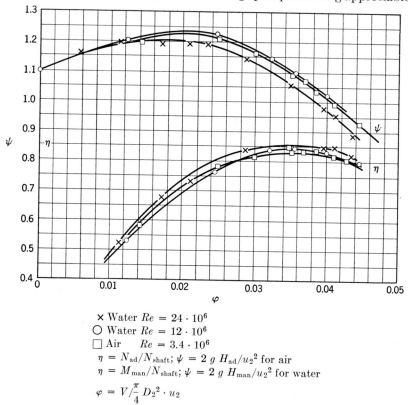

× Water $Re = 24 \cdot 10^6$
○ Water $Re = 12 \cdot 10^6$
□ Air $Re = 3.4 \cdot 10^6$

$\eta = N_{ad}/N_{shaft}; \psi = 2\ g\ H_{ad}/u_2{}^2$ for air
$\eta = M_{man}/N_{shaft}; \psi = 2\ g\ H_{man}/u_2{}^2$ for water

$\varphi = V/\dfrac{\pi}{4} D_2{}^2 \cdot u_2$

Fig. 9.14. Characteristic of the model pump with an impeller diameter of 550 mm. (Sulzer). The head coefficient ψ as shown is twice the value as used in this book, equation 5.12. The capacity coefficient ϕ as shown should be divided by $4/\pi^2$ to obtain the specific capacity q_s as defined by equations 5.10 and 6.24. N is power input.

improvement in efficiency as compared with older separate diffuser rings and return channel and unvaned U-turn.

REFERENCES

1. Kranz, "Strömung in Spiralgenhäusen," *V.D.I. Bull.* 370, 1935.
2. *General Electric Supercharger Symposium*, Lectures, 1943, Riverworks, West Lynn, Mass.

3. Sulzer, *Tech. Rev. (Switz.)* No. 3, 1951, Winterthur, Switzerland; also No. 1, 1947, p. 15.
4. Farve, Academie de Sciences, *Compt. Rend.* vol. 229, July 25, 1949, pp. 289–291 ("New Centrifugal Compressor Diffuser").
5. Stepanoff, *Centrifugal and Axial Flow Pumps*, Wiley, 1948.
6. Lendorf and Meienberg, "Developments in Design of Turbocompressors"; *Escher Wyss News*, Vol. 17/18, 1944/45, p. 60.
7. Lendorf, "Modern Compressors," *Escher Wyss News*, Nos. 1–2, 1939, p. 47.

CHAPTER 10

Leakage, Disk Friction,
Mechanical Losses, Axial Thrust

10.1 LEAKAGE LOSS

(a) **Volumetric Efficiency.** Leakage loss is a loss of capacity through the running clearances between the rotating element and the stationary casing parts. Leakage can take place in one or several of the following places, according to the type of blower: (1) between the casing and the impeller at the impeller inlet (around the impeller eye); (2) around the shaft through the external seals where shaft extends beyond the casing; (3) between two adjacent stages in multistage blowers; (4) through the axial thrust balancing devices in multistage units; and (5) past vanes of open impeller blowers.

The flow through the impeller is greater than the measured c.f.m. by the amount of leakage, and the ratio of the measured capacity Q to the impeller capacity $Q + Q_L$ is the volumetric efficiency.

$$Q/(Q + Q_L) = e_v \qquad (10.1)$$

Usually the volumetric efficiency takes into account only the leakage between the impeller and casing, as it takes place at every impeller. The interstage leakage and loss through the balancing devices are treated as additional items. In each case the amount of leakage should be multiplied by the pressure drop across the clearance to obtain the power loss due to leakage. Although the actual pressure at the clearance may be reduced as a result of the vortex action of the impeller, the full-stage pressure rise, or a multiple of the stage pressure rise, depending on the stage arrangement, should be used to calculate the loss of power due to leakage since the amount of leakage is given full input head when it passes through the impeller. Thus

$$\text{Leakage loss (hp.)}_L = GH/e_h 550 \qquad (10.2)$$

where G is the weight of the leakage flow, in pounds per second.
H is the total head in feet.
e_h is the hydraulic efficiency.

177

(*b*) **Calculation of the Leakage Loss.** Usually the sealing devices around the rotating element consist of one or more sharp-edged flat throttles forming either a straight-through or stepped labyrinth (Fig. 10.1). The following formula for leakage calculation was established by Egli (reference 1) from theoretical considerations. A number of

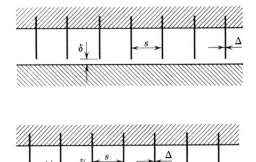

Fig. 10.1.   Straight-through and stepped labyrinths (Egli).

experimental factors account for the different physical modifications of the labyrinth.

$$G = A\alpha\phi\gamma \sqrt{gp_0/v_0} \tag{10.3}$$

where, following Egli's notation,

A is the net clearance area, square feet equal to $\pi D\delta/144$
α is a flow coefficient, given in Fig. 10.2.
ϕ is a factor depending on the pressure ratio across the clearance and the number of throttlings given in Figs. 10.3 and 10.4.
γ is a velocity of approach correction in a multiblade straight labyrinth given in Fig. 10.5; $\gamma = 1$ for a stepped and staggered labyrinth.
p_0 is absolute pressure ahead of labyrinth.
p_n is absolute pressure past labyrinth.
g is 32.16.
v_0 is specific volume, cubic feet per pound.
s is spacing between throttles.

The experimental data presented by the curves was obtained with a stationary testing rig. There is ample experimental knowledge that in the turbulent flow regime, which is to be expected in all practical

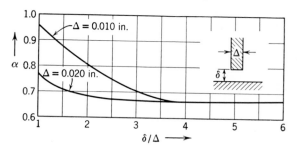

Fig. 10.2. Flow coefficient α for labyrinths with sharp-edged strips (Egli).

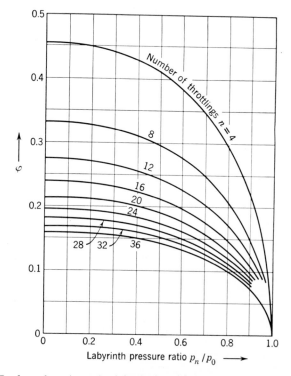

Fig. 10.3. Leakage function ϕ for labyrinths with four or more throttlings (Egli).

cases, the effect of the speed of the shaft on the amount of leakage is negligible (reference 2).

A study of data on Figs. 10.2, 3, 4, and 5 reveals that reduction of the clearance is the most effective means of reducing the amount of the leakage. With large clearances (say, over 0.020 in.) the single-strip seal is practically as good as the double strip. The clearances in common use are from 0.015 to 0.020 in.

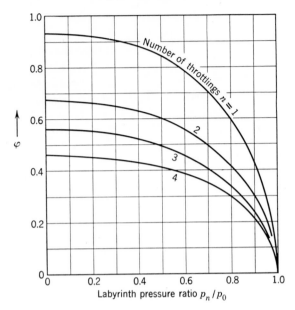

Fig. 10.4.   Function ϕ for one to four throttlings (Egli).

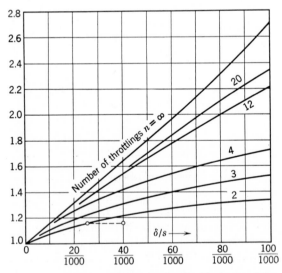

Fig. 10.5.   Carry-over correction factor γ versus δ/s for straight-through labyrinths (Egli).

(c) **Pressure Drop Across the Seal.** The pressure ratio across the seal p_0/p_n is lower than stage pressure (discharge pressure/inlet pressure for a single stage), because the pressure ahead of the seal is lower than the volute or diffuser casing pressure H_v, which in turn is lower than the blower discharge pressure. The determination of the volute pressure (H_v) has been discussed in Art. 9.2.

The reduction of pressure at the seal is caused by rotation of the fluid in the space between the impeller and casing walls. The pressure ahead of the seal can be determined from the head H_0, at this point, above the inlet pressure,

$$H_0 = H_v - \tfrac{1}{4}(u_2^2 - u_s^2)/2g \qquad (10.4)$$

where u_s is the peripheral velocity corresponding to the seal diameter. This relationship is based on the assumption that the fluid in space is rotating half of the impeller speed. This has been found to be approximately true by several experimenters (p. 203, reference 2). Refiguring of the heads H_0 and H_v into pressures is done by the use of the adiabatic formula with due regard to the difference in the symbols used.

(d) **Leakage Loss versus Specific Speed and Size.** The following statements established for centrifugal pumps are equally valid for centrifugal blowers:

1. Leakage loss, expressed in per cent of the hydraulic power input, is the same for blowers of the same specific speed if similarity is extended to the seal parts.

2. For a consistent line of blowers, leakage loss increases as the specific speed is reduced (approximately inversely as the 1.15 power of the specific speed). This can be easily visualized as at the same head the leakage volume of a higher specific speed unit (larger c.f.m.) will be a lower percentage than that for the lower specific speed blower. The increased leakage loss is one of the factors contributing to the lower total efficiency of lower specific speed blowers.

10.2 DISK FRICTION

(a) **Disk Friction Formula.** Disk friction loss is the most important single item among the blower losses. Although the loss is of a hydraulic nature it will be treated here as an internal mechanical loss, i.e., a loss of power, while hydraulic losses are losses of head or pressure. It is important to keep in mind this difference in the analysis of performance of centrifugal machines. Thus if the outside of an impeller is polished, the efficiency will improve, but the head will remain unchanged; whereas, if the impeller passages and vanes are polished, the efficiency will improve and the head will correspondingly increase.

Disk friction loss is grouped with other "internal" losses because heat
due to the disk friction is retained by the fluid.

The problem of disk friction has been extensively investigated both
theoretically and experimentally. Among other things, experiments
show that: (1) disk friction power is considerably higher when a disk
is rotated in an unlimited fluid space than when it is contained in a
casing as is the case for centrifugal blowers;* (2) disk friction loss
depends on the roughness of the disk in the same manner as pipe roughness affects pipe friction loss; (3) disk friction power is a function of

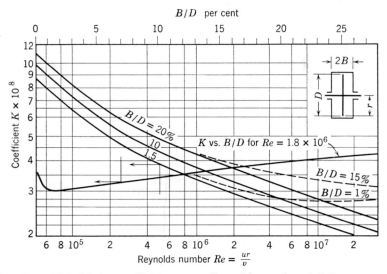

Fig. 10.6.   Disk friction coefficient versus Reynolds number; full lines, smooth
disk; dashed lines rough disk.

the viscosity of the fluid, thus is affected by the fluid temperature.
Variations of the experimental results of several investigators are
caused by the differences in the above-stated conditions.

Based on works of Zumbusch and Schultz-Grunow (reference 3),
Pfleiderer (reference 4) has prepared a chart of the friction coefficients
for calculating the disk friction loss (reproduced in Fig. 10.6) to be
used in connection with the following formula (two sides)

$$\text{hp.}_d = KD^2\gamma u^3 \tag{10.5}$$

* The often-quoted Stodola's and Kearton formulas for disk friction loss based
on Odell's experiments (1904) with rotating disk in the open atmosphere give values
of friction loss considerably in excess of later formulas derived from disk tests in a
suitable housing.   (Stodola, *Steam and Gas Turbines*, McGraw-Hill, 1928, p. 200;
Kearton, *Turbo-Blowers and Compressors*, Pitman, 1929, p. 91.)

where K is a numerical coefficient plotted against Reynolds number Re.
Re is the Reynolds number equal to ur/ν, dimensionless.
u is the outside peripheral velocity, feet per second.
r is the impeller radius, feet.
ν is the kinematic viscosity, feet squared per second.
D is the impeller diameter, feet.
γ is the fluid density, pounds per cubic foot.

The values of the coefficient K are given for three values of the side clearance B/D, where B is the distance between the disk and stationary walls of the casing. For normal designs B/D is from 2 to 5 per cent. This falls within the region of minimum disk friction loss, as is evident from a curve of K versus B/D drawn for $Re = 1.8 \times 10^6$.

The effect of the enclosure on the disk friction power can be visualized when it is realized that the particles of the fluid are given a rotary motion by the disk. As a result of centrifugal forces, particles move outward in the immediate vicinity of the disk and new particles approach the disk near the center. Thus a circulation is established. If the path of circulation is short, or if the volume of the fluid surrounding the disk is small, particles approaching the disk will retain part of their moment of momentum, thus requiring less power from the disk.

It has been a common assumption that the fluid between the disk and stationary walls rotates with one-half of the impeller angular velocity. This can be justified by theoretical reasoning and has been confirmed by the Schultz-Grunow experiments (reference 3) quoted above.

The values of the disk friction loss as determined from Fig. 10.6 should be increased by 5 to 10 per cent as the actual area of the revolving impeller shrouds is appreciably greater than that of a flat disk of the same diameter used by the experimenters. Two dotted curves show values of the coefficient K for rough disks for B/D ratio of 1 and 15 per cent. A considerable increase of K is observed at higher Reynolds numbers, where turbulent flow prevails at all radii of the impeller.

(b) **Disk Friction versus Specific Speed.** The formula for the disk friction loss (10.5) can be reduced to the form

$$\text{hp.}_d = K_1 n^3 D^5 \tag{10.6}$$

where K_1 is a numerical constant and n is r.p.m. Since, for all blowers of the same specific speed, the output varies also directly as the cube of the speed and fifth power of the impeller diameter, the disk friction loss expressed in per cent of blower output remains constant for similar blowers. This disregards the effect of the Reynolds number.

Expressing the disk friction loss in per cent of blower output and performing some evident algebraic substitutions, the following expression is obtained

$$\frac{\text{hp.}_d}{\text{Output}} = \frac{KD^2\gamma u^3}{Q\gamma H/550} = 550\frac{Kg\pi}{\psi q_s} \qquad (10.7)$$

Taking for K a value of $3.6/10^8$ from Fig. 10.6 for Reynolds number $Re = 1 \times 10^6$, the above expression becomes

$$\text{hp.}_d/\text{Output} = 0.002/\psi q_s \qquad (10.7a)$$

Substituting for q_s its value in terms of the capacity coefficient, the equation 10.7a becomes

$$\frac{\text{hp.}_d}{\text{Output}} = \frac{0.0002}{\psi\phi b_2/D_2} \qquad (10.7b)$$

Substituting for the specific capacity $q_s = Q/D^3 n$ the specific speed n_s from equation 6.15, we obtain

$$\text{hp.}_d/\text{Output} = \text{Constant}/n_s{}^2\psi^{5/2} \qquad (10.8)$$

For a constant value of ψ (or for a given value of the impeller angle β_2) disk friction loss increases inversely as the square of the specific speed. For the same specific speed the disk friction loss is lower for higher values of the impeller discharge angle β_2. However, this gain may be partly or entirely counterbalanced by the increased hydraulic losses: impellers become narrow and require more vanes, also conversion loss in the casing is higher with higher values of β_2.

The author is not aware of any examples showing better polytropic internal efficiency with higher impeller discharge angles than with $\beta_2 = 25°$, even in the lowest range of specific speeds.

10.3 MECHANICAL LOSSES

Mechanical losses include the power lost by friction in the bearings and seals. These losses depend upon the shaft size, type of seals, and the speed. These losses are easily measured, and each manufacturer has such information available for several shaft sizes plotted against the speed.

Kluge (reference 5) estimates mechanical losses for 2000 hp. and over 1.0 per cent, for 1000 and over 1.5 per cent, and for 500 and over 2.0 per cent.

It has been established by tests that power loss in bearings with sleeve radial bearings and Kingsbury thrust bearing varies approximately directly as the 1.45 power of the speed ratio. When the Kingsbury bearing disk is used as a viscosity pump for lubricating oil circulation, this exponent becomes about 1.85.

Since bearing and seal losses represent the "external" losses in respect to the flow through the machine, efficiency based on the net power input (minus bearing losses) is sometimes referred to as "internal" efficiency to differentiate it from the gross or total efficiency of the unit.[†] Separation of losses into external and internal losses becomes of particular importance when the efficiency of a blower is determined by using thermodynamic relationships for calculating the true output (it cannot be measured directly) or the power input. The method is called the "heat-balance" method, or "temperature-rise" method, discussed in Chapter 8.

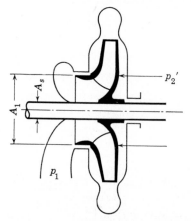

10.4 AXIAL THRUST

(a) **Single-Stage Blowers.** Double-inlet impellers are balanced for axial thrust due to symmetry. Single-inlet impellers are subjected to axial thrust because part of the back shroud is under inlet pressure (facing the impeller eye) whereas

Fig. 10.7.   Axial thrust on a single-inlet impeller.

the other side of the shroud is under the discharge pressure. The magnitude of the axial thrust is represented by

$$T = (A_1 - A_s)(p_2' - p_1) \qquad (10.9)$$

Where T is the axial thrust in pounds.

A_1 is the area corresponding to the outside impeller eye diameter D_r or diameter of the seal (Fig. 10.7).

A_s is the area of the shaft through the stuffing box or seal, square inches.

p_1 is the inlet pressure pounds per square inch.

p_2' is the pressure on the back of the shroud at diameter D_r, pounds per square inch.

[†] The polytropic internal efficiency is referred to as "hydraulic" efficiency by several writers (reference 4).   In this book the "hydraulic losses" term is applied to loss of head only, and hydraulic efficiency is given by equation 3.11 as a ratio of the measured head to the input head.   The gross efficiency is termed "shaft efficiency" in the A.S.M.E. Power Test Code PTC-10-1949.

The pressure p_2' is lower than that corresponding to the stage total head.   It can be more accurately calculated from H_0, the head across the seal, given by equation 10.4.   This pressure can be assumed to be uniform across the whole unbalanced area.   The actual thrust is somewhat lower than the value given by equation 10.9 owing to the change of the momentum of the flow through the impeller making a 90° turn at this place.   The opposing force F (to the right on Fig. 10.7) is equal to

$$F = (W/g)c_1 = A_e c_1{}^2(\gamma/g) = 2A_e\gamma(c_1{}^2/2g) \qquad (10.10)$$

where W/g is mass flow.

   c_1 is the inlet velocity.

   γ is the fluid density.

   A_e is the net impeller eye area.

If a single-stage blower has an overhung impeller with one seal on the high pressure side, there is an additional force opposing the axial thrust given by formula 10.9 equal to the area of the shaft at the seal A_s times the inlet gage pressure.

$$T_s = A_s p_1 \qquad (10.11)$$

When pumping gases under high pressure (boosters on natural gas pipe lines) the force T_s may exceed the axial thrust owing to unbalanced area, equation 10.9.

The universal practice of carrying the axial thrust by a thrust bearing is the most efficient way to take care of the thrust in a single-stage blower.   Balancing hydraulic thrust of a single-stage blower by hydraulic means, widely used in the centrifugal pump field, is rarely justified with single-stage blowers.   Figure 2.4 shows a single-stage blower provided with a balancing ring on the back of the impeller. By changing the diameter of the sealing ring any degree of balance can be obtained by exposing a portion of the impeller back shroud to atmosphere.

   (b) **Multistage Blowers.**   The problem of axial thrust becomes important when dealing with multistage blowers because of the higher pressures involved and the cumulative effect of several stages.   If impellers are arranged all facing in the same direction the axial thrust on the rotating element is equal to the sum of the axial thrust of the individual stages.   Note that owing to a temperature increase from stage to stage, and reduction of the impeller eye diameter, the axial thrust of the higher pressure stages is lower than that of the lower pressure stages, the head per stage being essentially the same.   There are two methods of balancing axial thrust of multistage blowers: (1) with impellers facing the same way a balancing piston or drum is provided on the high pressure end of the rotor (Fig. 11.10). This has full pressure on one side of it and inlet pressure on the other, thus exerting an axial force approximately equal and opposite to the axial thrust. An ample thrust bearing is provided to take care of any residual thrust. (2) Impellers are arranged in two opposing groups. The axial thrust of one group is balanced by that of the other, the thrust bearing taking care of a possible unequality of the two components of thrust (Fig. 11.6).

Axial thrust of a compressor can be partly or completely balanced externally through the rigid coupling by the axial thrust developed by the driver—steam or gas turbine—or by reduction gear. A thrust bearing is provided to take care of any residual thrust.

To reduce the amount of leakage across the balancing piston a multiblade labyrinth is universally used.

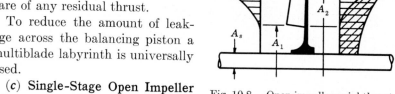

Fig. 10.8.   Open impeller axial thrust.

(c) **Single-Stage Open Impeller Blowers.** Open impellers produce higher axial thrust than closed impellers. The thrust on the back shroud is only partly balanced by the pressure inside the impeller passages (Fig. 10.8). The thrust on the back shroud is given by equation 10.12.

$$T_0 = (A_2 - A_s)[H_d - \tfrac{1}{8}(u_2{}^2 - u_s{}^2)2g]\gamma \qquad (10.12)$$

The pressure inside the impeller is H_d at the periphery, and the inlet pressure at the inlet edges of vanes is taken as zero here, as all heads are measured above the inlet head. The thrust on the inside of the back shroud is

$$T_i = (A_2 - A_1)\gamma H_d/2 \qquad (10.13)$$

The net axial thrust is the difference between the two

$$T = T_0 - T_i \qquad (10.14)$$

Here H_d is the head at the impeller discharge, given by equation 7.36; γ is the average gas density between inlet and discharge. For more accurate results the heads in the equation 10.12 should be converted into pressure ratios using the adiabatic formula, and using the pressure corresponding to H_d.

REFERENCES

1. Egli, "The Leakage of Steam Through Labyrinth Seals," *A.S.M.E. Trans.*, 1935, p. 115.
2. Stepanoff, *Centrifugal and Axial Flow Pumps*, Wiley, 1948, p. 203.
3. Schultz-Grunow, "Der Reibungswiderstand rotirender Scheiben in Gehäusen," *Z. angew. Math. Mech.* Vol. 15, *Bull.* 4, July, 1935, pp. 194–204; also, *V.D.I.*, Berlin, 1937, p. 357.
4. Pfleiderer, *Die Kreiselpumpen*, Springer, Berlin, 1949, pp. 17, 88.
5ˑ Kluge, *Kreiselgebläse und Kreiselverdichter*, Springer, Berlin, 1953.

CHAPTER 11

Compression with Cooling

11.1 INNER-COOLING

Introduction. Cooling of gas in the process of compression can be accomplished either internally (inner-cooling) or externally (intercooling). In internal cooling water jackets are provided in the diaphragms separating two adjacent stages of a multistage compressor (Fig. 11.1). External cooling is done in special heat exchangers mounted on the same base, or built into the compressor casing or in separate units.

The object of cooling is to reduce power and lower the final discharge temperature. In comparison with uncooled compressors, cooling results in a reduction of size or speed or number of stages. Cooling as such (reduction of temperature and increase of density) does not affect the input power in foot-pounds per pound of fluid, i.e., head produced. However, for a given generated pressure, a lower head is required. This means a lower speed or smaller machine. A reduction of specific volume also leads to a smaller size for a given weight flow. The saving in power results from the reduction in head necessary to produce the same pressure, the ratio of b.hp. requirements being proportional to the ratio at heads required for the given generated pressure.

Since it is impossible to cool the impellers of the compressor, the actual compression follows an adiabatic polytropic path and cooling has the effect of precooling and after-cooling. After-cooling has no effect on the power input of a preceding impeller, therefore benefits from cooling result only from the precooling ahead of each stage. It was pointed out in Art. 8.7 that it takes less power to precool gas and compress it adiabatically to a given final pressure and temperature than to compress it polytropically with a uniform rate of cooling along the whole compression path. Thus, inability to cool the impellers has no particular disadvantage as far as the final results are concerned.

Figure 11.1 shows a seven-stage compressor. The six diaphragms are provided with water jackets which are properly baffled and connected in series. The jackets in each half of the casing are separate to avoid

189

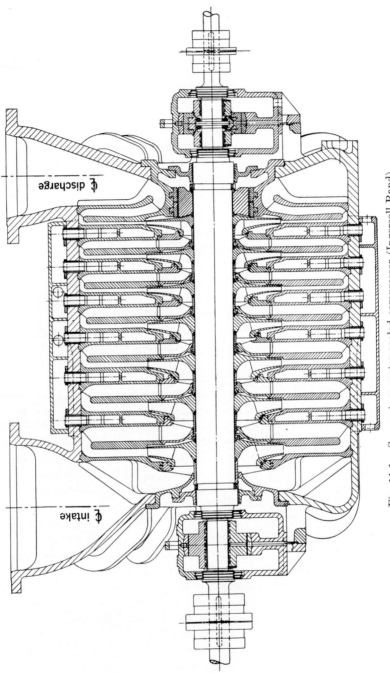

discharge ₵

₵ intake

Fig. 11.1. Seven-stage water-cooled compressor (Ingersoll-Rand).

water-sealing problems at the split flange. In each stage, heat transfer to the water jacket takes place along the outward flow through the vaneless diffuser wall and again to the next jacket along the inward path of gas through the vaned part of the return channel. Calculations follow the general methods using the usual formulas of heat transfer with the following modifications: (1) Since neither the gas temperature nor gas velocity remains constant along its path from the impeller discharge to the impeller inlet of the following stage, some average temperature and velocity is introduced into the calculations and results are corrected by one over-all constant established experimentally. (2) Actual tests and measurements of the heat removed by internal water cooling indicate that it is possible to apply the formulas and heat transfer data obtained on circular pipes to the irregular channels traversed by the hot gas and cooling water, provided an experimental factor is applied as determined by tests. In view of the fact that the construction and cooling arrangements of compressors vary little for several makes and sizes of machines such over-all corrective factors vary little if used in connection with the method of calculation for which they are intended.

(a) **Procedure for Heat Transfer Calculations.** Heat (q) transferred from the gas through the walls of the water jacket to cooling water is calculated from:

$$q = CUA(t_g - t_w) \text{ B.t.u./hr.} \tag{11.1}$$

where C is an over-all experimental numerical constant which accounts for all deviations of the heat transfer conditions from those for which the formulas and constants were established. A value of $C = 1.90$ was determined experimentally based on compressors of two different makes and by means of the method of calculation presented below.

U is an over-all heat transfer coefficient, B.t.u./(hr.)(sq. ft.)(°F.)

A is area of the heat transfer surface taken as equal to $(D_{wo}^2 - D_{wi}^2)0.785$ where D_{wo} and D_{wi} are the outside and inside diameters of the wetted area of the water jacket respectively; or A is the overall projected wet area of the water jacket; square feet (Fig. 11.2).

t_g is the mean gas temperature in °F. taken as equal to the gas temperature at the highest point of the crossover turn from the vaneless diffuser to the vaned return channel. From tests, it has been established that this temperature is equal to the inlet temperature of the stage plus two-thirds of the stage polytropic temperature rise, neglecting cooling.

t_w is the average cooling water temperature which progressively increases from jacket to jacket for a series arrangement with the high pressure water end at the low pressure compressor end, i.e., water and gas traveling in the same direction. With this arrangement t_w, for the first jacket, can be assumed to be equal to the water inlet temperature. For the second

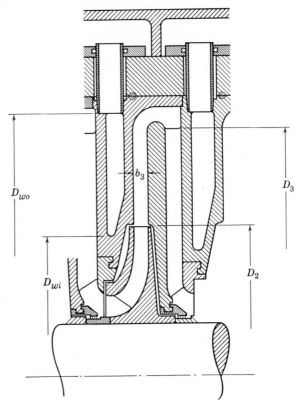

Fig. 11.2.   Water-cooled compressor stage.

water jacket, t_w will increase owing to the heat removed by the first jacket. This temperature increase can be calculated by dividing the number of B.t.u. removed from the first return channel and second diffuser by the amount of cooling water in pounds. The same procedure is followed for all succeeding water jackets.

The over-all heat transfer coefficient U is calculated from

$$U = \frac{1}{R_u} = \frac{1}{(1/h_g) + 1/(h_w) + L/K} \tag{11.2}$$

where R_u is the total thermal resistance.

h_g is the gas film heat transfer coefficient, B.t.u./(hr.)(sq. ft.)(°F.).

h_w is the water film heat transfer coefficient.

L is the metal thickness, ft.

K is the thermal conductivity of metal, B.t.u./(hr.)(ft.)°F. For cast iron, $K = 27$.

The heat transfer from the gas to each water jacket is calculated by means of formula 11.1 for the diffuser and return channel sides.

(b) **Gas Film Coefficient for Diffuser.** The gas film coefficient h_g is calculated with the formula (reference 1)

$$h_g = 0.024 \frac{c_p G^{0.8}}{D^{0.2}} \tag{11.3}$$

where c_p is the specific heat of the gas at constant pressure, B.t.u./(lb.)(°F.).

G is mass velocity, lb./(hr.)(sq. ft.).

D is equivalent diameter of gas passage, in.

For calculation of G for the diffuser the following formula is used

$$G_d = \frac{W}{\pi D_m b_3 \sin \alpha_2'} \tag{11.4}$$

where W is the weight of gas per hour.

D_m is equal to $(D_3 + D_2)/2$.

b_3 is the vaneless diffuser width, feet.

α_2' is the absolute velocity angle, found from $\phi/\psi = \tan \alpha_2'$. where ψ and ϕ are head and capacity coefficients. Values of ψ and ϕ are known from the tentative impeller selections.

The equivalent diameter D for the diffuser in formula 11.3 is

$$D = 4 \text{ (Flow area/Wetted perimeter)}$$

$$= \frac{4\pi D_m b_3}{2\pi D_m} = 2b_3 \tag{11.5}$$

(c) **Water Film Heat Transfer Coefficient.** For this the following formula was adopted (reference 1).

$$h_w = \frac{160(1 + 0.012t) V^{0.8}}{D_w^{0.2}} \tag{11.6}$$

where t is water temperature, °F.; a mean value can be used for all stages.

V is water velocity in ft. per sec.

D_w is equivalent diameter of water passage in inches, equal to 4 (Flow area/Wetted perimeter) for an average water passage of the jacket.

The velocity of cooling water through the jacket is assumed to equal 3 to 8 ft. per sec., depending on compression ratio. To obtain such velocity of water through the jacket and avoid local hot spots, baffling similar to that shown in Fig. 11.2a is provided. A velocity of 8 ft. per sec. requires about 10 p.s.i. water pressure per jacket excluding losses in pipes and fittings. Assuming the water velocity fixes the amount of cooling water.

(d) **Gas Film Coefficient for the Return Channel.** This is calculated with the same formula as for the diffuser (equation 11.3), but the values of the mass flow and hydraulic diameters are calculated as shown below

$$h_r = 0.024 \frac{c_p G_r^{0.8}}{D_r^{0.2}} \tag{11.7}$$

G_r is the weight of flow pounds per hour per unit area in square feet, which is taken as the total area of all gas passages between the return channel vanes at the middle of the channel; D_r is the hydraulic diameter of the individual air passage in inches at the same place where the mass of flow was calculated. D_r is equal to 4 (Flow area/Wetted perimeter).

(e) **Reduction of Temperature by Cooling.** The reduction of gas temperature due to cooling (Δt) is determined for each stage from

$$q = q_d + q_r = W c_p \Delta t \tag{11.8}$$

where q is the total B.t.u. removed from the gas discharged from the impeller on its way to the inlet of the following stage. The amount of heat q consists of two parts: that removed through the diffuser wall (q_d) and that removed through the return channel (q_r).

Then the inlet temperature to the succeeding stage is equal to $T_2 - \Delta t$ where T_2 is the stage discharge temperature obtained without cooling and following polytropic compression.

By dividing the total number of B.t.u. removed from all stages by the assumed amount of cooling water in pounds the cooling water temperature rise is obtained.

If the total compression ratio of the cooled compressor as calculated is higher than that required, the compressor speed, or impeller diameters are reduced to suit. *The ratio of the total head in feet of the cooled compressor to that of the uncooled compressor, for the same compression*

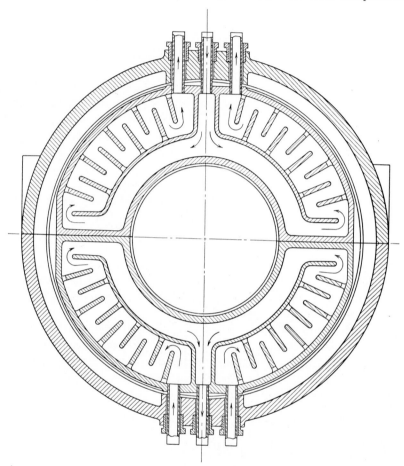

Fig. 11.2*a*.   Water jacket baffles (Clark).

ratio, is the ratio of the b.hp. required to drive the compressor with and without cooling.

For a ten-stage compressor and perfect cooling back to the inlet temperature at each stage, the head ratio is 68.3 per cent. Whereas the isothermal compression head ratio to that of an uncooled machine is 65.5 per cent. Table 1 is based on a polytropic efficiency of 75.0 per cent and polytropic exponent $(n - 1)/n = 0.378$.

The b.hp. and final discharge temperature of a cooled compressor depends upon the nature of the gas, the initial inlet temperature and speed, as all these values affect the compression ratio and temperature rise and impeller selection of each stage. Thus, even for an existing and tested compressor, it is necessary to go through the detailed calculations outlined in this article. The available test data will improve the accuracy of the results as the over-all constant $K = 1.90$ can be modified to comply with the observed test results. The water velocity in the jacket can be definitely fixed, if the pressure of the water supply source is known, and the values of the polytropic efficiency can be revised to agree with the actual combined polytropic efficiency of the unit.

In the method of heat transfer calculation presented above, it was assumed for simplification that the gas and cooling water travel in the same direction from one end to the other of the compressor. However, by reversing the water direction a minor gain in B.t.u. removed is accomplished (3 per cent on a six-stage air compressor). This change has a negligible effect on all intermediate calculations of the compressor performance.

When the object of the cooling is primarily one of reducing the discharge temperature, a water jacket over the outboard wall of the last-stage diffuser is provided, Fig. 11.3. In that case water inlet at the high pressure end of the compressor has a definite advantage over the low pressure end water connection.

Since the head for cooled or uncooled compressors varies directly as the square of the impeller peripheral velocity, the head coefficient remaining the same, reduction of the peripheral velocity (impeller size or speed) is proportional to the square root of the power ratio, thus

$$\text{Power ratio (Cooled/Uncooled)} = \frac{H_c}{H_p} \qquad (11.9)$$

Reduction in size, speed, or number of stages

$$\text{Size ratio (Cooled/Uncooled)} = \sqrt{H_c/H_p} \qquad (11.10)$$

Table 1 shows the head ratios (which is the same as power ratios) per pound of gas for hypothetical isothermal and actual polytropic (uncooled) compression for several compression ratios. The size ratios, which are the square root of the above ratios, are also tabulated. *Note that in an actual compressor, even in the case of "perfect" cooling back to the inlet temperature, the head required to produce a given pressure ratio will be higher than the isothermal head. This is because, as has*

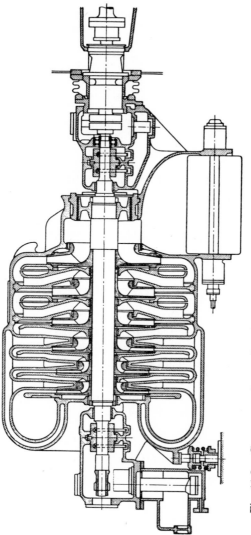

Fig. 11.3.   Compressor for methylene chloride, only high-pressure end is cooled (Escher Wyss).

been pointed out already, it is impossible in practice to cool impellers, and the process of compression is very nearly adiabatic, with precooling and after-cooling at each stage.

TABLE 1.   COMPARISON OF POLYTROPIC AND THEORETICAL ISOTHERMAL
          COMPRESSION FOR DIFFERENT COMPRESSION RATIOS

Compression ratio	2	3	4	5	6	7	8
Power or head ratio H_{iso}/H_p	0.920	0.810	0.760	0.728	0.700	0.680	0.655
Size or speed ratio $\sqrt{H_{iso}}/\sqrt{H_p}$	0.960	0.900	0.872	0.854	0.837	0.825	0.810

11.2   THERMODYNAMIC CONSIDERATIONS

Before proceeding to numerical examples of water cooling calculations, several of the fundamental thermodynamic principles developed in Chapter 7 will be reviewed and elaborated upon. Test results of actual water cooled compressors will be used to illustrate the application of these principles, and provide numerical proof of the validity of the deductions.

(*a*) **Impeller Characteristics.** *The head-capacity characteristic of each impeller expressed in terms of volume of impeller discharge and head in feet (equal to input in foot-pounds per pound) is a dynamic property of the machine and is not affected by any thermodynamic changes of the fluid.* However, for a given rate of flow (inlet c.f.m. or weight of flow per second) a decrease of inlet temperature (precooling between stages) increases the compression ratio of the stage and thus reduces the discharge volume at impeller outlet. This would move the operating point inward along the head-capacity characteristic and results in a variation of head contributed by the stage. Hence the design of impellers for several stages, or the selection of impellers from those already available, is affected by cooling. These effects are secondary to the main considerations of this article.

(*b*) **Polytropic Exponent.** Since generation of head or actual compression of the fluid is confined to the impeller and the impeller is not cooled, the process is adiabatic and the polytropic relationship (equation 7.47 holds).

$$(n - 1)/n = (k - 1)/ke_p \qquad (11.11)$$

The polytropic exponent $(n - 1)/n$ given by this equation is used to calculate the pressure ratio and temperature rise in a cooled stage. Table 2 shows the calculated and measured pressures and temperatures of a four-stage water cooled compressor. In this test pressures and temperatures were measured in the high point of the turn from the vaneless diffuser into the vaned return channel. Calculated discharge temperatures are 0.67 of the stage temperature rise plus the inlet temperatures, as indicated in the preceding article.

TABLE 2. STAGE PRESSURES AND TEMPERATURES OF FOUR-STAGE
COOLED COMPRESSOR
(Run 122–8, Table 3b, reference 2)

| | Discharge Pressure, in. Hg | | Discharge Temperature °F. | |
Stage Number	Calculated	Actual	Calculated	Actual
1	−6.35	−6.21	134.7	133.8
2	+0.65	+0.64	186	187.7
3	8.95	9.13	232	228
4	19.05	19.25	275	274

(c) **Head Produced by a Cooled Stage.** For a given rate of flow (design point) the enthalpy equilibrium equation for a steady adiabatic flow through the impeller states that

$$w_{in} = c_p(T_2 - T_1) = H_p + q_f$$

$$c_p(T_2 - T_1) = H_p/e_p \qquad (11.12)$$

where w_{in} is the energy input to the fluid (enthalpy), equal to shaft power minus mechanical losses, foot-pounds per pound.

H_p is energy input in foot-pounds per pound of fluid, or head in feet. It may be thought of as a height to which fluid is lifted and discharged at the inlet pressure.

q_f is heat resulting from hydraulic internal friction, including disk friction; foot-pounds per pound.

The amount of heat q_f is retained by the fluid. It contributes nothing to the head produced or elastic work stored in the fluid, but it appears as an increase in temperature above that corresponding to the isentropic compression. On Fig. 7.10, the energy input w_{in} appears as an increase in enthalpy, represented by area $BELH$. Area $ABELJ$ represents energy input to the fluid corresponding to the head H_p which is available for doing mechanical work in a steady flow process. The area $ABHJ$ corresponds to the heat q_f due to hydraulic friction. The symbol H_p is used here for the true output head and is calculated with the polytropic formula with a proper polytropic exponent $(n - 1)/n$.

(d) **Head Produced by a Cooled Compressor.** The enthalpy equilibrium equation 7.15, applied to the compressor unit as a whole, states

$$w_{in} = c_p[(T_2)_4 - (T_1)_1] + q_{out} \qquad (11.13)$$

where w_{in} represents the shaft work input to the fluid.

$(T_1)_1$ is the fluid inlet temperature to the first stage.

$(T_2)_4$ is the fluid outlet temperature, fourth stage; a four-stage compressor will be considered for this deduction.

q_{out} is the heat removed by cooling, internally or externally, between stages 1 and 4.

The quantity of heat q_{out} is composed of three parts, removed between stages 1–2, 2–3, and 3–4, respectively.

$$q_{out} = c_p[(T_2)_1 - (T_1)_2] + c_p[(T_2)_2 - (T_1)_3] + c_p[(T_2)_3 - (T_1)_4] \quad (11.14)$$

where T_1 is stage inlet temperature.

T_2 is stage outlet temperature.

The subscripts outside of the parentheses refer to the stage number. Substituting this value for q_{out} into equation 11.13 and rearranging the terms we obtain

$$w_{in} = c_p(T_2 - T_1)_1 + c_p(T_2 - T_1)_2 + c_p(T_2 - T_1)_3 + c_p(T_2 - T_1)_4 \quad (11.15)$$

and making use of equation 11.12, it follows that

$$w_{in}e_p = H_{p1} + H_{p2} + H_{p3} + H_{p4}$$

or

$$H_p \text{ total} = \Sigma H_p \text{ stages} \quad (11.16)$$

The physical meaning of equation 11.16 is: (*1*) *in a steady flow process, the addition or subtraction of heat externally* (*not the heat due to losses*) *does not change the amount of elastic energy stored in the fluid.* (*2*) *It requires the same amount of work in foot-pounds per pound of fluid to lift 1 lb. of fluid to the height H = head in feet whether the gas is hot or cold* (*Art. 1.4 and Fig. 1.5*).

The polytropic head of a complete unit can be calculated with the polytropic formula, using a polytropic exponent $(n - 1)/n$ determined from the relationship

$$(p_2/p_1)_t^{(n-1)/n} = (T_2/T_1)_t \quad (11.17)$$

where subscript t indicates that the pressure and temperature ratios are total for the whole compressor.

Equation 11.17 is for compression with a continuous cooling along line AM, Fig. 11.4, instead of cooling between stages (equation 11.11 is for adiabatic processes only). It has been proved by test, two examples of which are included in this chapter, and one example is given in Art. 7.4c. The significance of equation 11.17 can be seen from Fig. 11.4, showing a pv diagram of a multistage compressor with three intercoolers. The area $ABCD$ represents the compression work of the first group of impellers, followed by cooling along BE at constant pressure. The area $EFGC$ is the work performed by the second group of impellers, later cooled along FH. Similarly, area $HJKG$ shows the same for the third group, and area $LMNK$, for the fourth. The final state M also can be reached by a single polytropic compression with a suitable exponent, defined by equation 11.17. Note that the area $AMND$ is very closely equal to the combined areas $ABCD$, $EFGC$, $HJKG$, and $LMNK$ listed above. Attention is called to the fact that the polytropic exponent $(n-1)/n$ determined from equa-

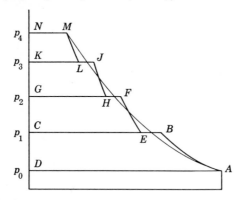

Fig. 11.4. Pv diagram of a multistage compressor with three intercoolers.

tion 11.17 does not satisfy equation 11.11 as can be seen by substituting the numerical values from the examples that follow later in this chapter.

(e) **Head Coefficient ψ_t for a Cooled Compressor.** The total head of a multistage compressor (cooled or uncooled) can be represented by

$$(H_p)_t = \psi_t \Sigma u_2{}^2/g \qquad (11.18)$$

where, u_2 is the peripheral velocity of the individual stages, and ψ_t is the "weighted" head coefficient of the combination of several impellers. It differs from the design head coefficients (at the best point of efficiency) of individual impellers because these impellers may be of different specific speed and the operating point of the complete unit may fall off peak on the individual stage characteristics. The coefficient ψ_t can be used for an approximate estimation of the performance of a complete unit for different conditions, but it is not a "design constant" because it does not remain constant. The head coefficients based on isothermal or adiabatic heads have little physical meaning and have no useful application.

11.3 NUMERICAL EXAMPLE

Calculate the power requirement and discharge temperature of a six-stage water cooled compressor, as shown in Fig. 11.5 and referred to in Art. 7.4, pumping air for the following conditions:

Inlet c.f.m., 2630.
Inlet pressure, 14.53 p.s.i.a.
Inlet temperature, 541.7°R.
Average polytropic head per stage, 5650 ft.
Weight of flow, 3.16 lb. per sec.
Impeller diameters, 17¾ in.
Speed, 7400 r.p.m.
Projected area of water jacket, 3.98 sq. ft.
Jacket metal thickness, ½ in. on diffuser side and ⅝ in. on return channel side.
Polytropic efficiency, 77.0 per cent.

Polytropic exponent, uncooled, $(n - 1)/n = \dfrac{0.283}{0.77} = 0.368$.

Water inlet temperature, 90°F.

Following the procedure outlined above, calculations will be carried out for the first two stages. Table 3, p. 206, gives the results of calcu-

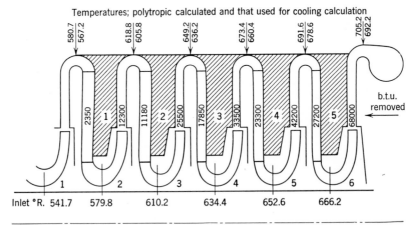

Fig. 11.5. Cooling diagram of a six-stage compressor.

lations for the complete compressor. The diagram in Fig. 11.5 shows the air temperatures and B.t.u. removed by each jacket.

(a) **First-Stage Return Channel.** (1) Gas film heat transfer coefficient (equation 11.7)

$$h_r = 0.024(0.24 G_r{}^{0.8}/D_r{}^{0.2}) \tag{11.7}$$

$$G_r = \frac{3.16 \times 3600 \times 144}{2.12 \times 18} = 43{,}000 \text{ lb per hr. sq. ft.}$$

where, 2.12 sq. in. is the area between two return vanes normal to the flow, and 18 is the number of vanes.

$$D_r = \frac{4 \times 1\frac{3}{16} \times 1\frac{25}{32}}{2(1\frac{3}{16} + 1\frac{25}{32})} = 1.43 \text{ in.}$$

$$h_r = 27.76 \qquad 1/h_r = 0.036$$

(2) Water film coefficient, using equation 11.6,

$$h_w = \frac{160(1 + 0.012t) V^{0.8}}{D_w{}^{0.2}}$$

where t is water temperature in °F. Estimating the water temperature rise at 10°, the average water temperature of 95°F. will be used for all stages.

Water velocity $V = 3$ ft. is assumed for parallel connection of top and lower halves of water manifolds. This arrangement will require about 8.5 p.s.i. water pressure drop for five jackets in series. (Pressure drop varies as square of the water velocity.)

When the power input for the test is measured by heat balance (equation 7.15) to obtain a higher cooling water temperature rise, a low velocity should be maintained, otherwise determination of the amount of heat removed by cooling and the power input will be subject to inaccuracy.

The hydraulic diameter of the water passage is equal to

$$D_w = \frac{4 \times 3.25 \times 1.125}{2(3.25 + 1.125)} = 1.67 \text{ in.}$$

$$h_w = 757 \qquad 1/h_w = 0.001317$$

(3) Metal thermal resistance for cast iron

$$L/K = 0.625/(27.0 \times 12) = 0.001937 \text{ B.t.u./ft.}$$

(4) The over-all heat transfer coefficient from equation 11.2

$$U_r = \frac{1}{R_u} = \frac{1}{0.0265 + 0.001317 + 0.001937} = 25.45 \text{ B.t.u./hr. (sq. ft.)}$$

(5) Heat to the first jacket from the first return channel

$$(q_r)_1 = 1.90 \times 25.45 \times 3.98(T_g - 555)$$

$$T_g = 567.2°R.$$

The average air temperature T_g for the first stage is taken as equal to

$$T_g = T_1 + 0.67(T_2 - T_1)$$

and

$$T_2 - T_1 = T_1 \times X$$

where X is taken from

$$H = 5650 = \frac{T_1 R}{(n-1)/n}(X)$$

$$T_2 = 580.7 \qquad T_2 - T_1 = 39.0 \qquad T_1 = 541.7$$

$$(q_r)_1 = 2350 \text{ B.t.u.}$$

(6) Temperature reduction before the second stage inlet

$$\Delta t_1 = \frac{2350}{3600 \times 3.16 \times 0.24} = 0.86°F.$$

Second stage inlet temperature $(T_2 - \Delta t_1)$

$$(T_1)_2 = 580.7 - 0.86 = 579.84$$

(b) Second-Stage Diffuser. (1) Gas film ceofficient for the diffuser using formula 11.3.

The mass flow rate lb. per hr. (sq. ft.) is found from

$$G_d = W/\pi D_m b_3 \sin \alpha_2'$$

$$= \frac{3.16 \times 3600 \times 144}{\pi \times 24.625 \times 0.9375 \times 0.374} = 60,300$$

The hydraulic diameter for the diffuser

$$D_d = 2b_3 = 1.875 \text{ in.}$$

Using these numerical values the gas film coefficient is calculated.

$$h_d = 34.1 \text{ B.t.u./hr. (sq. ft.)}$$

(2) The same water film coefficient applies to the first diffuser as that for the first return channel as heat is removed from both by the same water jacket.

$$h_w = 757 \text{ B.t.u./hr. (sq. ft.)}$$

(3) The metal thermal resistance for the diffuser is equal to

$$L/K = \frac{0.500}{12 \times 27} = 0.00154$$

(4) Using the above numerical values, the over-all heat transfer coefficient for the second diffuser is

$$U_d = 32.0$$

(5) The average air temperature in the second diffuser

$$(T_g)_2 = 0.67(\Delta T)_2 + (T_1)_2$$

$$= 0.67 \times 39.0 + 579.8 = 605.8$$

(6) The amount of heat removed from the air through the second-stage diffuser is equal to

$$(q_d)_2 = 1.9 \times 32.0 \times 3.98(605.8 - 555)$$

$$= 12,300 \text{ B.t.u./hr.}$$

(7) Following the procedure outlined above, the amount of heat removed from the second channel is found to be

$$(q_r)_2 = 11,180$$

(8) Total heat removed from the second stage

$$(q)_2 = (q_d)_2 + (q_r)_2 = 23,480$$

(9) Temperature reduction due to cooling of the second stage

$$\Delta t_2 = \frac{23,480}{3600 \times 3.16 \times 0.24} = 8.6$$

(10) The inlet temperature of the third stage

$$(T_1)_3 = (T_2)_2 - \Delta t_2$$

$$(T_1)_3 = 618.8 - 8.6 = 610.2$$

Note that, since the same head is assumed for all stages, the polytropic temperature rise per stage is the same, equal to $\Delta T = 39.00$.

(c) **Compression Ratio.** The sole effect of cooling in a stage is a reduction of inlet air temperature for the following stage, compression by the impeller following the polytropic process with $(n - 1)/n = 0.368$. The compression ratio of the first stage is determined from the polytropic equation used before for the discharge temperature calculations.

$$X_1 = \frac{H(n-1)}{nT_1R} = r_1^{0.368} - 1 = 0.0714$$

$$r_1 = 1.206$$

Similarly,

$$r_2 = 1.192$$

(d) **Summary of Results.** (1) Table 3 presents results of calculations for a complete six-stage compressor.

TABLE 3. WATER COOLING CALCULATIONS SIX-STAGE COMPRESSOR

1 Stage number		1	2	3	4	5	6
2 Impeller inlet temperature	T_1	541.7	579.8	610.2	634.4	652.6	666.2
3 Impeller discharge temperature	T_2	580.7	618.8	649.2	673.4	691.6	705.2
4 Temperature for cooling	T_g	567.2	605.8	636.2	660.4	678.6	692.2
5 Return channel	h_r	27.76	32.5	32.5	32.5	32.5	——
6 Return channel	h_w	757	602	602	602	602	——
7 Return channel	U_r	25.45	29.1	29.1	29.1	29.1	——
8 Return channel	q_r	2,350	11,180	17,850	23,300	27,200	——
9 Diffuser	h_d	——	34.1	47.7	47.7	52.4	82.8
10 Diffuser	U_d	——	32.0	41.5	41.5	45.0	65.5
11 Diffuser	q_d	——	12,300	25,500	33,500	42,200	68,000
12 Temperature reduction	Δt	0.86	8.6	15.85	20.8	25.4	25.0
13 Compression ratio	r	1.206	1.192	1.182	1.176	1.172	1.167

Final temperature, 705.2 − 25.0 = 680.2°R.
Total B.t.u. removed by cooling is equivalent to 103.6 hp.
Total compression ratio = 2.731.
Total polytropic head = 5650 × 6 = 33,900 ft. (cooled).
Total polytropic head uncooled for compression ratio 2.731, H_p = 35,250 ft.
Ratio of cooled/uncooled heads = 0.962.
Power saving (1 − 0.962) × 100 = 3.68 per cent.
Final temperature uncooled = 785°R.
Temperature reduction due to cooling, 104.8°R.

(2) The same compressor operated at the conditions assumed for this numerical example has shown on test:

Discharge pressure, p_2 = 38.06 p.s.i.a.

Discharge temperature, T_2 = 664.4°R.

Compression ratio, 2.62.

Cooling water, 53.5 g.p.m.

Water inlet temperature, t_1 = 90.2°F.

Water temperature rise, 9.58°F.

Heat removed by cooling, equivalent to 99.4 hp.

Calculated temperature rise, using 53.5 g.p.m. of water, 9.82°F.

Power input by formula 7.15 including 1.6 hp. radiation loss, b.hp. = 234.1.

Polytropic exponent, formula 11.17, $(n - 1)/n = 0.2115$.

Total polytropic head $H_p = 31,850$ ft.

Polytropic efficiency 0.781.

Polytropic exponent for uncooled operation and 0.781 efficiency, formula 11.11, $(n - 1)/n = 0.362$.

Total polytropic head for the same compression ratio 2.62 uncooled, $H_p = 33,550$ ft.

Power saving ratio, 31,850/33,550 = 0.95.

Power saving, per cent, 5.0.

(3) *Remarks.* Note that the test compression ratio is slightly lower than the calculated ratio indicating that the assumed polytropic head per stage was on the high side. By using a lower head per stage to obtain exactly the test compression ratio, the difference between the calculated and test values of the amount of heat removed and the final temperature will be reduced.

It may be pointed out that, since the primary object of cooling is reduction of power and size or speed of the unit and since this reduction of the above value is only a few per cent, no great accuracy of calculations of the cooling effect on the performance is necessary. Thus, in the above numerical example, if the error in calculations were, say, 10 per cent, the final result in power (or head) would be in error less than 0.5 per cent or well within the accuracy of testing.

If a reduction of the discharge gas temperature is required, the last stage casing should be completely jacketed. In Fig. 11.3, water jackets are omitted from the first and second stages due to a low cooling effect of those stages.

For higher compression ratios (heavier gas, higher speed, more stages) a state can be reached when the reduction of gas temperature due to cooling may be higher than the stage temperature rise and the gas temperature will gradually decrease having reached a maximum.

11.4 INTERCOOLING

(a) **External Cooling.** When cooling is accomplished not by jacketing the individual stages but in special heat exchangers either mounted on the same base with the compressor or in separate units, it is known as "intercooling." External cooling is by far more effective than internal cooling but requires more expensive equipment. As the head per stage grew higher, as a consequence of the progress in material and improvements in the manufacturing technique, the over-all dimensions of high compression machines became smaller and internal cooling became less effective. This is because the increase in head per stage was accomplished by increasing the rotative speed rather than the size. Higher rotative speeds led to better hydraulic types (higher specific speed) and better efficiency. Later high pressure compressor designs, here and abroad, use external cooling.

Internal cooling may be more practical when pumping gases saturated with water vapor, but, if cooled below the dew point during compression, a corrosive solution is formed with some components of gas. However, if vapor is kept in the superheated state, no corrosion takes place. For this purpose internal cooling may be sufficient, and by suitably controlling the quantities of cooling water, condensation can be avoided (reference 8). Scaling of water jackets, when there is no easy way of cleaning water passages, is a serious drawback of inner cooling.

(b) **Humidity Control.** External cooling permits control of moisture content in high pressure compressed air plants. For example, it is important to reduce the humidity of air supplied to mines, since a high moisture content makes working conditions unpleasant and damage is likely to be caused to air-operated machinery. Excessive cooling due to air expansion in pneumatic tools limits the maximum air pressure to about 100 p.s.i.g. to avoid danger from icing.

A majority of compressed air tools work without expansion, because tools of equal power are lighter and controls simpler. However, use of air motors in which air can expand, doing useful work, is steadily increasing. Such motors require compressed air sufficiently dry to avoid damage due to icing (reference 10). When air dryness is of importance an after-cooler with a liquid separator is added. A reduction of the discharge temperature tends to improve the general economy of the installation by reducing the distribution system friction losses.

In some cases special equipment is used to reduce air temperature and moisture content by allowing air to expand through a number of nozzles. In practice this involves the following steps (Fig. 11.6).

1. Air is compressed by a compressor A to a pressure higher than the air main pressure (110 p.s.i.g., with 75 p.s.i.g. in air main, in one example) and is passed through an after-cooler (B) where air temperature is reduced to 95°F.

2. From the after-cooler, air is passed through a heat exchanger (C) where it is cooled to 70°F. by cool air delivered into the mine system.

3. From the heat exchanger, air is directed to an air turbine (D), through the first water separator (E). The air turbine is coupled to

the compressor shaft. The drop in pressure and temperature through the turbine is controlled by the adjustment of nozzle valves. The temperature of air at the turbine discharge is kept above freezing (40°F.) to avoid freezing in the second water separator (F) after the gas turbine.

4. After the second water separator (F), cold air passes through the above mentioned heat exchanger (C) where it receives heat from the air leaving the after-cooler.

The second water separator is provided with a by-pass valve (G) to admit hot air from the compressor for defrosting if ice has formed.

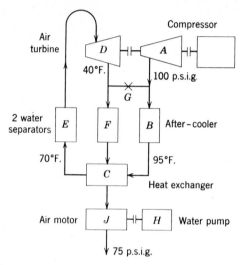

Fig. 11.6.   Diagram of dehumidifying installation.

Water is removed from the system by a water pump (H), air motor driven (J) (reference 11).

(c) **Polytropic Efficiency of Compressors with External Cooling.** The polytropic efficiency of multistage compressors with intercooling can be calculated on test if the pressures and temperatures of the gas at the inlet and outlet of the intercooler are measured. The output of each group of impellers can be calculated as independent units ($H_pW/550$), and the polytropic efficiency is determined from

$$e_p = \Sigma(H_pW)/\text{b.hp. } 550 \qquad (11.18)$$

where b.hp. is the power input to the whole unit.

W is weight of flow per second.

H_p is polytropic head of the group of impellers.

Formula 11.18 does not charge the loss of pressure through the coolers to the compressor.   When coolers are built into the compressor frame, measurements of inlet and discharge pressure and temperatures of the several impeller groups may present difficulty.   For a comparison of several cooling arrangements, or of cooled compressors of different makes, it may be necessary to include the pressure losses through the coolers for efficiency calculations.   In this case the polytropic head is measured at the compressor discharge, using polytropic exponent $(n - 1)/n$ from equation 11.17.

The input (b.hp.) can be determined using the conservation of enthalpy equation (7.15)

$$w_{in} = c_p(T_2 - T_1) + q_{out}$$

where the first term on the right represents the change of enthalpy of the gas, and q_{out} is the heat removed by the coolers, which is easily measured.

(d) **Isothermal Efficiency of Cooled Compressors.**   Efficiency of compressors cooled either internally or externally is frequently expressed in terms of isothermal efficiency, defined as

$$e_{iso} = \frac{WRT_1 \log_e (p_2/p_1)}{\text{b.hp.} - \text{Mechanical losses}} \tag{11.19}$$

It is only in a hypothetical process where gas is maintained during the process of compression at the initial temperature, that isothermal efficiency is equal to the true output/input efficiency and isothermal head is equal to the polytropic head $(n = 1)$. *In practice this is never realized even in the case when gas is cooled back to its inlet temperature, because the gas is not cooled while it is compressed in the impeller but before or after it passes the impeller.*   The difference depends upon the number of compressor stages and number of intercoolers.   Theoretically, isothermal compression can be realized with an infinite number of stages.   Table 4, discussed later, shows the effect of the number of intercoolers upon the power and isothermal efficiency.

The difference between the input for a theoretical isothermal compression (with an infinite number of stages) and actual compression with a limited number of stages and internal or external cooling after each stage appear as the crosshatched areas on Fig. 7.2.

Isothermal efficiency is a "conventional" efficiency, used for comparison of compressors of different makes.   For the same output (head or compression ratio and weight of flow as specified) isothermal efficiency represents correctly the relative merits of the several machines.   This follows from the fact that in formula 11.19 the numerator is the same for all units and the power demand is inversely proportional to the isothermal efficiency. This is true only if the discharge temperatures are the same for the several compressors, because a compressor with a higher discharge temperature would have a higher total head to produce the same discharge pressure, and hence higher b.hp. However, this may result from less effective cooling and not from an inferior hydraulic design.

There is no way (and there really is no need) to predict isothermal efficiency of a machine for which tests are available, except when the requirements are duplicated. To determine the power required, which is of primary interest to the user, it is necessary to go through all steps outlined in this chapter. Available tests will assure a good approximation, as the over-all performance of the cooling means (internal or external) can be more closely established based on constants derived from the actual observations.

(e) **Effect of Cooling on Compressor Performance.** To study the effect of the number of intercoolers and number of stages on the compressor performance, i.e., efficiency, power demand, and size or speed, Table 4 was compiled. A compression ratio of 8:1, inlet temperature of 70°F., and polytropic efficiency of 75 per cent were selected, all impeller groups and all impellers producing equal heads. For items 1 and 2 in Table 4, the discharge temperature is equal to the inlet

TABLE 4. EFFECT OF COOLING ON COMPRESSOR PERFORMANCE CALCULATED
All values per pound of air.
Compression ratio, 8:1.
Polytropic efficiency, 75%; $(n - 1)/n = 0.378$.
Air inlet, 70°F. = 530°R.
Air cooler outlet 100°F. for all items, except 1 and 2.

Item Number	Number of Intercoolers	0	1	2	3	7	9	Infinite (isothermal)
1	Total polytropic head, ft.	89,800	72,200	67,400	64,880	61,800	61,400	58,800
2	Power required %; air cooler outlet, 70°F.	100	80.4	75.2	72.2	68.8	68.3	65.5
3	Total polytropic head, ft.; cooler outlet, 100°F	89,800	74,250	69,870	67,670	64,820	64,500	——
4	Power required %; cooler outlet, 100°F.	100	82.6	77.7	75.3	72.2	71.8	——
5	Relative size, speed, or number of stages	100	91.0	88.2	87.2	85.0	84.8	81.0
6	Shaft input, ft.-lb., required	118,700	99,100	93,200	90,300	86,400	86,000	78,400
7	Isothermal efficiency, %	49.7	59.4	63.1	66.1	67.9	68.4	75.0
8	Final discharge temperature, °R.	1,167	830	728	682	618	606	530
9	Total B.t.u. removed by cooling	0	54.0	71.25	79.0	89.16	91.44	100.7
10	Enthalpy increase B.t.u.	153	72.0	47.5	36.5	21.1	18.24	0
11	Power input, (9) + (10) = (6) B.t.u.	153	126	118.75	115.5	110.26	109.68	100.7

temperature (70°F.). These figures give a comparison of power demand of several arrangements with theoretical isothermal compression. The rest of the items are based on cooling air to 100°F. The following remarks elaborate on the calculation procedure and results obtained.

1. It is assumed that the total compression ratio 8.0 is equally divided between several groups of impellers with a cooler in between. Thus, with two intercoolers each group out of three produces a compression ratio $\sqrt[3]{8} = 2$.

2. A polytropic compression is assumed in every stage. Isothermal compression as such cannot be realized in an actual compressor with any kind of cooling and is mentioned only for comparison.

3. If a reduction of the final discharge temperature is contemplated, after-coolers should be provided which will be of the same size as the rest of the intercoolers, if the final temperature is set at 100°F.

4. The number of stages does not enter directly into consideration, although it is evident that seven intercoolers would call for an eight-stage unit and nine intercoolers are meant for ten stages.

Perhaps the procedure followed in preparation of Table 4 should be outlined briefly so that the significance of the tabulated information can be appreciated.

Item 1. The total head required to produce the compression ratio 8 is the sum of heads of several groups of impellers, calculated for an inlet temperature of 70°F. and compression ratio $\sqrt[m]{8}$, where m is the number of groups. The last column shows the value of head for isothermal compression, which can be considered as compression with an infinite number of intercoolers.

Item 2 is the ratio of heads shown in the several columns to that of the uncooled compressor, which represents the percentage of power input, the polytropic efficiency of 75 per cent being assumed constant for all stages.

Item 3 is the same as item 1, but it is calculated on a basis 100°F. inlet to all groups of impellers except the first, where the inlet temperature is kept 70°F.

Item 4 is similar to item 2, showing power ratio to that of the uncooled compressor with air cooled to 100°F.

Item 5 represents the square root of the values of item 4 and represents a reduction in size, speed, or number of stages for different cooling arrangements. It will be noticed that even with two coolers, one out of eight stages is saved by cooling for the same value of the maximum peripheral velocity.

Item 6 is item 3 divided by the polytropic efficiency 0.75 and represents the work input to the air (mechanical losses excluded).

Item 7 is obtained by dividing the isothermal output of 58,800 ft.-lb. by the values of input given by item 6. Note that for three coolers, to reach a 70.0 per cent isothermal efficiency with cooling to 100°F. requires a polytropic efficiency of 80.6 per cent. This follows from the fact that 70.0 per cent isothermal efficiency requires a power input equal to 58,800/0.70 = 84,000 ft.-lb. For this input a polytropic output (head) of 67,670 ft.-lb. (item 3 for three coolers) requires a polytropic efficiency of 67,670/84,000 = 0.806.

Item 8. This is calculated using polytropic relationships for the last group of impellers and 100°F. for the inlet temperature, except for the first and last columns where the inlet temperature remains 70°F.

Item 9. If the air temperature entering and leaving each cooler is known, heat removed by cooling per pound of air can easily be determined.

Item 10. Enthalpy increase of the air at discharge is equal to

$$h_2 - h_1 = 0.24(T_2 - 530)$$

where T_2 is taken from item 8.

Item 11 proves the conservation of enthalpy statement, equation 7.15.

The comparison of the several cooling arrangements presented in Table 4 does not include the hydraulic loss through the coolers. Table 5 shows the loss through the first cooler as 0.568 lb., the loss decreasing in the second and third coolers due to reduction in volume (all three coolers are identical). Obviously more coolers incur more loss of pressure. For that reason, besides the mechanical simplicity and cost, the number of coolers is usually limited to three. In modern designs great care is exercised to reduce velocities before discharging air into the cooler.

It will be observed from the above discussion and calculations that estimating the performance of an existing compressor with external cooling, or designing a new one, does not present any difficulties or uncertainties such as are encountered in the calculation of performance of the internally cooled machines. This is because the heat transfer values of external coolers are well established. Thus, coolers are selected of suitable size to produce the desired cooling effect.

(*f*) **Example of a Multistage Compressor with Three External Coolers.** Table 5 shows test results of a nine-stage air compressor with three external coolers. The test permitted taking pressure and temperature readings at the inlet and outlet of the four groups of impellers, and thus it was possible to calculate the polytropic heads of each group and polytropic efficiency based on ΣH_p, excluding the pressure losses in the coolers. The polytropic head for a complete unit, based on the polytropic exponent $(n-1)/n$, according to equation

TABLE 5. TEST RESULTS OF A NINE STAGE AIR COMPRESSOR WITH THREE EXTERNAL COOLERS. Data by Kluge (reference 12)

	Symbol	Impeller Groups 1	2	3	4	For a complete unit
Inlet pressure, p.s.i.a.	p_1	8.66	16.63	27.97	44.35	8.66
Discharge, pressure, p.s.i.a.	p_2	17.2	28.3	44.65	61.3	61.3
Compression ratio	r	1.985	1.70	1.595	1.38	7.08
Inlet temperature °R.	T_1	545	564	560	556	545
Discharge temperature, °R.	T_2	681	681	677	628.5	628.5
T_2/T_1	T_2/T_1	1.25	1.208	1.208	1.131	1.152
Polytropic exponent	$(n-1)/n$	0.325	0.357	0.403	0.378	0.0729
Cooler pressure loss, p.s.i.	p		0.568	0.397	0.298	
Polytropic head, ft.	H_p	22,350	17,540	15,350	10,170	62,700

Weight of flow, lb./sec. = 20.2; c.f.m. = 28,700.
b.hp − Mechanical loss = 3085 hp.
Polytropic efficiency based on a polytropic head of 62,700 ft. as measured at final discharge = 74.6 per cent.
Sum of polytropic heads of four groups measured individually, ΣH_p = 65,360 ft.
Polytropic efficiency based on ΣH_p per cent = 77.7, (pressure losses in coolers excluded).
Polytropic head for r = 7.08, without cooling = 76,000 ft.
Power reduction ratio = 0.825.
Size, speed, or number of stages reduction ratio = 0.91.
Isothermal head for the same compression ratio, feet, H_{iso} = 56,800.
Isothermal efficiency based on b.hp. (Mechanical efficiency 0.982) in per cent = 66.4.
Impeller diameters 49.25 to 30.5 in.
r.p.m. = 4450; u_2 = 957 ft./sec., maximum.

11.17, is lower, resulting in lower polytropic efficiency of a complete unit with pressure loss through the coolers charged to the compressor.

11.5 EXAMPLES OF HIGH PRESSURE COMPRESSORS WITH COOLING

In Art. 11.2 it was pointed out that the benefits from cooling increase as the compression ratio rises. In Europe, where the efficiency of all industrial equipment is evaluated higher than in this country, owing to prevailing economic conditions, cooling is applied to all compressors where the compression ratio exceeds 2.5 to 3.0. Turbo-blowers for blast furnace are built without cooling. Also standard blowers for steel works (compression ratio 4:1) in Europe are uncooled. There is less justification for cooling of compressors in the United

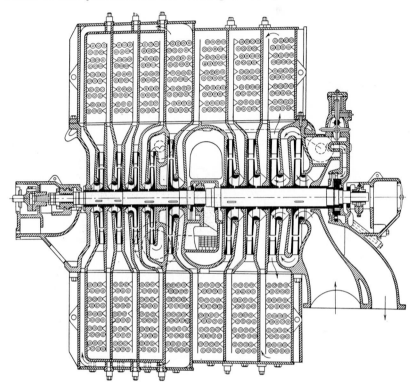

Fig. 11.7a. Brown Boveri isotherm compressor.

States for similar application on account of lower costs of power and fuel.

The greatest number of water cooled high pressure compressors were built in Europe for central compressed air supply installations for mines, shipyards, and large manufacturing plants. The pressure ratios lie between 6:1 to 8:1. Sizes vary from 12,000 c.f.m. to 35,000 c.f.m., with several units up to 85,000 c.f.m. The most popular size is around 30,000 c.f.m.

Figure 11.7a and 11.7b Brown Boveri "isotherm" compressor with all stages cooled except the first and the last. Each cooler consists of two halves placed above and below the compressor casing. The

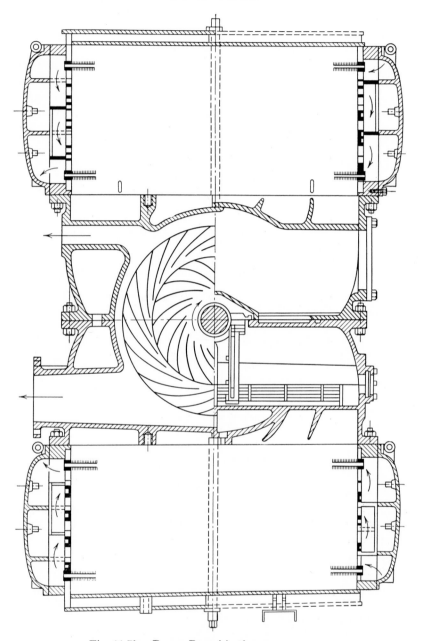

Fig. 11.7*b*.   Brown Boveri isotherm compressor.

maximum peripheral velocity is 770 ft. per sec. Figure 11.8 shows the performance of the "isotherm" compressor both with vaneless and vaned diffusers. Gain in efficiency with vaned diffusers is at the expense of range of operation. Under average operating conditions the temperature at the final discharge is 95 to 105°F. above the cooling water temperature. Isotherm compressors are built in seven sizes covering a range of capacities from 2500 to 88,000 c.f.m. Surrounding the compressor casing completely by the cooler housings results in an appreciable reduction of noise.

Three-bearing design of the isotherm compressor permits using a lighter shaft, which leads to a better hydraulic type of impellers.

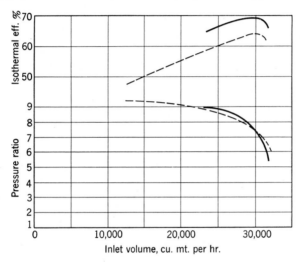

Fig. 11.8. Performance of an isotherm compressor; full lines with vaned diffuser; dashed lines with vaneless diffuser.

Impellers are arranged in two opposing groups for axial thrust balance. The unit is provided with a recovery gas turbine on the inlet side of the compressor. The bodies of both coolers are of the welded-steel construction. Cooler brass tubes carrying water have copper fins pressed on the outside. Bearings are provided with forced lubrication.

Figure 11.9 shows an Escher Wyss seven-stage compressor with two intercoolers mounted on one side of the compressor casing. The vaneless diffuser discharging into the coolers have an extra large diameter ratio partly for mechanical reasons and partly to reduce velocities so that the pressure loss through the coolers are reduced.

Figure 11.10 shows a Gutehoffnungshütte (GHH) ten-stage compressor with three intercoolers placed on both sides of the casing. The

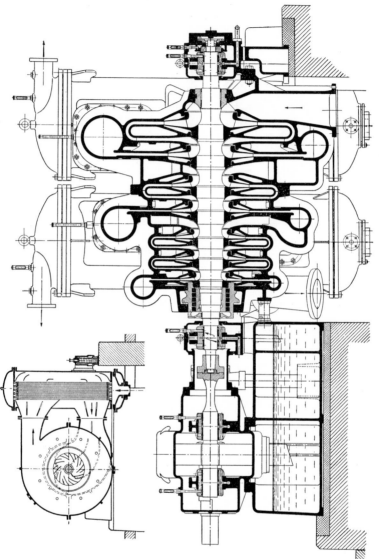

Fig. 11.9.   Escher Wyss compressor with two intercoolers.

first cooler consists of two coolers in parallel. Stages leading to the coolers have double volutes, whereas the rest of stages are provided with vaneless diffusers.

In the United States, owing to extended electrification of mines and industrial plants, there is no great need for large central compressed air installations. In isolated cases high pressure ratios are met by arranging several units in series with common or independent drive. For large volumes a low pressure unit consists of two identical compressors in parallel. External coolers are used between the high and low pressure units. In one case, two units were furnished for tonnage oxygen production in Texas, each to deliver 110,000 c.f.m. of air at 108 p.s.i.a. and driven by a 24,000 hp. steam turbine at 3900 r.p.m. The unit is built with three casings, the low pressure part having two in parallel. All three casings are mounted in tandem for a common driver with an external cooler between the low and high pressure components (reference 13).

Although the trend in high compression ratio compressor design is definitely toward external cooling, both in this country and abroad, this goal was reached by several manufacturers by way of dual cooling, i.e., inner-cooling combined with external cooling. Figure 11.11 shows an example of a nine-stage Demag air compressor designed for 47,000 c.f.m. at a compression ratio of 9.7 to 10.5 at 3060 r.p.m. It is internally cooled and has in addition two external coolers between stages 3–4 and 6–7.

A number of high pressure units have been built in the United States with combined inner and external cooling and were built in two casings with jacketed diaphragms similar to Fig. 11.2 and with external coolers between the casings (reference 13).

11.6 INJECTION COOLING

Injection cooling is widely used in Europe and is hardly known in this country. Lendorff reports more than one hundred turbocompressors by Escher Wyss in successful operation with injection cooling in 1949 (reference 8). In this method of cooling a suitable liquid is sprayed through atomizers into the return channel of a multistage compressor where it evaporates immediately and reduces the temperature of the flow. In machines pumping water vapor the injected liquid is condensate and in the case of refrigerating installations using turbocompressors the liquid is the refrigerant. Water can also be injected into compressors pumping air or gas when the increase in water content of the flow can be tolerated by the process and presence of water does not make a corrosive solution.

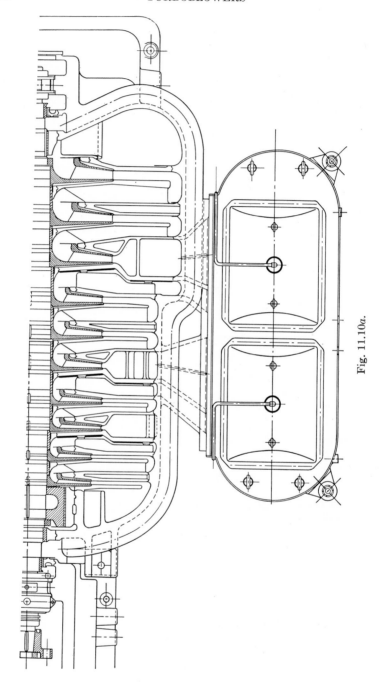

Fig. 11.10a.

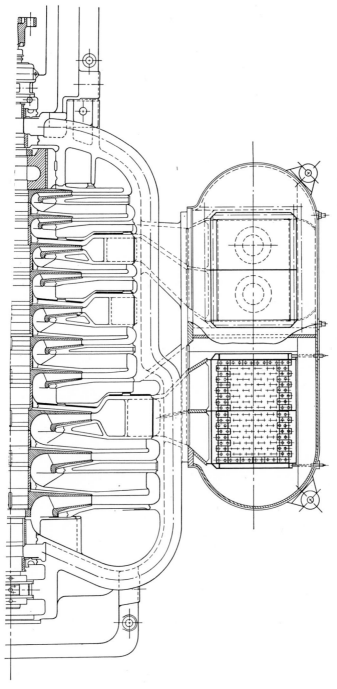

Fig. 11.10a.   Gutehoffnungshütte ten-stage compressor with three intercoolers.

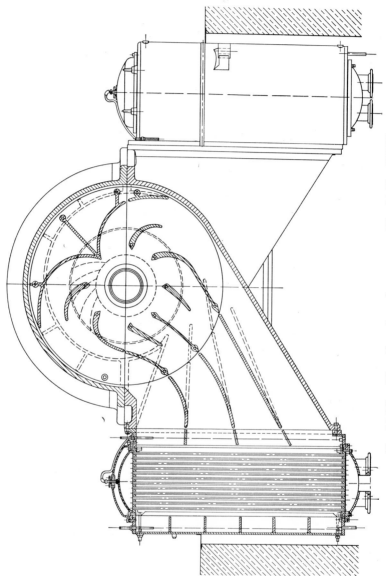

Fig. 11.10b.   Elevation view of compressor Fig. 11.10a (GHH).

Figure 11.12 shows the effect of injection cooling on the power demand for different compression ratios as compared with the uncooled compression. Under proper conditions and medium compression ratios (2.5:3) injection of water may be more effective than the

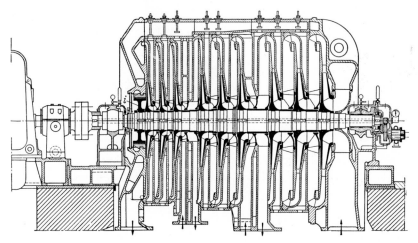

Fig. 11.11.   Demag compressor with internal and external cooling.

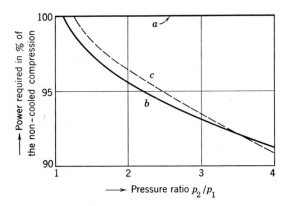

Fig. 11.12.   Power reduction by injection cooling.   (a) uncooled; (b) vapor compression with injection; (c) air compression with injection (Escher Wyss).

external (intercooling) cooling.   Figure 11.13 shows the view of the injection piping arranged on the compressor casing.

Note the multiplicity of injection points and provision for bleed-off and draining of all parts of the casing.   When pumping water vapor, the size of units and number of stages needed to produce a given pressure ratio are considerably larger in comparison with air compressors,

Fig. 11.13.   Ammonia vapor compressor with liquid injection.   Four units of this type in one plant have 13.6 millions cal./hr. refrigeration, requiring 4500 kw. at the terminals (Escher Wyss).

owing to the low density of water vapor.   Thus vapor compressors in sugar refinery applications compare in size or exceed the large blast furnace blowers.   By proper control of the amount of injected liquid it is possible to realize a compression approximately parallel to and above the saturation line, thus avoiding condensation.

In addition to the power saving, injection cooling has several advantages as compared to internal or external water cooling for certain applications. These advantages are: (1) In certain processes (like sugar making) rejection of heat to cooling water is objectionable for the economical operation of the whole plant. (2) Injection cooling permits a better control of the amount of foreign matter carried by gas. (3) Injection can be used for removing incrustations or deposits from the flow passages by overdosing the amount of injected liquid with drains open.

Application of centrifugal compressors to evaporation processes in Europe is justified by the high cost of fuel. Compressors are used for concentration of solutions containing water. Vapor is compressed sufficiently to be utilized as heating means in the heating chamber of the evaporator, hence the name "heat pumps" frequently used for compressors in such service. Economic factors leading to the successful application of compressors for evaporation service do not exist in the United States.

Injection cooling is never used by Swiss firms for high pressure (7–9 atm.) air compressors, which as a rule have external cooling (reference 9). Apparently the difficulties with erosion, corrosion, and scaling outweigh the power saving resulting from injection cooling, as condensate either is not available or is valued more than the benefits derived from injection in compressed air plants. Besides, an increase in humidity of air makes this method of cooling unsuited for central compressed air plants.

11.7 GENERAL REMARKS ON COOLING

(a) **Economy of Water Cooling.** It has been shown in this chapter how power saving resulting from cooling can be accurately calculated. This saving should balance the cost of cooling equipment and its operation and also the extra cost of compressor housing. *It is obvious that no part of the heat removed by cooling water comes from the power input from the driver. No installation could stand such a waste of available energy.* Perhaps the process can be easier to visualize if all cooling is assumed to be done ahead of the first stage, then obviously all the heat removed has to come from the surroundings (see Fig. 7.2a). Equation 11.15 clearly indicates that the energy input to the fluid, which is proportional to the temperature rise and equal to the polytropic head of the stage divided by the polytropic efficiency, does not depend upon the initial temperature of the individual stages. Thus the input does not depend upon where the heat is removed from the gas on its way from inlet to discharge.

It is true that the resulting pressure ratio is affected by how and where heat is removed. To produce a given pressure the best place to remove heat is ahead of the first-stage inlet, and the poorest place is beyond the last-stage discharge. In practice the location of points of heat removal are determined by the temperature of the available water. But it is the heat from the surroundings which is boosted to a higher level for convenience of removal.

Although these statements become axiomatic to the compressor designer their deduction is impossible without the concept of available energy which enables us to keep a separate account of available energy (power input) and unavailable energy (losses and major portion of the heat.)

(b) **The Effect of Cooling.** If the same compressor is operated at the same speed, uncooled first and then cooled; it has the following effects: (1) The head at b.e.p. remains the same, but pressure will increase due to increase of density. (2) Since the capacity at b.e.p. (volume) at impeller discharge remains the same, b.e.p. will take place at a higher weight of flow or higher inlet c.f.m. owing to increase of density. (3) The b.hp. at b.e.p. will increase in direct ratio of increase of density at impeller discharge. However, to produce a given pressure ratio at the same inlet c.f.m., either speed or impeller diameter should be reduced so that b.hp. will be below that of the uncooled machine.

When the degree of cooling is changed, owing to change in cooling water temperature and inlet gas temperature, the effects will follow the direction indicated above.

REFERENCES

1. McAdams, *Heat Transmission*, McGraw-Hill, p. 174, equation 4k and p. 183, equation 9d; also Marks, 5th ed., p. 372.
2. Trumpler, Frederick, and Trumpler, "Heat Transfer Rates in Centrifugal Compressors," *A.S.M.E. Trans.* Vol. 72, 1950 p. 797
3. Bruno Eck and W. J. Kearton, "Turbo-Gebläse," Springer, Berlin, 1929, p. 274.
4. *Konstruktion*, Vol. 2, 1950, p. 135.
5. Baumann, Brown Boveri Rev., 1941, p. 196.
6. Tzitkin, *Centrifugal Compressors and Fans*, U.S.S.R., Maschgis, 1950, p. 263 (In Russian).
7. *Escher Wyss Mitt.* 11, 1938, pp. 7, 9.
8. Lendorff, "Designs and Uses of Compressors," *Escher Wyss News*, Vol. 14, 1941, p. 20; also Vol. 21/22, 1948/49, pp. 49, 92.
9. Lendorff, "Turbo Compressoren Zur Brudenverdichtung in Zuckerfabriken," *Escher Wyss Mitt.*, Jan. 20, 1946/47, p. 46, also available in English as "Turbo-Compressors for Vapors in Sugar Factories," *Escher Wyss News*, 1946/47, pp. 46–50.

10. *Brown Boveri Rev.*, April/May, 1941, p. 112.
11. Millar, "Compressor Plant Design," *J. Inst. Certified Engrs.*, South Africa, May, 1950, pp. 128–152.
12. Kluge, Kreiselgebläse und Kreiselverdichter, Springer, Berlin, 1953, p. 203.
13. Foster, "Application of Centrifugal and Axial Compressors," *Petroleum Refiner*, Vol. 28, No. 8, p. 98, Aug., 1949; also, *Centrifugal and Axial Flow Compressors*, Clark Bros. Co., publication, 1949.

CHAPTER 12

Centrifugal Fans

INTRODUCTION

Fans represent a class of turbomachines designed to move fluids such as air, gases, and vapor against low pressures. The A.S.M.E. Test Code groups all turbomachines producing a fluid density increase of 7 per cent, or less, as fans. This corresponds, for atmospheric air, to a compression ratio of about 1.10. Fans are used for low inlet pressures (atmospheric or lower) therefore a very light casing construction is generally adopted to hold the low discharge pressure. Thus the mechanical features—welded steel plate construction, and simplified hydraulic forms—are the outstanding characteristics of fans as distinguished from blowers of the same compression ratio. In small sizes the two classes of turbomachines definitely overlap, particularly in the range of low specific speeds.

Capacities of fans vary from a few hundred c.f.m. to over 100,000 c.f.m. and cover a range of specific speeds of 150 to 5000 (based on static heads in feet of fluid). Figure 12.1 shows efficiencies, based on static heads, attained within the above range. A variation in efficiency from 15 to 30 points for a given specific speed results from the use of various mechanical and hydraulic means to produce the desired performance in small and low cost machines.

In discussing the theory and design it is convenient to divide fans into three groups: (a) centrifugal fans, (b) multivane squirrel cage or Sirocco type fans, and (c) axial flow fans. The last group is discussed in Chapter 13.

12.1 CENTRIFUGAL FANS

These cover a range of specific speeds up to 2000 in Fig. 12.1. In centrifugal fans power is applied to the fluid and pressure is produced in the same manner as in centrifugal blowers and compressors; thus the same theory applies. The difference in performance between the two classes of machines using the same design elements appears, in

228

the case of fans, as lower efficiency, a lower head coefficient ψ and lower capacity coefficient ϕ. This impairment of performance in fans is the result of sacrificing the minimum requirements for good hydraulic guidance and handling of the fluid for simplicity of manufacture, small size, and low cost. Except in smaller sizes the design is intended for fabricated steel plate construction. In smaller sizes the cost of patterns and volume of business justify cast impellers and casings in which case the fans may be classed as blowers.

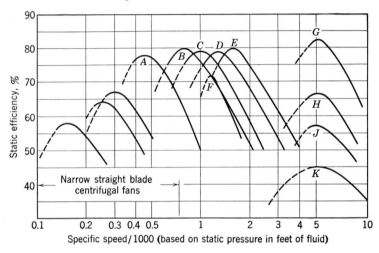

Fig. 12.1.   Fan efficiencies for different specific speeds (data by Buffalo Forge Co.)

A	high-pressure compressor
B, C, D, E	backward curved vane fans
F	forward curved vane fans
G	streamlined vane-axial fans
H	commercial vane-axial fans
J	commercial tube-axial fans
K	propeller fans

Figure 12.2 shows four types of impellers representing centrifugal impellers of high specific speed (1500–2000). The figure also shows their performance in suitable casings. The optimum efficiency for this hydraulic type (centrifugal pumps) is over 90 per cent when use is made of best hydraulic elements such as mixed flow impeller vanes and cast volute casings. This efficiency has been approached in fans of modern design by using cast impellers, similar to those used in centrifugal pumps, in normal welded steel fan casings (reference 2).

Factors that adversely affect the hydraulic performance of centrifugal fans, fall into four groups:

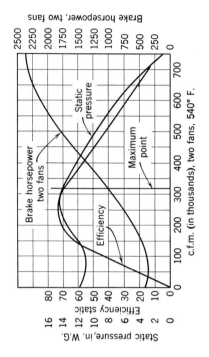

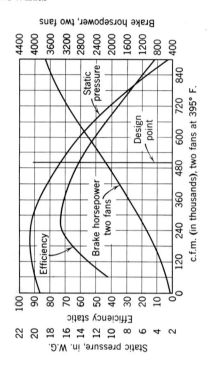

Fig. 12.2. Four types of impellers and their performance; specific speed, about 1500 (American Blower Corporation).

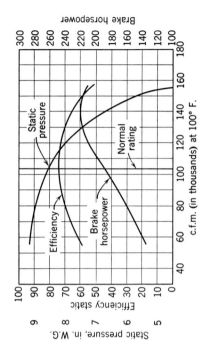

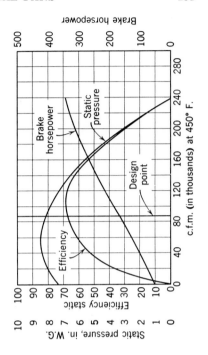

Fig. 12.2. (Continued.)

1. Use of high impeller discharge vane angles (up to 90°). It has been shown in Chapter 5 that backward curved vanes having a vane angle β_2 in the range of 25 to 30° should be used for optimum efficiency. The difference in efficiency between impellers with 90° vane angle and those with 25° vane angle is estimated to be at least 5 points.

An entrance angle of 90° also impairs efficiency because the gas has to acquire prerotation in the direction of rotation to enter the impeller channel as is shown on the velocity triangle, Fig. 12.3. If the fluid is to enter the vanes without shock, the tangential component c_{u1} should be equal to the peripheral velocity u_1. The head produced is reduced by the prerotation effect by $u_1{}^2/g$. Although this value of

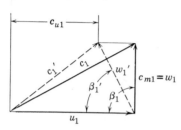

prerotation is never reached, the head generated and through-flow capacity is appreciably reduced by the use of a 90° entrance angle. Thus a bigger machine is required to produce the same head-capacity requirement. It has been shown experimentally (reference 3) that use of an inlet angle of 90° (straight radial vanes) causes a reduction of efficiency of about 10 points, as compared with the entrance angle as determined by the entrance velocity triangle.

Fig. 12.3. Inlet velocity triangle for $\beta_1 = 90°$.

2. Impeller profiles, as adopted for fan design, were established for simplified production by welding of simple steel plate parts. Such designs usually do not provide the best possible approach to the impeller entrance, and there is little or no guidance inside the impeller to turn the flow 90°. Minor improvements of the impeller profile, such as the use of conical hubs and outer shrouds, never fail to produce an improvement in efficiency.

3. In order to keep the fan casing as small as possible, only volute casings are used; neither vaneless nor vaned diffusers are ever employed. Again, to reduce the over-all size of the unit the base circle of the volute is reduced to a minimum. Reduction of the clearance between the impeller and the volute tongue below the optimum established for centrifugal volute pumps and blowers has an adverse effect on the efficiency because the flow discharged by the impeller enters the active volute area before its velocity distribution is equalized.

Also, there is no attempt to recover any pressure from the velocity energy of the volute, as normally an efficient expanding nozzle is not used between the volute outlet and discharge flange. Furthermore, the discharge opening of the casing is made considerably larger than the volute throat area thus allowing a sudden drop in velocity from the impeller to the volute discharge opening. Figure 12.4 shows diagrams comparing a normal volute having a minimum discharge nozzle with an abbreviated volute as built for fans when size is the controlling consideration. In the normal volute, the volute area increases progressively in proportion to the angular displacement from the zero point (cut-off point or tongue) along the full circumference of the impeller. In the abbreviated volute about one quarter of the impeller periphery discharges directly into the discharge opening without establishing normal volute pressure and velocity distribution prevailing in the controlled volute sections. Note that the average volute

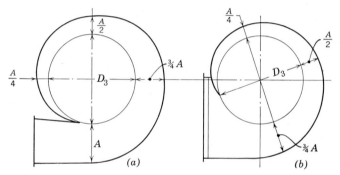

Fig. 12.4. Normal volute (a) and abbreviated volute (b).

velocity may be only one-half of the absolute velocity at impeller discharge.

Failure to provide a complete volute and efficient velocity conversion at the discharge can be responsible for a loss of efficiency of from 5 to 15 points, depending upon the specific speed and degree of deviation from the normal volute design. For a square or rectangular discharge opening the volute sections are made rectangular, trapezoidal, or a combination of the two. Combination shapes are used for low specific speed impellers, which require a narrow volute at the base circle. Although rectangular volute sections are inferior to those having circular or pear-shaped forms used in centrifugal blowers and pumps, actual tests have shown that the efficiency of fabricated volutes is within one point of that of the best cast iron volute with circular or pear-shaped sections.

4. For low pressure and large volume fans (high specific speed) the leakage loss between the rotating impeller and stationary casing is negligible. For that reason no effective means are provided to reduce this loss. For low specific speed fans the leakage loss expressed

in per cent of power input rapidly increases as the specific speed is decreased and may be responsible for a reduction in efficiency of several points.

12.2 FAN DESIGN CONSTANTS

The fan design procedure is identical with that for blowers and compressors. The leading impeller and volute dimensions are established based on the performance at the best efficiency point. Due to the deviation of hydraulic forms from those established for blowers of optimum design the head and capacity coefficients shown in Fig. 6.10

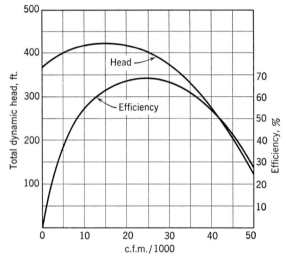

Fig. 12.5.   Performance of double-inlet impeller Fig. 12.6. 900 r.p.m. $\psi = 0.576$; $\phi = 0.303$; $n_s = 1590$.

are not realized with fans. Furthermore, for several types of fan construction in use, the design data of Fig. 6.10 cannot be corrected or made applicable by the use of a single coefficient. Using the same considerations and methods employed in the preparation of Fig. 6.10, it is possible to establish the design constants (ψ and ϕ) for a continuous line of fans of one particular design if test data are available for one type (specific speed) using a certain value of the impeller discharge angle. To arrive at head and capacity coefficients for another type, using different impeller discharge angles, the following method is suggested. The procedure was developed, and proved satisfactory, for small sizes of centrifugal pumps of simplified design having performance considerably below the optimum for which Fig. 6.10 is applicable.

Figure 12.5 shows the performance of a fan with a double-inlet impeller as in Fig. 12.6 (reference 4). Pressure coefficient $\psi = 0.576$; capacity coefficient $\phi = 0.303$. These values are considerably below those shown in Fig. 6.10 for the optimum design. To draw a new chart of ψ and ϕ similar to Fig. 6.10 and applicable to a line of fans similar to Fig. 12.6, draw the net work on ψ and ϕ scales and dimensionless specific speed ω_s in the same manner as on Fig. 6.10 (Fig. 12.7). Locate point E for which the test and design data are available. Draw a straight line through E parallel to the β_2 line on the Fig. 6.10 which is parallel to the ϕ axis in this particular example for $\beta_2 = 90°$. Use point C_1 of the intersection of the line through E and ψ axis to draw the

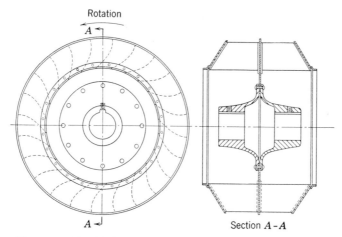

Fig. 12.6. Double-inlet, 38-in. impeller $b_2 = 24$ in.; $\beta_2 = 90°$.

rest of β_2 lines through C_1 and parallel to the corresponding lines in Fig. 6.10. The slope of these lines is given by the relationship

$$\tan \delta = CO/\tan \beta_2 = 0.691/\tan \beta_2 \qquad (12.1)$$

This completes the chart, which has all the properties of Fig. 6.10 but is less accurate.

When the test values of the head coefficient ψ and capacity coefficient ϕ are available for one particular design the values of ψ and ϕ for the same impeller discharge angle β_2 can be estimated with the help of Fig. 6.12 for a different specific speed by drawing a line through the test point following the direction of the two adjacent curves on the chart. The new values of ψ and ϕ are read off from this line for the required specific speed. To determine the values of ψ and ϕ for the same specific speed but different impeller discharge angle, the chart values for the new β_2 should be reduced in the same ratio as the test values of ψ and ϕ bear to the chart values for the test impeller. To obtain ψ and ϕ when both β_2 and n_s are different, both above steps are applied simultaneously.

The reduction of the pressure coefficient, as compared with the optimum values, signifies increased hydraulic losses due to lack of

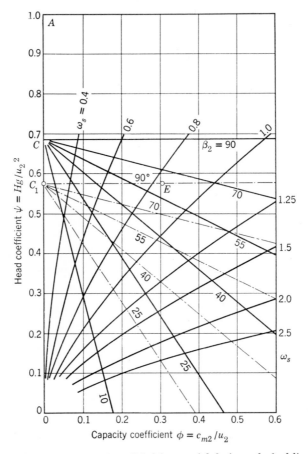

Fig. 12.7.   Figure 6.10 modified for special designs, dashed line.

streamlining of the flow passages through the fan.   At the same time, low capacity coefficients mean that the impeller passages are not fully utilized owing to sharp turns of the passages.

It should be pointed out that centrifugal fans have been built, which produce a head coefficient ψ equal to that given by Fig. 6.10 or even exceeding it, although efficiency is considerably below the optimum possible for the same specific speed.   This usually takes place when the volute tongue is located close to the impeller outside diameter. This results in impulse action by the vanes in the same manner as in multivane type fans, discussed in the next article. The method of selection of the ψ and ϕ values described above is applicable to this type of design also.

12.3 FORWARD CURVED MULTIVANE IMPELLERS OF IMPULSE TYPE

These are also known as "squirrel cage" or "Sirocco" type fans and represent a class by themselves as they do not fit into a general continuous row of mechanical and hydraulic design of gas turbo-pumping machinery. The impeller of this type of fan has a multitude of cupshaped cylindrical vanes arranged to produce a maximum "impulse" effect on the fluid. Although the dynamics of the vane action is very

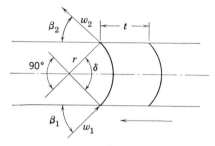

Fig. 12.8.   Sirocco blade elements.

similar to that of the Pelton water wheel reversed, the effect and efficiency of such impellers is low, as there is no way to convert efficiently the resulting absolute velocity into pressure.

(*a*) **Head Produced.** The head produced by the impulse type of impeller is considerably in excess of that possible with normal centrifugal impellers with an impeller vane angle not exceeding 90°. Values of $\psi = 1.2$ at best efficiency point have been attained with this type

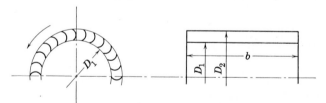

Fig. 12.9.   Impulse impeller.

of impeller. The average values of ψ for smaller units are about $\psi = 1.10$, based on the total head. Considerations of the velocity relations at the best efficiency point indicate that they are the same as established for Pelton water wheels, thus suggesting that the impulse action is the primary means of producing head.

The mechanical and hydraulic design elements of impulse wheels are well established within narrow limits. By referring to Figs. 12.8 and 12.9 the vane is usually made as a circular arc with an included angle $\delta = 90°$, In general

$$\delta = 180 - (\beta_1 + \beta_2) \tag{12.2}$$

With very thin vanes and parallel side walls (shrouds) continuity gives

$$\pi D_1 b_1 w_1 \sin \beta_1 = \pi D_2 b_2 w_2 \sin \beta_2 \tag{12.3}$$

Since $b_2 = b_1 = b$ and $w_1 = w_2$

$$D_1/D_2 = \sin \beta_2/\sin \beta_1 \tag{12.4}$$

for $\beta_1 + \beta_2 = 90°$,

$$D_1/D_2 = \tan \beta_2 \quad \text{and} \quad D_2/D_1 = \tan \beta_1$$

The value of D_1/D_2 varies from 0.8 to 0.95, 0.875 being used most frequently. For $D_1/D_2 = 0.875$ the value of $\beta_2 = 41°$ approximately and $\beta_1 = 49°$. Note that according to the notation adopted in Chapters 3 and 4 this corresponds to $\beta_2 = 139°$ for a forward curved vane.

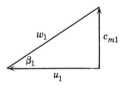

From the inlet velocity triangle, Fig. 12.10, we see that

Fig. 12.10. Entrance velocity triangle.

$$c_{m1} = u_1 \tan \beta_1 = u_1(D_2/D_1) = u_2 \tag{12.5}$$

A consideration of velocities on the theoretical discharge velocity triangle (Euler's), Fig. 12.11, yields

$$c_{u2} = u_2 + c_{m2} \tan \beta_1$$

but

$$c_{m2} = c_{m1}/\tan \beta_1 \quad \text{and} \quad c_{m1} = u_2$$

$$c_{u2} = 2u_2 \tag{12.6}$$

Thus the absolute velocity leaving vane (theoretical) is twice the peripheral velocity of the impeller at discharge. These are the conditions for the maximum output of an impulse water turbine, i.e., the peripheral velocity of the wheel is one-half the velocity of the jet.

From equation 12.6 we obtain

$$\psi_e = c_{u2}/u_2 = 2.0 \tag{12.7}$$

The ratio of the actual to the Euler's head coefficient gives:

$$\frac{\psi}{\psi_e} = 1.20/2.00 = 0.60 \tag{12.8}$$

which is considerably lower than that for centrifugal blowers (0.691, as it appears on Fig. 6.10) and, no doubt, is due to a bad velocity conversion by the casing.

(b) **Number of Vanes.** If t is the linear vane spacing, the number of vanes z is equal to

$$z = \pi D_2/t \qquad (12.9)$$

t is taken as 0.7 to 1.0r, where r is the vane radius, equal to

$$r = (D_2 - D_1)/2 \sqrt{2} \qquad (12.10)$$

The number of vanes varies from twenty-four for small sizes to sixty-four for 30-in. impeller diameter or larger.

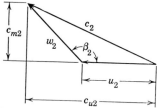

Fig. 12.11.   Discharge velocity triangle.

(c) **Capacity and Specific Speed.** Capacity of the impulse wheel is varied by changing the wheel width b. The normal capacity is determined by the size of the impeller eye diameter. For continuity, the area at the entrance to the vanes $\pi D_1 b$ should be equal to that of the impeller eye, which gives $b = D_1/4$. An increase of the impeller width beyond this value will increase the capacity but not in proportion to the impeller width. It may also reduce the efficiency.

The average specific speed of impulse fans, based on the static head in feet of fluid and capacity in c.f.m., is around $n_s = 1175$ for single inlet units. Efficiencies attained, based on static head, are slightly over 70 per cent under favorable conditions. Impulse fans are built in sizes of 3 to 132 in. impeller diameter. They are less popular in Europe than they are in this country, on account of the higher evaluation of efficiency. One of the drawbacks of the impulse type of fans is their narrow range of operation. On both sides of the best efficiency point the fan becomes noisy. Besides, at higher pressures the pumping limit is reached soon, whereas at low heads the driver may become overloaded, as the b.hp. curve is sharply rising with increasing capacity.

12.4 EXAMPLES

(a) **Impeller Proportions.** Table 1, compiled from data by Bruno Eck (reference 1), gives performance and the leading proportions of the impeller of several fans. The lack of continuity of the design elements is most apparent when compared with modern blowers and particularly centrifugal pumps covering the same range of specific speeds. When performance is approaching the optimum the design elements of centrifugal pumps of different makes, domestic or foreign, display a definite regularity when arranged on the basis of specific speed.

Figure 6.10 is one of the methods of correlating the design data. On the other hand, when designs are impaired by mechanical simplifications at the expense of hydraulic performance, there is no continuity in deviations from the optimum design. To state it differently: although all good designs are very much alike, there is a variety of ways to obtain a given head-capacity when efficiency is disregarded. It is believed that when an optimum design is known it is possible to improve the hydraulic performance of the majority of fans with little or no mechanical complications or increase in cost.

TABLE 1.   PERFORMANCE AND DESIGN OF SEVERAL FANS
Data by Eck (reference 1)

	n_s	ϕ	ψ	e, %	$\beta_2°$	$\beta_1°$	D_1/D_2	b_2/D_2	b_1/D_2	u_2 f.p.s.	D_2 in.	hp	z
1	820	0.387	0.44	54	90		0.68	0.40	0.40	213		13	8
2	905	.398	.375	50	90		.86	.37	.44			100	40
3	420	.197	.600	70	90	90	.57	.33	.33	147		1.0	10
4	700	.550	.485	60	90	90	.56	.24	.57	137			8
5	330	.457	.600	72	34		.42	.09	.17	410		50	20
6	465	.224	.502	57	40	30	.56	.27	.27	262		5	16
7	385	.433	.600	78	32		.50	.13	.28	432		280	32
8	318	.327	.575	59	90	90	.24	.13	.13		5.40		8
9	445	.440	.327	63	48	35	.35	.07	.15		5.12		12
10	295	.275	.530	50	90	90	.35	.10	.10		9.60		6

(*b*) **Controls.** In the application of fans to processes where the head-capacity requirements vary, several methods of control are in use. They are essentially the same as those used on the large blower installations discussed in Chapter 15. Power plant forced draft installations are the most prominent examples where variation of the rate of flow of air is important for the over-all control of the plant. The power saving at the partial rates of flow is an appreciable item in the economy of the plant. The choice of controls depends on the size of the plant and cost of equipment, as compared with benefits derived from more elaborate controls.

1. With constant speed drive, throttling the discharge is the most common way to vary the capacity. The power requirements follow the constant speed b.hp. curve. Power waste is essentially proportional to the head destroyed by the throttling. Figure 12.12 shows an illustration of the double-inlet forced draft fan equipped with streamlined sectional dampers on the discharge. The power variation is given on Fig. 12.13, curve 1.

2. Inlet guide vanes, shown on Fig. 12.14 for a forced draft fan, work as a throttle, and power saving is derived from the reduction of the air density. This is the simplest effective means of control; the

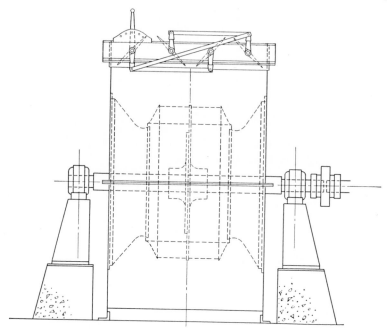

Fig. 12.12. Head-capacity control with damper on discharge (American Blower).

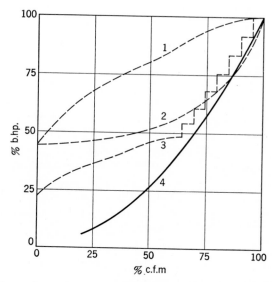

Fig. 12.13. Power demand with several means of control for forced draft installation (American Blower).

power saving can be seen by comparing curves 1 and 2, Fig. 12.13, for constant speed drive.

3. Variable speed steam turbine drive for a forced draft fan is by far the most economical means of volume control and is also favored from the point of view of heat balance in industrial power plants. Slip ring a.-c. motor control operates by steps and requires damper regulation between the steps. Speed reduction to about 60 per cent of rated can be realized with slip ring motors, requiring damper throttling below 60 per cent capacity. Curve 3 on Fig. 12.13 shows the relative power demand for this case.

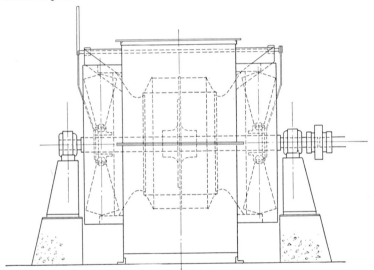

Fig. 12.14. Output control with inlet guide vanes (American Blower).

4. Curve 4, Fig. 12.13 shows the power variation for constant speed drive through a hydraulic coupling. Minimum speed of 20 per cent of rated is possible with this method of drive, requiring no dampers on discharge.

Any of the above controls can be arranged for manual or full automatic control.

REFERENCES

1. Madison, *Fan Engineering*, Buffalo Forge Co., 1949.
2. Bruno Eck, *Ventilatoren*, Springer, Berlin, 1952, p. 93.
3. Bruno Eckert, *Ladeeinrichtungen für Verbrennungsmotoren*, Franckh'sche Verlag, Stuttgart, Germany, p. 27.
4. Marks, Lomax, and Ashton, "Influence of Bends in Inlet Ducts on the Performance of Induced Draft Fans," *A.S.M.E. Trans.*, Sept., 1933, p. 133.
5. Madison, *Fiat Final Report* 489, 1945, *Survey of Fans and Turbo-blowers*, Field Information Agency, U. S. Govt. in Germany.

CHAPTER 13

Axial Flow Fans and
Compressors, Single Stage

INTRODUCTION

Although the theoretical treatment of axial flow fans and compressors has much in common, the field of application and the forms necessary to meet the hydraulic requirements of each are so different that it is convenient to discuss these two groups of axial flow machines separately.

As a class, axial flow fans include high capacity, low head, single-stage machines covering the extreme range of the high specific speed field shown in Fig. 12.1. In small sizes, motor driven axial fans are sometimes built in two stages owing to speed limitations but are classed essentially as low head machines.

Axial compressors are high pressure multistage machines specially developed for use in connection with gas turbines. In contrast with axial flow fans, they are operated at a maximum speed to reduce the number of stages. Usually the mechanical strength of the impeller and critical Mach number determine the speed. In the general field of specific speeds the axial flow compressor competes with the centrifugal compressor. The advantages of the axial flow compressor are: small space and frontal projected area (important for aircraft application), high speed (permitting direct coupling to the gas turbine,) and high efficiency. Its main disadvantage is a small operating range.

13.1 TERMINOLOGY AND GEOMETRY OF THE AXIAL FLOW IMPELLER VANES

(a) **Vane Cascades.** To discuss the action of the impeller vanes in an axial flow fan or compressor it is convenient to represent vanes on the development of several cylindrical sections. Three such developments are of particular interest: at the outside impeller diameter D_o; at the impeller hub D_h and at the mean effective diameter D_m. It will be recalled that the mean effective diameter is defined by equation 5.19 as

$$D_m = \left[\frac{D_o{}^2 + D_h{}^2}{2} \right]^{1/2} \qquad (13.1)$$

This can be given a different form for axial flow machines:

$$D_m = \left[\frac{D_o{}^2}{2} (1 + \nu^2) \right]^{1/2} \qquad (13.2)$$

where $\nu = D_h/D_o$ is the hub ratio, an important design element for axial flow machines. On the cylindrical development, vanes appear equally spaced at a distance $t = \pi D/z$, sometimes referred to as "pitch," where z is the number of vanes and D is the diameter of the cylindrical section. The ratio of the vane chord length to the vane

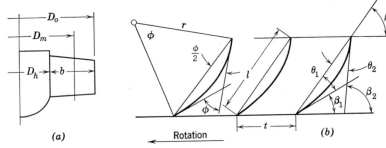

(a)   Rotation   (b)

Fig. 13.1. Cascade notation.

spacing (l/t) is an important design element, being an index of the "vane solidity." Vane solidity is a descriptive term relating the vane area (actual or projected) to the area of the annulus normal to the flow. The chord-spacing ratio generally increases from the vane tip to the hub (Fig. 13.1).

To effectively exert any driving action on the fluid, the vane angle is gradually increased from β_1 to β_2. The difference between the two, $\beta_2 - \beta_1$, is a measure of the vane curvature along any particular vane section. From the geometry of Fig. 13.1, the following relationships between the several angles can be written

(a) Vane curvature

$$\beta_2 - \beta_1 = \phi = \theta_1 + \theta_2 \qquad (13.3)$$

(b) Chord angle

$$\beta_c = \beta_1 + \theta_1 \qquad (13.4)$$

$$\beta_c = \beta_2 - \theta_2$$

(c) Circular arc vane

$$\theta_1 = \theta_2 = \theta = \phi/2 \qquad (13.5)$$

$$\beta_2 - \beta_1 = \phi = \text{Central angle}$$

$$l = 2r \sin \theta$$

(b) **Airfoils.** In view of the very low head produced by an axial flow impeller, the skin friction loss, or what is known as drag, acquires a greater importance than in centrifugal or mixed flow impellers. For that reason a high degree of impeller vane streamlining and polishing is required to obtain the optimum peak efficiency. To satisfy this requirement and that of mechanical strength the impeller vane profiles take the form of airfoils. Although developed primarily for the airplane supporting wing application, airfoils have found wide use in the field of axial flow turbomachines and therefore familiarity with the properties of airfoils is essential.

A great many airfoil sections have been tested in several countries for the last 30 years in order to determine the profile which, when applied to airplane wing design, will support a maximum load with a

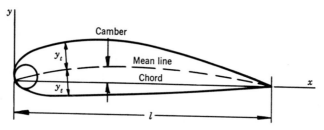

Fig. 13.2.   Airfoil nomenclature.

minimum expenditure of power. In *N.A.C.A. Report* 460 (reference 1) all useful airfoil sections have been classified according to their curvature and thickness. For this purpose airfoils are considered as made up of a certain profile thickness form disposed about certain mean lines (Fig. 13.2). The form of the mean line determines completely most of the important hydraulic properties of airfoils, whereas thickness is dictated by the strength requirements. All good airfoils have nearly the same thickness variation along the mean line, the maximum thickness being different for different profiles. The maximum distance from the chord to the mean line is called "camber" and is usually expressed in per cent of the chord length or c/l, Fig. 13.2.

Each N.A.C.A. profile is assigned a four-digit number such as 4312. The first number indicates the camber of the mean line; the second, the location of the camber from the leading edge in tenths of the chord length. The last two digits show the maximum vane thickness in per cent of the chord.

The angle of attack is the acute angle (α, Fig. 13.3) between the vane chord and the direction of the relative velocity of the flow. The aspect ratio is the ratio of the length of the airfoil to the length of the chord. All N.A.C.A. sections were tested with an aspect ratio 6:1, but results were also recalculated for an infinite aspect ratio. Since, in a turbomachine, fluid is confined between the hub and casing side walls and is not free to escape radially, use of the airfoil data for infinite aspect ratio is justified.

(c) **Lift and Drag : Gliding Angle.** If an airfoil is exposed to an air flow, the forces acting upon it can be resolved into two components: component L, normal to the direction of the approaching undisturbed flow which is called the lift, and component D, in the direction of the air flow which is called the resistance or drag (Fig. 13.3). The magni-

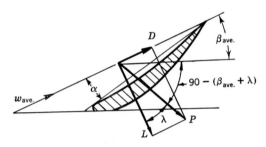

Fig. 13.3. Forces acting on an airfoil.

tude of these forces can be represented by the following formulas:

$$L = C_L bl\rho \frac{w_{ave}^2}{2} \tag{13.6}$$

and

$$D = C_D bl\rho \frac{w_{ave}^2}{2} \tag{13.7}$$

where C_L and C_D are experimental coefficients of lift and drag.

b is the width of the airfoil.

l is the length of the chord of the airfoil.

w_{ave} is the undisturbed relative air velocity.

ρ is the density of the fluid.

Both C_L and C_D depend upon the profile of the airfoil, the angle of attack α, and the aspect ratio. Their values have been experimentally determined for a great number of profiles. C_D is very small in comparison with C_L. The ratio C_D/C_L defines λ which is called the gliding angle. At this angle an airplane can perform a steady gliding flight. The drag force D includes (1) the skin friction, which depends greatly on the smoothness of the surface, and (2) losses due to eddies in the wake behind the wing. This part of the drag is greater for thick profiles. A well-rounded nose and a sharp tail edge reduces this part of the drag.

Figure 13.4 shows performance of airfoils 4306 and 4312 replotted from *N.A.C.A. Report* 460 to show the effect of the thickness upon the lift and drag coefficient C_L and C_D respectively. For the useful range, C_L is identical for both airfoils. The ratio L/D serves as an index of the airfoil efficiency. This is better for the thin airfoil. The maximum value of the lift coefficient C_L is obtained with 12 per cent airfoil thickness. Airfoils 4315, 4318, and 4321 have a lower maximum lift.

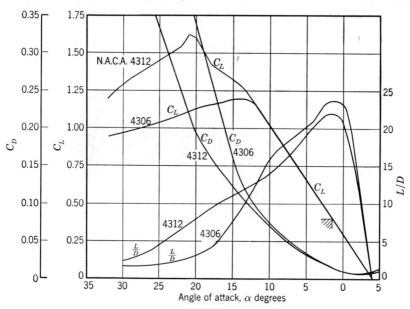

Fig. 13.4. Effect of vane thickness on airfoil performance (*N.A.C.A. Report* 460).

For this plot the scale for the angle of attack α was deliberately reversed from that of *N.A.C.A. Report* 460 to show the resemblance of curve C_L versus α to the ordinary head-capacity curve of an axial flow fan; C_L standing for head; the angle of attack α, for capacity; and the ratio L/D representing efficiency.

Figure 13.5, plotted in the same manner, shows the effect of the vane camber. Higher lifts at a lower angle of attack are obtained with 6 per cent camber than with 2 per cent camber at the optimum L/D ratio, but the airfoil with 2 per cent camber is the more efficient of the two.

(*d*) **Airfoil Profiles, Munk Method.** Munk (reference 2) has shown that the mean camber lines of the N.A.C.A. four-digit airfoil

profiles and their aerodynamic properties are completely defined by
two tangents with their points of contact to the leading and trailing
ends of the mean line (AC and BC in Fig. 13.6). This follows from the
properties of parabolic curves comprising the mean camber lines of
this family of airfoils. Tangents AC and BC may be given by specifying angles θ_1 and θ_2 between the chord and the tangents. Additional tangents can be drawn by dividing the tangents AC and BC
into a number of equal parts and joining the corresponding points
(1, 2, 3, and 4). The point C of the intersection of the two tangents

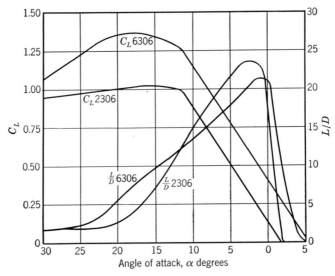

Fig. 13.5.   Effect of vane camber (curvature) on airfoil performance (*N.A.C.A.*
Report 460).

determines the location of the maximum camber station, and the value
of the camber ED is equal to one half of the distance EC. It is evident
that Munk's geometrical method of drawing the mean camber line
of airfoils parallels the author's procedure of drawing axial flow impeller
sections based on the inlet and discharge angles β_1 and β_2 established
from Euler's velocity triangles. From Fig. 13.6 the following relationships between angles β_1, β_2, θ_1, and θ_2 are evident.

$$\beta_2 - \beta_1 = \theta_2 + \theta_1 \tag{13.3}$$

The vane curvature $(\beta_2 - \beta_1)$ can be expressed in terms of camber and
its location. From Fig. 13.6, $\tan \theta_1 = 2ED/AE = 2c/l_c$ and $\tan \theta_2$
$= 2ED/EB = 2c(l - l_c)$ where c is the camber and l_c is its location

relative to the leading edge, both expressed as fractions of the airfoil chord length. Since angles θ_1 and θ_2 are usually small, the values of the angles in radians are approximately equal to their tangents. Then the vane curvature becomes

$$\beta_2 - \beta_1 = \frac{2c}{l_c} + \frac{2c}{l - l_c} = \frac{2c}{l_c(l - l_c)} \tag{13.8}$$

Equation 13.8 shows that the vane curvature $(\beta_2 - \beta_1)$ establishes the hydrodynamic properties of the airfoil just as completely as the camber and its location in the N.A.C.A. classification.

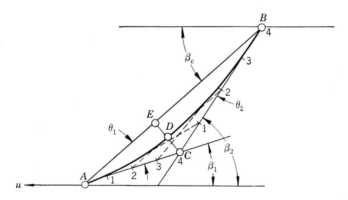

Fig. 13.6. Airfoil characteristics in terms of curvature $\beta_2 - \beta_1 = \theta_2 + \theta_1$.

13.2 EXPERIMENTAL DESIGN FACTORS

There are a number of design elements of axial flow fans and blowers which do not enter into the theoretical discussion, although they affect directly the performance of the axial impeller. These include (1) hub ratio, (2) number of vanes, (3) vane thickness, (4) turning of vanes on the hub as it occurs in adjustable vane impellers, and (5) fan casing, with or without diffusion vanes. Selection of any of these design elements depends upon experience. Correlation of test information, on the basis of specific speed, shows a definite pattern consistent with that of lower specific speed centrifugal and mixed flow blowers. As more test data are accumulated it depends upon the skill of the designer to discern the effects of these several variables, leading to the optimum hydraulic performance.

A blower or fan designer should avail himself of the test data and design information available on axial and propeller pumps, as these are directly applicable to blowers and fans. Examples from axial flow pumps will be quoted below when similar information is not available on fans.

(a) **Impeller Hub Ratio.** The ratio of the impeller hub diameter (D_h) to the impeller outside diameter (D_o) is directly connected with the specific speed. Higher specific speed fans have smaller hubs. This provides a greater free area for the flow and a smaller mean effective diameter thus leading to a greater capacity and a lower head.

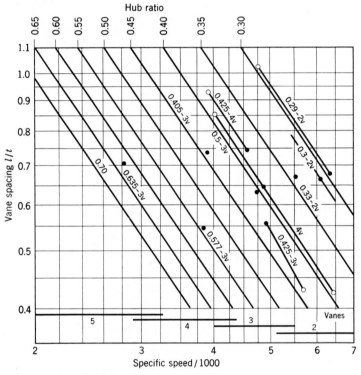

Fig. 13.7. Hub ratio, number of vanes, and l/t ratio for axial flow fans.

Selection of the impeller hub ratio fixes the radial height of the impeller vanes b Fig. 13.1. This radial height is usually stated as the ratio b to the impeller outside diameter or b/D_o. Different b/D_o ratios correspond to definite hub ratios:

b/D_o	$\frac{1}{3}$	$\frac{1}{4}$	$\frac{1}{6}$	$\frac{1}{7}$	$\frac{1}{8}$	$\frac{1}{9}$	$\frac{1}{10}$
D_h/D_o	$\frac{1}{3}$	0.5	0.667	0.715	0.75	0.778	0.80

By referring to equation 5.27 it will be noticed that b_2 becomes

$$b_2 = (D_o - D_h)/2 = b$$

Using this value of b and D_m from equation 13.2 the relationship between the performance specific speed n_s and the dimensionless specific speed ω_s, equation 5.27, becomes

$$n_s = 2495[(1 - \nu^2)/(1 + \nu^2)]^{\frac{1}{2}}\omega_s \qquad (13.9)$$

where $\nu = D_h/D_o$ is the hub ratio.

This shows that after the hub ratio is selected, ω_s can be calculated and Fig. 6.10 may be entered to select the design constants for any desired values of the impeller discharge angle β_2. Figure 13.7 repre-

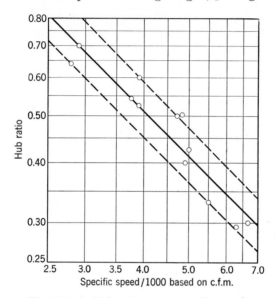

Fig. 13.7a. Hub ratio versus specific speed.

sents a compilation of test points covering a wide range of hub ratios and obtained with impellers having different numbers of vanes and chord-spacing ratio. When there are two points referring to the same impeller the dark point represents the more efficient arrangement of the two. Fig. 13.7a shows the common values of the hub ratio as a function of specific speed only.

Figure 13.8 shows the ψ - ϕ characteristics of three fans having the same number of impeller vanes (seven) and approximately the same vane setting (20 to 23° at outside diameter). The best efficiency points based on the total head are marked A, B, and C. The hub ratios, efficiency and specific speeds in terms of c.f.m. and head in feet are tabulated below. The formula connecting the dimensionless coefficients ψ and ϕ with the performance specific speed is given by equation 13.9. It will be noticed that the best efficiency points A, B, and C fall very well on the chart in Fig. 6.10.

PERFORMANCE DATA FOR FIGURE 13.8

Best efficiency points	A	B	C
Hub ratio	0.702	0.573	0.426
Total efficiency per cent	84	85	82
Vane setting degrees at outside diameter	20	21	23
Specific speed n_s	1900	3000	5400
Dimensionless specific speed ω_s	1.133	1.70	2.46

It should be pointed out that the hub ratio depends also upon the selection of the capacity coefficient ϕ which in turn depends upon the

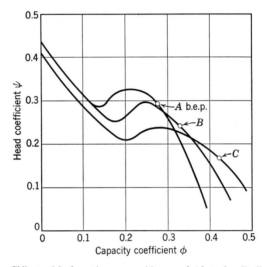

Fig. 13.8. Effect of hub ratio on specific speed (data by Buffalo Forge).

impeller discharge angle and specific speed ω_s (Fig. 6.10). This is because the continuity equation

$$\text{c.f.m.}/60 = c_m \pi D_o^2 (1 - \nu^2)/4 \qquad (13.10)$$

has to be satisfied. Thus the impeller design involves adjustment of several variables to agree with the above requirements.

(b) **Chord-Spacing Ratio.** The cord-spacing ratio l/t is another important design element which is selected on the basis of previous experience. Equation 6.15 below gives the value of l/t in terms of the head coefficient ψ, which in turn depends upon specific speed,

$$l/t = 4.75\psi \qquad (6.15)$$

The numerical coefficient was established from available test data on axial fans and pumps. For axial fans l/t is less than unity. For impellers cast in one piece, non-overlapping vanes are desirable as they only require a simple molding procedure without core work. The ratio l/t varies along the radius, increasing toward the hub. This increase is also necessary for mechanical strength. The value of l/t at the hub may be 1.25 to 1.30 times that at the outside diameter of the impeller, depending on the hub ratio. The same values of l/t can be realized with different number of vanes. Figure 13.7 shows a number of experimental points for different hub ratios, l/t values, the number of vanes all plotted against specific speed as abscissa.

(c) **Number of Vanes.** Kaplan (reference 3) who is the originator of the axial flow hydraulic turbine with adjustable vanes, has found experimentally that for a given wetted area of the vane (l/t) the number of vanes should be a minimum. This was also confirmed by Schmidt's tests (reference 4) with a 12-in. fan of constant projected vane area of 63 per cent and which disclosed the tabulated efficiencies.

Vane number	6	5	4	3	2
Efficiency, per cent	68.0	70.3	72.5	75.0	79.0

These figures should be considered as exaggerated because Schmidt's impeller vane was of constant thickness with tapered ends. With modern airfoil vanes and high degree of streamlining and polish the effect of the number of vanes is less pronounced.

Reduction of the number of vanes leads to a longer and heavier impeller hub which is objectionable with an overhung impeller mounting.

For single-stage fans and blowers, the following formula for the number of vanes has been suggested (reference 9).

$$z = 6\nu/(1 - \nu) \tag{13.11}$$

This gives the tabulated numbers for different hub ratios.

Hub ratio	0.3	0.4	0.5	0.6	0.7	0.8
Number of vanes	3	4	6	9	14	24

By substituting for the hub ratio ν its value D_h/D_o, equation (13.11) becomes

$$z = 6\,\frac{D_h}{D_o - D_h} = 3\,\frac{D_h}{b} \tag{13.11a}$$

This shows that the number of vanes is proportional to the hub diameter and is inversely proportional to the vane height (which is not devoid of some logic).

Figure 13.9 shows a test of an axial flow pump with identical vanes numbered from 2 to 5. Note that capacities at normal and zero head are the same for several impellers indicating that the capacity constant $\phi = c_m/u$ does not depend on the number of vanes or the ratio l/t. The normal head and head at zero flow increase for a higher number of vanes or higher value of l/t. With heavy vanes and a low chord angle (low β_2 too) the maximum number of vanes is almost fixed, since adding vanes restricts the free area of the flow. As a result the normal capacity and efficiency drop. Thus, in one example, good performance was obtained with three and four vanes only. With two vanes the l/t ratio was too low for good efficiency (reduction of two to three

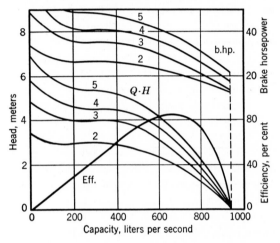

Fig. 13.9.   Effect of number of vanes on performance (Schlimbach).

points) and with five vanes the output was less than with four vanes and at a lower efficiency.

Figure 13.10 shows the effect of the ratio l/t with three impellers having four vanes each and l/t ratios of 0.4, 0.6, and 0.8. The curves are very similar to those in Fig. 13.9. Figure 13.11 shows the efficiency variation for different values of l/t (projected area), the same number of vanes (two), and the same vane inlet and outlet angle (the same vane curvature or camber). It is expected that the optimum value of the l/t would be different for a different vane curvature and vane loading (speed).

(*d*) **Vane Curvature and Vane Setting.**   Figure 13.12 shows the performance of a four-vane impeller with different vane settings, i.e., the vane curvature $\beta_2 - \beta_1$, or vane camber, remained the same, the discharge angle β_2 and the inlet angle β_1 being changed by the same amount. The point of interest is that the head produced is essentially the same for all vane settings and thus is a function of the vane curvature $(\beta_2 - \beta_1)$ alone. This means that although the tangential component at the impeller discharge (c_{u2}) is higher at higher values of β_2,

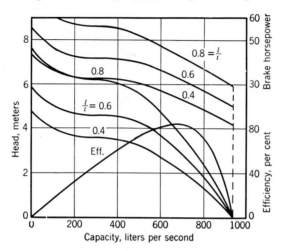

Fig. 13.10. Effect of l/t on performance; 730 r.p.m.; $\beta_2 = 20°$ average (Schlimbach).

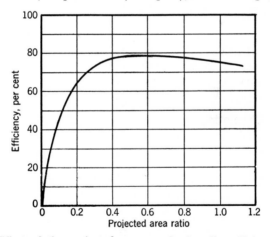

Fig. 13.11. Effect of the projected area on the impeller efficiency (Schmidt).

the tangential component at inlet (c_{u1}) is increased by approximately the same amount. The peripheral velocity being the same at inlet and outlet—no change in head results. Efficiency is good over a wide range of capacities. In fact if the casing vanes could be changed for every impeller vane setting, the decrease in efficiency on both sides of the optimum setting would be still smaller. Capacity varies approximately directly as the inlet pitch or tan β_1. This particular point was also proven by Schmidt's tests (reference 4).

It should be pointed out that in multistage axial flow compressors having stationary vanes ahead of each impeller increasing the vane-setting angle is accompanied by an increase of head (Fig. 14.4) because gas is not free to acquire the necessary prerotation to enter the impeller blades with the same angle of attack, thus a higher gas deflection results. In a single-stage axial blower no inlet guide vanes are provided and gas tends to adjust itself to the blade entrance angle, the gas deflection remaining essentially the same.

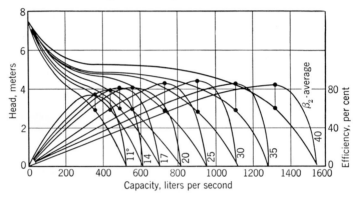

Fig. 13.12. Performance 4-vane impeller, 500-mm. diameter, at different vane angles, 650 r.p.m. (Schlimbach).

(e) **Vane Thickness.** Figure 13.13 shows test results by Eckert (reference 6) of two impellers, one with airfoil vanes well streamlined and polished, the other of the same solidity and camber line but made of stamped steel sheet vanes welded to the hub. The performance of the two impellers is identical. Similar results were obtained by several investigators.

Eckert also found by test that another impeller of the same airfoil pattern but made of cast iron with the trailing edge about $\frac{1}{8}$ inch thick was 5 points lower in efficiency. Part of the efficiency reduction was caused by the greater relative roughness of the cast-iron vane as compared to the polished alloy vane. For cast vanes it is necessary to add metal to the trailing edge to be removed after machining. Excessive vane thickness results in separation and noise with high pressure high speed impellers.

Figure 13.14 is reproduced from an Escher Wyss publication (reference 11) to illustrate the effect of hub and blade solidity on the specific speed.   Note that (1) to realize the same specific speed, pumps require considerably more vane area than fans because of difference in density of air and water (ratio of densities is of the order of 800); (2) for low specific speeds, water impellers are wider because the impeller discharge angles as a rule are lower than those of blower impellers; (3) the blowers and fans change abruptly from axial to centrifugal between

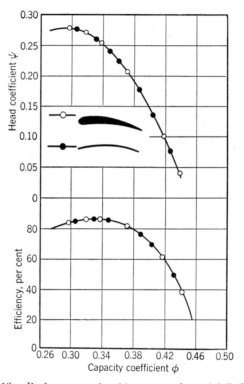

Fig. 13.13.   Performance of a thin vane and an airfoil (Eckert).

specific speeds 1000 and 2000.   With pumps, continuity of profile change is maintained from axial to mixed flow and straight axial flow. Impellers with conical hubs and extreme Francis vanes are mechanically weak for operation at high rotative speeds necessary to meet blower head requirements, but they have been used for low heads for fans with optimum efficiencies.

13.3 AXIAL FLOW IMPELLER DESIGN PROCEDURE

The design procedure for a single-stage axial flow impeller is essentially the same as for a centrifugal impeller.   In fact in the centrifugal pump field the axial flow impeller is the high specific speed extreme of a continuous row of types from low specific speed plain centrifugal types through the various types of mixed flow impellers with conical hubs to the straight axial flow impeller. In the field of blowers and fans this continuity is broken as the types with conical impeller hubs are rarely used because of mechanical (strength) and cost considera-

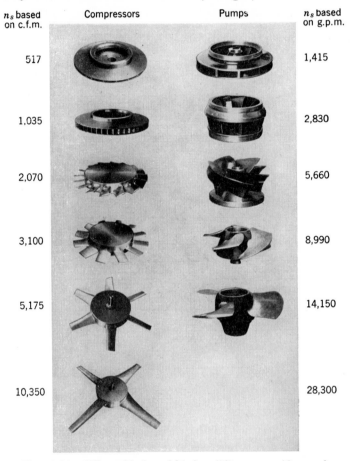

n_s based on c.f.m.	Compressors	Pumps	n_s based on g.p.m.
517			1,415
1,035			2,830
2,070			5,660
3,100			8,990
5,175			14,150
10,350			28,300

Fig. 13.14. Effect of hub and blade solidity on specific speed.

tion. Single-stage axial flow machines have no inlet guide vanes therefore the inlet velocity can be considered as axial. For such conditions the design values of the head coefficient ψ and capacity coefficient ϕ can be selected from Fig. 6.10. The following steps are involved:

1. To meet a given set of head-capacity conditions, the speed (r.p.m.) is selected. Thus the specific speed of the impeller is fixed.

Due consideration should be given to the head range the proposed unit should cover in future applications.

2. For the specific speed thus obtained the hub ratio is selected from Fig. 13.8.

3. For the selected hub ratio the chord-spacing ratio l/t is selected, Fig. 13.7 being used as a guide. The number of vanes is assumed at the same time.

4. The head and capacity coefficient for the best efficiency point, which is the design point, are chosen next from Fig. 6.10. To enter the chart the performance specific speed n_s is converted into the dimensionless specific speed by formula 13.9 and the values of ψ and ϕ are read off for the assumed value of the impeller discharge angle β_2 at the mean effective diameter. A value of the latter equal to $25°$ can be taken as a good average. Higher values of β_2 can be chosen if a maximum output from a given size of machine is wanted. By referring to Fig. 13.12 it will be noticed that at a fixed speed a considerable range of capacities can be obtained in a given casing with a single vane design applied to several impeller patterns having vane settings (on the hub) at 5 or $10°$ intervals.

5. From the values of ψ and ϕ obtained in (4) the peripheral velocity u_m at the mean effective diameter and the axial velocity c_m are calculated. If the mean effective diameter and the hub ratio are known, the impeller outside and hub diameters, can be established.

6. Then both the inlet and outlet Euler's velocity triangles can be drawn for several streamlines (outside, mean effective, and hub diameter) thus establishing the vane profile inlet and discharge angles for each streamline. The forced vortex, or what is also known as "solid rotation" (constant angular velocity for all streamlines) pattern of velocity distribution along the radius is selected following the reasoning given in Chapter 4. A constant axial velocity is assumed along the radius. By referring to Fig. 4.11, the point E is established by drawing the velocity triangle for the mean effective diameter and the chosen value of β_2. The discharge velocity triangles for each streamline can be drawn by connecting point E with points between A and B corresponding to the several streamlines. To draw the inlet triangles the ratio $P_{1s}/c_m = 1.15$ to 1.25 is assumed. This accounts for the contraction of flow area due to vane thickness and allows a nominal prerotation, or a small positive angle of attack at entrance.

7. If the inlet and outlet angles β_1 and β_2 are known for each streamline, the vane profile mean camber line can be drawn following Munk's method described earlier in this chapter. The vane thickness is selected, using a minimum necessary for mechanical strength

and manufacturing procedure. It is increased uniformly toward the hub.

8. Note that the velocity triangles mentioned above are Euler's (theoretical) triangles drawn on the vane angles and the actual axial velocity. The input velocity triangles based on the actual velocities will be drawn to establish the direction of the absolute flow at impeller discharge in order to design the stationary vanes of the casing, discussed later in this Chapter.

13.4 AIRFOIL THEORY

Introduction. A lack of reliable test and design data on axial flow turbomachines in the early stages of their development is responsible for the attempts of several investigators to make use of the extensive test data on airplane airfoil profiles for axial flow blower and pump impellers. The airfoil theory of axial flow impeller design establishes a connection between the lift coefficients of airfoil test data and the impeller total head. The design procedure consists of the selection of suitable airfoil profiles for several radii of the impeller and determination of the vane setting on the hub, or chord angle β_c for each radius. A constant head for several streamlines is usually assumed in this method even though other assumptions are possible. The other important impeller design elements, such as (1) hub ratio, (2) l/t ratio at each radius, (3) revolutions per minute or specific speed, (4) axial velocity, and (5) impeller diameter are selected on the basis of previous experience. There is nothing in the airfoil theory to help or guide in making such selections. Thus the impeller design is still entirely experimental, airfoil experimental knowledge being used for establishing the vane curvature only. It is only natural that after sufficient experience was accumulated on efficient axial flow fans, blowers, and pumps the interest in the airfoil theory subsided. In the meantime, other more direct methods of design were advanced based on the experience with rotating profiles in suitable casings.

(*a*) **Total Head Equation.** If a cylindrical cut is made through an axial flow impeller and the cylinder is developed onto a plane, a row of vane profiles will result. The action of fluid on the profile can be considered similar to that taking place on an airfoil in a wind tunnel, provided the relative velocity w_{ave} is an average value of the relative velocity of approach and discharge w_1 and w_2 which exist before and after the vane at a distance where the effect of the flow through the row of vanes is equalized (Fig. 13.3). The effect of the cascade arrangement of vanes on the lift coefficient C_L is little known and has been neglected by several advocates of the airfoil theory for axial flow impellers.

The total force P exerted by the fluid per unit of vane length is a resultant of lift L and drag D and makes an angle λ with L (Fig. 13.3). P forms an angle $90° - (\beta_{\text{ave}} + \lambda)$ with the peripheral velocity of the impeller. The tangential component of P is

$$P \cos [90° - (\beta_{\text{ave}} - \lambda)] = P \sin (\beta_{\text{ave}} + \lambda) \qquad (13.12)$$

The work per second is

$$E = Pu \sin (\beta_{\text{ave}} + \lambda) \qquad (13.13)$$

Considering a slice of vane between two concentric cylindrical surfaces of radius r and $r + dr$, the corresponding work per second for z vanes is

$$zdE = zPdru \sin (\beta_{\text{ave}} + \lambda) \qquad (13.14)$$

If dQ denotes the volume of fluid included between the two cylindrical surfaces, the work per pound of fluid is

$$H_t = \frac{zdE}{dQ\gamma} = \frac{Pu \sin (\beta_{\text{ave}} + \lambda)z}{dQ\gamma} dr \qquad (13.15)$$

But $dQ = ztdrc_m$, $P = L/\cos \lambda$, and $L = C_L(\gamma w_{\text{ave}}{}^2 F)/2g$ where $F = l \times 1 = l$, area per unit length. Then

$$P = C_L(\gamma l w_{\text{ave}}{}^2/2g \cos \lambda) \qquad (13.16)$$

and equation 13.15 becomes

$$H_t = C_L \cdot \frac{l}{t} \cdot \frac{u}{c_m} \cdot \frac{w_{\text{ave}}{}^2}{2g} \frac{\sin (\beta_{\text{ave}} + \lambda)}{\cos \lambda} \qquad (13.17)$$

or

$$C_L \frac{l}{t} = H_t \frac{2g}{w_{\text{ave}}{}^2} \cdot \frac{c_m}{u} \cdot \frac{\cos \lambda}{\sin (\beta_{\text{ave}} + \lambda)} \qquad (13.18)$$

The theoretical head H_t is obtained from $H_t = H/e_h$, where e_h is the hydraulic efficiency and has to be assumed.

w_{ave} and β_{ave} are obtained from the velocity diagram (Fig. 13.15) constructed for an average tangential component $(c_{u2} - c_{u1})/2$. The value of c_{u2} is obtained from

$$c_{u2} - c_{u1} = \frac{gH_t}{u} \qquad (13.19)$$

Usually c_{u1} is assumed to be equal to zero.

From equation 13.18 it is seen that for a greater value of u and w_{ave} the value of $C_L(l/t)$ is lower; that is, at larger radii l/t and C_L are lower than at the hub.   Equation 13.18 includes the l/t ratio, and does not give any indication of the number of vanes.   For higher heads, higher values of C_L and l/t are required; or, more vane area and a higher cambered profile are required.

Equation 13.18 is used for the calculation of C_L (l/t) for several radii of the impeller.   It is assumed that H_t and c_m are constant along a radius.   Next l/t is assumed.   For a fixed hub ratio, l/t can vary only within narrow limits for a given specific speed.   Vane profiles are selected for a chosen l/t ratio.   Experience is necessary to select

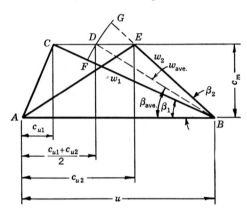

Fig. 13.15.   Velocity diagrams of flow ahead of and past the airfoil.

proper values of l/t to obtain C_L and the vane profile in order to produce an efficient impeller and head-capacity and efficiency curves of good shape.

(b) **Lift Coefficient versus Head Coefficient.**   The right hand side of equation 13.18 can be further simplified by the following approximations:

$$\cos \lambda \approx 1 \qquad c_m/w_{ave} \approx \sin \beta_{ave}$$

since λ is of the order of one degree.   Also substituting for $H_t = uc_{u2}/g$, equation 13.18 becomes

$$C_L(l/t) = 2c_{u2}/w_{ave} \qquad (13.20)$$

The right hand side of this equation can be transformed to express the lift coefficient C_L for an assumed value of the chord-spacing ratio l/t in terms of (1) vane curvature $(\beta_2 - \beta_1)$, (2) camber and its location, and (3) head and capacity coefficients ψ and ϕ.

In Fig. 13.15 the area of triangle $CEB = \frac{1}{2}c_m(c_{u2} - c_{u1}) = \frac{1}{2}$ $c_m c_{u2}$ if $c_{u1} = 0$. This is approximately but very closely equal to the area of the sector $FGB = \frac{1}{2}w_{\mathrm{ave}}^2(\beta_2 - \beta_1)$. Hence

$$c_m c_{u2} = w_{\mathrm{ave}}^2(\beta_2 - \beta_1)$$

and

$$C_L l/t = 2(\beta_2 - \beta_1)/\sin \beta_{\mathrm{ave}} \qquad (13.21)$$

By referring to Fig. 13.6 we notice that $\tan \theta_1 = 2ED/AE = 2c/l_c$ and $\tan \theta_2 = 2ED/EB = 2c/(l - l_c)$, where c is the camber and l_c is its location relative to the leading edge, both expressed as fractions of the airfoil chord length. Since values of θ_1 and θ_2 are usually small, the values of the angles in radians can be substituted as an approximation for their tangents. Then the vane curvature becomes

$$\beta_2 - \beta_1 = 2cl/l_c(l - l_c) \qquad (13.22)$$

and equation 13.21 can be further modified to

$$C_L l/t = \frac{4cl}{l_c(l - l_c) \sin \beta_{\mathrm{ave}}} \qquad (13.23)$$

To express the lift coefficient in terms of ψ and ϕ the following substitutions are made in equation 13.20

$$\frac{c_{u2}}{u} = \psi \quad \text{and} \quad w_{\mathrm{ave}} = \frac{c_m}{\sin \beta_{\mathrm{ave}}} = \frac{u\phi}{\sin \beta_{\mathrm{ave}}}$$

then

$$C_L l/t = \frac{2\psi \sin \beta_{\mathrm{ave}}}{\phi} \qquad (13.24)$$

Note that w_{ave} as defined in Fig. 13.15 is not an exact average of w_1 and w_2 and similarly β_{ave} is not an exact average of β_1 and β_2. It can be shown that

$$\beta_{\mathrm{ave}} = \beta_c + \frac{\theta_2 - \theta_1}{2} \qquad (13.25)$$

and thus $\beta_{\mathrm{ave}} = \beta_c$ when $\theta_2 = \theta_1$, as is the case with a circular arc mean camber line. In general $\beta_{\mathrm{ave}} \approx \beta_c$ and represents the profile position in respect to the hub for each radius. Equations 13.21 and 13.24 show that the lift coefficient in formula 13.18 does not reveal any new relationship between the head produced and the design elements which could not be expressed in terms of familiar design elements used for centrifugal and mixed flow impellers.

(c) **Discussion of the Airfoil Theory.** The airfoil data available for selection of axial flow impeller profiles following the airfoil theory were obtained under conditions vastly different from the flow pattern existing in a fan or blower. A number of simplifying assumptions were necessary to make possible a comparison of the flow of the two. In practice, corrective factors had to be applied after tests of units designed on the basis of airfoil theory in order to bring the test results to some kind of agreement with the anticipated design performance. There are a number of factors responsible for such a state of affairs, the most important of which will be listed below:

1. The mutual vane interference under the conditions prevailing in the impeller is not sufficiently known. Even when the cascade test data of several airfoils with a required chord-spacing ratio are available, the performance of a vane of variable profile and at different vane settings along the radius is greatly different from that of a cascade in the straight flow of a wind tunnel.

2. Profiles selected on the basis of "over-all" performance may produce the assumed axial velocity only by accident. Axial velocity (or in general meridional velocity) results from the proper selection of the impeller entrance and discharge angles. Besides the through-flow velocity and specific capacity q_s depends upon the hub ratio, and vane solidity. All these factors fix the specific speed of the impeller. In the airfoil theory and design procedure little or no consideration is given to all these factors.

3. N.A.C.A. data are limited to cambers of 0, 2, 4, and 6 per cent. In practice higher and intermediate cambers may be required. Thus either new profiles have to be drawn for which test data are not immediately available, or the nearest existing profile has to be used, thus impairing continuity of the vane surface and the flow along the radius.

4. Airfoil cascade tests do not provide for the effects of the impeller approach and casing beyond the impeller. Thus the same impeller will perform differently in different casings, such as one with straightening vanes, the other without.

5. The effect of the end conditions of the vane (running clearance between the outside diameter and stationary wall, and revolving hub wall) are impossible to estimate accurately from the cascade tests.

6. The method becomes less accurate and workable for lower specific speed axial flow impellers and fails entirely for mixed flow types such as are in use in the mixed flow propeller pump field. A continuity of mental pattern of flow, theoretical reasoning, and geometrical design procedure is indispensable for a turbo designer to enable him to interpret the test results and to correlate the experi-

mental design constants for the whole field of specific speeds. The airfoil theory does not satisfy this requirement.

7. The airfoil theory method of axial impeller design is invariably associated with a free vortex energy distribution along the radius— i.e., vane sections at different radii are designed for the same head (at design point only). Two reasons could be discerned for this: (1) At the time the airfoil theory of the axial flow impeller was introduced it was a general belief that only the free vortex pattern provides a stable flow radially. (2) The theory was originally proposed for axial flow water turbines where a constant head is actually applied at all radii. There is nothing in the airfoil theory to prevent any desired head distribution along the vane radius—later designs with other than free vortex pattern of flow were applied in connection with a different theoretical treatment. The high pressure multistage axial compressors for gas turbines imposed such severe requirements as to performance size and weight that all theory and practice heretofore employed were reviewed critically.

As a result new design methods evolved which are based on inlet and outlet velocity triangle considerations and corrective factors determined from cascade airfoil tests and actual impeller performance in a suitable casing. There has been a steady drift away from the free vortex hypothesis of flow in the direction of the forced vortex. A detailed account of the later methods of axial flow impeller design, as developed for high pressure multistage axial flow compressors, is given in the next chapter.

13.5 FAN OR BLOWER CASING

(a) **Function of the Casing.** The purpose of the fan casing beyond the impeller is to convert into pressure the tangential component of the absolute velocity leaving the impeller. This is accomplished by "straightening" the flow as it leaves the impeller and reducing the velocity.

The diffusion vane curvature is selected so that the fluid enters the diffusion vanes with a minimum loss (zero or small angle of attack) and leaves the casing axially. With an impeller designed for a forced vortex pattern of flow, the angular velocity of the flow leaving the impeller at all radii is constant. This regime is maintained at all rates of flow, the angular velocity increasing as the head is increased. The diffusion vane angle is adjusted so that the flow continues with a constant angular velocity, the value of which is reduced until all the tangential component is taken out of the flow. To accomplish this the diffusion vane entrance angles are laid out for a constant pitch,

P_{3s}, Fig. 13.16. The value of the absolute velocity angle $\alpha_m{}'$ at the mean effective diameter D_m appears in Fig. 6.10 and can be taken out when the values of the head and capacity coefficients are established, or it can be calculated from tan $\alpha_m{}' = \phi/\psi$. The diagram in Fig. 13.16 now can be completed as the axial velocity c_{m2} is known from impeller design. Vane profiles can be drawn at several radii following the same procedure as that outlined for the impeller vanes. Since casing vanes are stationary their thickness is determined by the minimum foundry requirements.

The number of vanes in the casing varies from 5 to 8, a smaller number being used in smaller units. The vane length at the hub is made shorter ($DC < AB$, Fig. 13.17) because the vane spacing is closer at the hub (higher l/t value) than it is at the outside diameter.

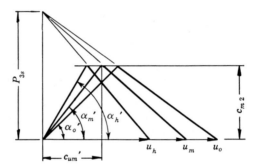

Fig. 13.16.   Velocity diagram at entrance to diffusion casing.

This also tends to shorten the axial length of the unit. The axial distance d between the impeller and the diffusion vanes has some bearing on the performance; the optimum value of the ratio d/D_o is about 0.05. When the value of d is being selected, provision should be made for accommodating impellers with a higher vane angle setting which require more axial space. The impeller hub length is fixed also with this idea in mind.

(b) **Modifications of the Casing Vane.** There are a number of further minor considerations which enter into the selection of the casing vane angles. It will be recalled that Fig. 6.10 is based on the total head as it is measured at the fan or blower discharge. The head at the impeller discharge is somewhat higher by the amount of losses in the casing and can be estimated as follows. The total head H and blower gross efficiency e are considered as known. Taking hydraulic efficiency as $e_h = \sqrt{e}$ the input head H_i is then approximately equal to

$$H_i = H/\sqrt{e} \qquad (13.26)$$

The head at impeller exit is less than H_i by the amount of hydraulic losses in the impeller. If the casing losses are assumed equal to those of the impeller (each represents a set of vanes) the head at the impeller exit H_d is

$$H_d = \frac{H_i + H}{2} = \frac{H/\sqrt{e} + H}{2} \qquad (13.27)$$

At this point it will be shown that the head produced at the mean effective diameter is equal to the total integrated head. Thus, although the generated head varies along the radius following forced vortex pattern, the head given by the equation 13.27 is developed at the mean effective diameter D_m, defined as

$$D_m = \sqrt{(D_o{}^2 + D_h{}^2)/2} \qquad (13.28)$$

In Chapter 4, equation 4.10 and Fig. 4.6, it has been shown that the integrated head is equal to the arithmetical average of the heads produced at the hub and at the periphery and

$$H_e = (u_o c_{uo} + u_h c_{uh})/2g = u_m c_{um}/g \qquad (13.29)$$

where u_m and c_{um} are the peripheral velocity and the tangential component of the absolute velocity at the diameter D_m. From this equation we obtain

$$2 = \frac{u_o c_{uo}}{u_m c_{um}} + \frac{u_h c_{uh}}{u_m c_{um}} \qquad (13.30)$$

In a forced vortex, peripheral and tangential velocities vary as the radii or diameters, therefore

$$2 = (D_o{}^2/D_m{}^2) + (D_h{}^2/D_m{}^2)$$
$$D_m = \sqrt{(D_o{}^2 + D_h{}^2)/2} \qquad (13.31)$$

It may be pointed out also that a cylinder of a diameter equal to D_m divides the flow into two equal parts.

Expressing the head H_d of equation 13.27 as

$$H_d = \frac{u_m c_{um}{}'}{g} \qquad (13.32)$$

the value of the $c_{um}{}'$ can be determined and the construction of Fig. 13.16 repeated corresponding to the head H_d. This will give values of the vane angles slightly lower. Thus the vane angles based on the total head H allow a small angle of attack δ (Fig 13.17) which does

not affect efficiency. This means that the refinement in the vane
angle determination outlined above may not be justified.

The value of the diffusion vane angle is not very critical, and variations as great as $\pm 5°$ from the optimum values have hardly any notice-
able effect on the performance. This is rather fortunate as frequently
the same casing may be used with several impellers requiring different
diffusion vane angles. Again, in practice, for cost reasons the vane is
made of constant curvature (rolled steel plate) without any damaging
effects on efficiency. For compact units the axial diffusion vane length
is kept to a minimum. A greater number of vanes and a positive
angle of attack are then employed. In extreme cases when a large

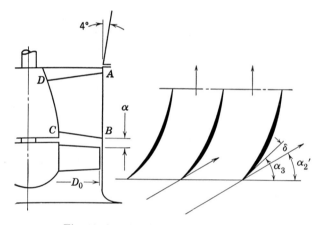

Fig. 13.17.   Axial flow diffusion casing.

volume of gas at very low pressure is moved the diffuser vanes or
even the whole diffusion casing are omitted at some sacrifice of
efficiency.

In addition to the conversion of the impeller discharge velocity into
pressure by means of stationary vanes, a further reduction of velocity
is accomplished by increasing the diffusion casing diameter toward the
discharge flange. A small divergence angle (8° total) is essential for
an effective conversion. Tapering of the diffuser hub within the vaned
part of the casing also contributes to the diffusion of the discharge
velocity, although its primary purpose is streamlining the flow passage.

(c) **Propeller and Tube-Axial Fans.** These terms are used to designate axial flow fans without the diffusion vanes on the discharge side.
The first group includes fans in which the casing is reduced to the
mounting ring around the impeller periphery and supporting bracket
for the fan shaft and driving means (Fig. 2.3). The tube-axial fans

have a simplified cylindrical shell enclosing the impeller and supporting the driving means and are provided with end flanges for inlet or outlet duct connections (Fig. 2.2). Mechanical simplification is attained at the expense of efficiency as it appears in Fig. 12.1 where vane-axial fan designates machines with fully developed diffusion vane casing and bell-shaped inlet. A deterioration of static efficiency from 76 to 45 per cent follows the various degrees of mechanical simplification at the expense of hydraulic performance. In a well-designed fan omission of the diffusion vanes incurs appreciable reduction in efficiency, the loss depending upon specific speed and type of the discharge casing— with or without a conical diffuser.

(d) **Open Propeller Fans.** These have no casing whatsoever. Owing to back flow at the hub and at the propeller blade tips the output of the impeller is greatly reduced in comparison with that of the tube-axial fan: Measuring the output of open-propeller fans presents great difficulties as the velocity of flow and dynamic pressure vary along the radius, the flow being reversed at the hub and outside periphery of the propeller. Providing a cylindrical ring around the propeller increases the head and capacity approximately twice (reference 20). Since power input remains essentially the same, efficiency increases approximately four times. (From 18 to 72 per cent, for an automobile fan.)

The following formula can be used for estimating the free delivery capacity of a propeller (p. 238, reference 9).

$$\text{c.f.m.} = KD_2{}^3 \text{ (r.p.m.) sin } \beta_c$$

where, D_2 is the propeller diameter in feet; and K is an experimental factor equal to 1.0 to 1.4 for a simple ring frame, 1.2 to 1.6 for a simple impeller ring frame and coned inlet, 1.5 to 2.00 for an impeller mounted in a duct of the same size. The angle β_c is the average blade setting angle with plane of rotation or chord angle.

If it is necessary to change the blade setting of a propeller for which capacity, pressure, and horsepower are known, then capacity varies as the sine of the angle, pressure varies as the square root of the sine of the angle and power varies as $\frac{3}{2}$ of the sine of the angle. Usually 2 to 4 blades are used. The blade setting angle (chord angle β_c) is normally between 15 and 30°.

13.6 EXAMPLES AND ILLUSTRATIONS

Figures 13.18, 13.19, and 13.20 show the performance of an axial flow fan published by Peck and Ross (reference 10). Figure 13.18 shows the test of the impeller alone; Fig. 13.19, impeller and conical diffuser, and Fig. 13.20, a complete assembly including the casing straightening vanes as shown in Fig. 13.21. Below are given some data pertaining to the fan physical dimensions:

c.f.m. = 52,500.
Static pressure, in. of water, 10.2.
Speed, 3600 r.p.m.
Specific speed, 5000.
Outside diameter, in., 38.31.
Hub ratio, 0.40.
Number of impeller vanes, 8.
Number of casing vanes, 6.

The data on Figs. 13.18 and 13.19 were obtained with a model about ¼ size of the prototype, whereas data on Fig. 13.20 were

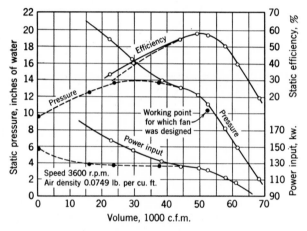

Fig. 13.18.   Performance of the fan alone, Fig. 13.21 (Peck and Ross).   Dashed lines indicate test with inlet box baffles removed.

obtained with the full-size unit. Results of the first two were recalculated for the full-size unit performance. In Fig. 13.18 efficiency of the impeller based on the total dynamic head was 75.8 per cent. Note the effect of the radial baffles in the intake box is not felt at b.e.p. and capacity over the normal. At partial capacities with baffles removed, the head and b.hp. dropped considerably, indicating that when prerotation is not checked at the impeller inlet it tends to unload the impeller.

Addition of the conical diffuser (no vanes) increased the static efficiency from 56 to 66 per cent (Fig. 13.19). Removal of the middle

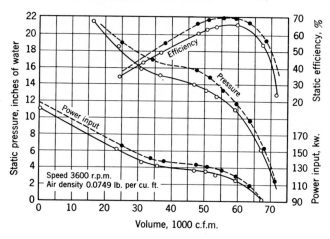

Fig. 13.19. Performance of the fan with cone diffuser only; no guide vanes (Peck and Ross). Full lines indicate clearance of 1.25 per cent; dashed lines, minimum clearance.

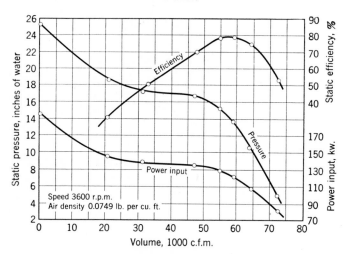

Fig. 13.20. Performance of the full-size unit with guide vanes and cone diffuser (Peck and Ross).

hub streamlining cone reduced the static efficiency from 66 to 64 per cent. The same figure shows the increase of efficiency due to a reduction of the radial running clearance from 1.25 per cent of the impeller radius to the minimum possible.

The maximum static efficiency of the complete model unit with the vaned casing was 77 per cent. Figure 13.20 shows the static efficiency of the prototype with the cone and vaned casing as 78.5 per cent.

Efficiency based on the total head of the full-size assembly was 82.5 per cent. All efficiencies are the gross efficiencies, i.e., including the bearing losses. Efficiencies as given above are in close agreement with those shown in Fig. 12.1 for 5000 specific speed.

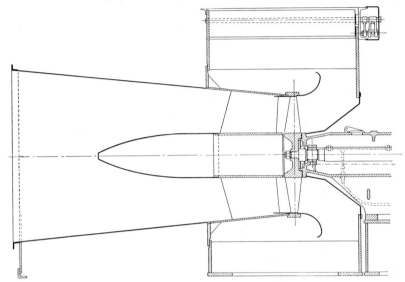

Fig. 13.21.   Full-size fan (Peck and Ross).

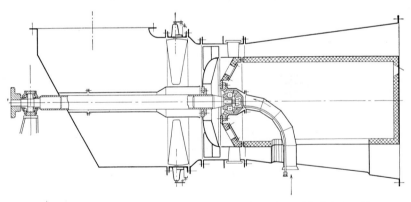

Fig. 13.22.   Kühele-Kopp and Kausch axial flow fan with inlet guide vanes.

Figure 13.22 shows a Kühele-Kopp and Kausch (German), single-stage axial flow fan of low specific speed, with hub ratio 0.78, with adjustable inlet vanes, built for handling hot gases. The bearing supporting impeller is located inside the insulated core of the long discharge cone, and is air cooled. There is a set of discharge diffusion vanes between the impeller and discharge cone. Figure 13.23 shows a typical performance characteristic of a fan of this type at constant speed and several inlet guide vane positions. It will be shown in Chapter 15 (Fig. 15.8) that for high head centrifugal blowers the inlet guide vanes are not effective in producing counterrotation in the

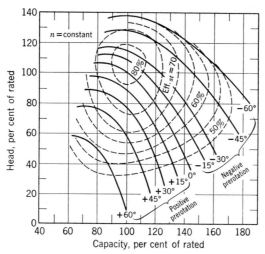

Fig. 13.23. Typical performance of the fan, Fig. 13.22.

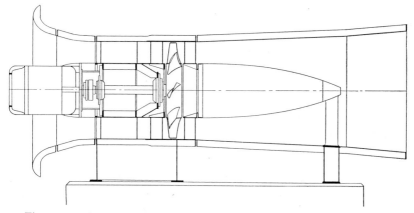

Fig. 13.24. Demag mine ventilating fan with adjustable impeller vanes.

impeller approach to increase the flow and are used only to reduce the flow mostly by throttling.

Figure 13.24 shows Demag axial flow fan with adjustable vanes used for mine ventilation. Motor is brought out of the inlet bell for easy servicing. Both horizontal and vertical mounting are employed.

For pumping moist or dust-laden air the motor is mounted on discharge side beyond the 45° discharge elbow.   Figure 13.25 shows the
performance of the largest Demag fan for several impeller vane positions and two speeds.

Blowers with Two Counterrotating Propellers.   There are a few isolated installations of blowers in Europe in which another propeller
rotating in opposite direction to the blower impeller is used to straighten

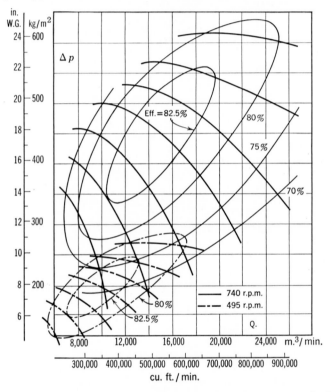

Fig. 13.25.   Performance of the largest Demag fan for mine ventilation.

out the flow past the impeller instead of the stationary casing vanes.
The largest installation of this kind is that in Modane, France, built
by Dingler-Werke A. G., Germany, and used for the large wind tunnel.
The impeller diameter is 49.3 feet, requiring 80,000 hp. to drive at
100 r.p.m.   With both propellers having adjustable blades a wide range
of operation with good efficiency (over 80 per cent) is possible from
0.5 to 2.0 of the rated capacity, the optimum efficiency being over
89.0 per cent.   An axial flow is produced at all rates of discharge.
The pumping element is extremely short.

A similar installation of a smaller size was equipped by Escher Wyss, with 27.9 ft impeller diameter and 5,510,000 c.f.m. capacity.

Figure 13.26 shows a smaller blower with two counterrotating impellers both provided with adjustable blades and capable of pumping air in either direction with equal efficiency. This is accomplished by reversing the driver rotation and changing the impeller blade setting. The driving shaft is at 90° to the axis of the blower, thus keeping both ends of the casing unobstructed (reference 20).

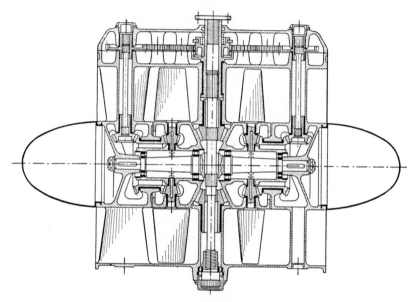

Fig. 13.26.   Axial blower with two counterrotating impellers.

The involved mechanical design of the blowers with counterrotating impellers limits their application to the special requirements only. Blowers with two counter-rotating impellers are sometimes referred to as "two-stage," because the head generated by a set of two similar counterrotating impellers is essentially twice that of the individual impeller in a normal stage. Note that in the stationary casing force exerted by the vane to effect the flow deflection is stationary (vane reaction) and hence no work is done by this force. But, when deflection is accomplished by a counterrotating impeller, the deflecting force exerted on the fluid is moving, hence work is applied to the fluid equal to the $(\Delta c_u u)$ where Δc_u is change in tangential velocity of the fluid and u is the peripheral velocity of the impeller at the same point.

REFERENCES

1. *National Advisory Committee for Aeronautics, Report* 460, 1935.
2. Munk, "On the Geometry of Streamlining," *Theodore von Kármán Anniversary Volume*, Calif. Inst. Technol., Pasadena, Calif., 1941, p. 8.
3. Kaplan and Lechner, *Theorie und Bau von Turbinen-Schnelläufern*, Oldenburg, Munich, 1931, p. 145.
4. Schmidt, "Some Screw Propeller Experiments," *J. Am. Soc. Naval Engrs.* Vol. 40, No. 1, Feb. 1928.
5. Schlimbach, "Der Man-Schraubenschaufler," *Mitt. Forsch. Anst. GHH Konzern*, Oct., 1935, p. 54 (Maschinenfabric Augsburg-Nurnberg).
6. Eckert, "Neuere Erfahrungen an Überdruckaxialgebläsen," *Z.V.D.I.*, Vol. 88, No. 37/38, Sept. 16, 1944, p. 516.
7. Marks and Weske, "The Design and Performance of an Axial Flow Fan," *Trans. A.S.M.E.*, Vol. 56, No. 11, 1934, pp. 807–812.
8. Ackert and Kobel, "Design of an Axial Flow Cooling Fan with Adjustable Inlet Guide Vanes," *FKFS Report* 398, *BuShips* 338, U. S. Navy Dept. p. 6.
9. Madison, *Fan Eng.*, Buffalo Forge Co., 1949, p 232.
10. Peck and Ross, "An Air Flow-Type of Propeller Blower," *A.S.M.E. Trans.*, Oct., 1935, p. 417.
11. Keller, "Common Principle and Research for Compressors and Pumps," Escher Wyss News, Vol. 14, Zurich, 1941.
12. Pfleiderer, Die Kreiselpumpen, Springer, Berlin, 1949, p. 352; also, 1932 edition, p. 319. (Specific speed n_s = 5000.)
13. Barton Bell, *N.A.C.A. Report* 729, 1942 (n_s = 2400, inlet counterrotation); also, Bell and De Corter, *N.A.C.A. Report*—without number—Dec., 1942. (Tests of same blower with impellers of different solidity.)
14. Marks and Weske, "The Design and Performance of an Axial Flow Fan," *A.S.M.E. Trans.*, Nov., 1934, p. 807. (n_s = 4750.)
15. Marks and Flint, "The Design and Performance of a High Pressure Axial Flow Fan," *A.S.M.E. Trans.*, Oct., 1935, p. 383. (n_s = 2900.)
16. O'Brien and Folsom, *The Design of Propeller Pumps and Fans*, Univ. Calif. Vol. 4, No. 1, 1939. (n_s = 2800.)
17. Ruden, "Investigation of Single Stage Axial Fans," *N.A.C.A. Tech. Min.* 1062, 1944; translated from German. (n_s = 4800.)
18. Eckert "Experiments with an Axial Cooling Fan-Blower," *BuShips* 338, May, 1946, U. S. Navy Dept., Vol. 21.
19. Ruden, "Investigation of Single Stage Axial Fans," *N.A.C.A. Tech. Mem.* 1062, 1944; translated from German. Results of tests at Göttingen Aerodynamic Laboratory.
20. Eckert, *Axialkompressoren und Radialkompressoren*, Springer, Berlin, 1953, pp. 110, 143.

CHAPTER 14

High Pressure Multistage
Axial Flow Compressors

INTRODUCTION

Axial flow multistage compressors were developed for use with gas turbines. In this field, particularly for aircraft applications, axial compressors possess several advantages such as higher efficiency than heretofore realized with centrifugal compressors; small weight and bulk, particularly important for aircraft; and high speed of rotation, which permits direct connection to the gas turbine. An optimum of the above advantages may be realized by:

1. Varying the specific speed of individual stages by selecting different numbers of stages to produce the required pressure ratio.

2. Allowing different degrees of prerotation ahead of the impeller. This in turn affects the maximum rotative speed. The term "degree of reaction" is used for classifying compressor blading with respect to the desired prerotation and is discussed in Art. 14.1.

Owing to the military importance of the gas turbine, efforts in several countries were concentrated in a search for the best designs in the shortest possible time. Although the present stage of development of the axial compressor can hardly be considered as final, the relative advantages of several solutions are well established and will be discussed. Also in this chapter emphasis will be placed upon principles underlying the design of individual stages rather than upon the design of the complete compressor unit.

14.1 DEGREE OF REACTION

(a) **Definition.** The term "degree" of reaction, or, for brevity, "reaction," was originated in the steam turbine field where it is used instead of specific speed to differentiate between different hydrodynamic types. Since the performance specific speed (n_s) can be met with different hydrodynamic designs the degree of reaction is used to distinguish the degree of prerotation provided at the impeller inlet of axial flow multistage compressors which may be of the same specific

277

speed.   The degree of reaction is never applied to centrifugal machines even when they are provided with inlet guide vanes (adjustable or removable).   The degree of reaction is defined as the ratio of the pressure rise in the impeller to the total head produced by the stage, or,

$$R = \frac{\Delta p_i}{H} = 1 - \frac{c_2'^2 - c_1'^2}{2gH} \qquad (14.1)$$

where R is reaction.

Δp_i is the static pressure rise in the impeller in feet of fluid.

H is total head per stage.

c_2' is the true impeller outlet velocity, absolute.

c_1' is the true impeller inlet absolute velocity which is also the outlet velocity from the stationary vanes of the preceding stage.

The last term of equation 14.1 represents the pressure rise in the stationary vanes expressed as a fraction of the total head.   In a multi-stage compressor, since the inlet and outlet velocities of the stage are identical in value and direction, the total head produced by the stage is all in pressure rise; part of it is generated within the impeller passages, and the remainder is recovered from the kinetic energy in the stationary vanes.

(b) **Single-Stage Axial Blowers and Fans.**   These usually have axial inlet velocities.   Since the inlet is taken from a vessel or the surrounding atmosphere where the velocity is negligible, full velocity head at the blower discharge is credited to the machine and c_1' in equation 14.1 is taken as equal to zero.   The expression for the reaction, equation 14.1, can then be transformed algebraically as follows:

$$R = 1 - \frac{c_2'^2}{2gH} = 1 - \frac{c_{u2}'^2 + c_m^2}{2gH} \times \frac{u^2}{u^2} = 1 - \frac{\psi^2 + \phi^2}{2\psi} \qquad (14.2)$$

The subtractive term in the last expression represents the kinetic energy (K.E.) at the impeller discharge as a fraction of the total head.*

* The part of the kinetic energy term in equation (14.2)

$$\frac{\phi^2}{2\psi} = \frac{c_m^2}{2gH} = \sigma \qquad (14.3)$$

is frequently found in German literature on axial flow compressors and is called "throttling number" (Die Drosselzahl).   It is a form of through-flow capacity constant and has the property of remaining constant when the speed or impeller vane setting is changed without any change in the discharge system.   There is

The lines of constant reaction (really lines of constant K.E. but marked with numerical values of reaction) are shown in Fig. 6.10. These are half-circles with radii equal to

$$r = 1 - R = \text{K.E.} \tag{14.4}$$

and centers located on the axis of ψ. This can be ascertained by comparing equation 14.2 with that of a circle in the form

$$(x - a)^2 + (y - b)^2 = r^2 \tag{14.5}$$

where a and b are the coordinates of the center. In our case $a = 0$; $b = r$; $x = \phi$ and $y = \psi$. Substituting these values we obtain

$$\phi^2 + (\psi - r)^2 = r^2$$

Hence

$$r = \frac{\psi^2 + \phi^2}{2\psi} \tag{14.6}$$

Note that lines of constant reaction are a part of the network in Fig. 6.10 depending upon the coordinate system only and are free from any assumptions or experimental observations.

(c) **Multistage Axial Compressors.** For these the expression for the reaction, equation 14.1, can be transformed to:

$$R = 1 - \frac{c_u'{}_2{}^2 + c_m{}^2 - c_u'{}_1{}^2 - c_m{}^2}{2gH}$$

$$= 1 - \frac{c_{u2}'{}^2 - c_{u1}'{}^2}{2gH} = 1 - \frac{(c_{u2}' - c_{u1}')}{u} \frac{(c_{u2}' + c_{u1}')}{2u} \frac{u^2}{gH}$$

$$= 1 - (\Delta c_u'/u)(c_{u\,\text{ave}}'/u)(1/\psi)$$

$$R = 1 - \frac{\psi}{\psi} \frac{c_{u\,\text{ave}}'}{u} = 1 - \frac{u - w_{u\,\text{ave}}'}{u}$$

$$= \frac{w_{u\,\text{ave}}'}{u} \tag{14.7}$$

---

no particular advantage in introducing the characteristic σ in the discussion of axial flow compressors (reference 8). From equation 14.2 it follows that

$$R + \sigma + \frac{\psi}{2} = 1$$

For similar blowers, or the same blower at different speeds $\sigma = $ constant connects points of the same specific speed and is referred to as "corresponding points" in Art. 2.5.

where $w_{u\ ave}'$ is the tangential component of the average relative velocity

$$w_{ave}' = (w_2' + w_1')/2 \qquad (14.8)$$

Note that equation 14.7 is of the same form as equation 4.3 if, in equation 4.3, all terms are expressed as a fraction of $u_2{}^2/g$. Equation 4.3 was derived from a general consideration of the impeller action.

A further discussion of "reaction" is given in the following article where its use for identification of different types of axial flow impeller blading is demonstrated.

14.2 HYDRODYNAMIC STAGE TYPES

General. In a multistage arrangement where each impeller is followed and preceded by a stationary set of vanes it is possible to control the direction of flow into the impeller. From elementary theory and from experience it is known that prerotation against the impeller rotation results in a higher head per stage for a given peripheral velocity and that prerotation with the impeller direction reduces the head per stage. The early designs of axial flow compressors employed prerotation against impeller rotation (reference 1).† This resulted in a lower specific speed stage type, greater over-all projected area (frontal area), and lower maximum possible rotative speed. Lower maximum possible rotative speed is limited by the local Mach number as determined by the relative velocity of flow through the impeller. The high relative velocity also affected the optimum obtainable efficiency. The ultimate stage design for the aircraft gas turbine is based on prerotation with the impeller and leads to: higher stage specific speed, smaller frontal area, higher maximum rotative speed, and higher efficiency. For locomotive, marine, and stationary installations a stage design based on axial flow inlet (no prerotation) is used to some extent as size and weight of the unit is not as critical as in the aircraft application (reference 2). Here long life and reliability are the prime considerations.

A detailed discussion of the types of compressor stage designs involves a consideration of the impeller inlet and outlet velocity triangles based on design conditions (best efficiency point) at the mean effective diameter. Variation of the velocity triangles along the vane radius admits several solutions and is treated under a separate title.

All velocity triangles are drawn assuming a constant axial velocity and true directions of flow into and away from the impeller. In

† Sir Charles Parsons had designed and operated a number of axial flow compressors from 1904 onward, using axial outlet type of blading (reference 2, p. 411).

other words, the velocity triangles are "input velocity triangles" as defined in Chapter 3 and are so designated to distinguish them from Euler's velocity triangles drawn on the vane angles.   The term blade is used synonymously with the term vane, the first being used extensively in the literature on axial flow compressors.

Selection of entrance and discharge vane angles and value of the axial velocity necessary to meet the required head-capacity conditions depends on experimental knowledge of the deviation of the actual, or "input velocity triangle," from Euler's triangles, which is the same as a deviation of the direction of the flow from that prescribed by the vane. For a stage with axial flow inlet a relationship between the actual head and pressure coefficients and the impeller discharge angle was discussed

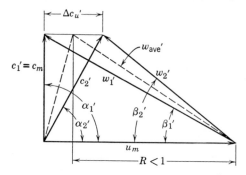

Fig. 14.1.   Velocity triangles for axial inlet.

in Chapter 13 following the procedure established for centrifugal and mixed flow impellers.   It is possible to devise a chart similar to Fig. 6.10 for an axial flow stage with prerotation, but the complication would render the chart unattractive for illustrative purposes.   In practice there are several means in use to correct the design elements selected on a theoretical basis in order to obtain the desired performance.

It will be pointed out again that the symbols for the input triangle (true flow velocities and angles) carry a prime (') mark in order to differentiate between values of velocities and angles of input and Euler's triangles.

(*a*) **Types of Blading, Axial Flow Inlet.**   Figures 14.1, 14.2, and 14.3 show velocity diagrams for three basic types of blading used for axial flow compressor design.   A number of modifications and intermediate types are also in use.   Figure 14.1 shows a diagram for a type in which the inlet velocity to the impeller is axial.   This velocity, at the same time, is the outlet velocity of the stationary vanes of the preceding stage. This is the normal design for single-stage blowers and fans as discussed in the preceding Chapter. An axial inlet design is also the only one used for axial flow water pumps.

Designs for axial flow water pumps have reached a high degree of perfection, and gross efficiencies of over 90 per cent have been realized over a wide range of specific speeds. The axial flow inlet type of blading occupies the median position between the two other types

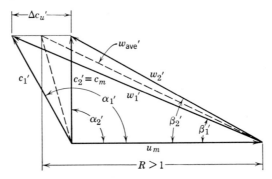

Fig. 14.2. Velocity triangles for axial exit.

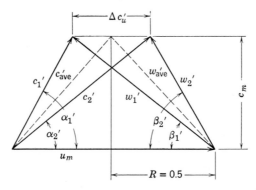

Fig. 14.3. Velocity triangles for 50 per cent reaction; symmetrical diagram.

described below and leads to the moderate axial and peripheral velocities shown in Table 1. This type is favored for stationary installations where size and weight is a secondary consideration. Although the number of units in operation is very small, gross efficiencies of 88 per cent have been attained (reference 3), and further progress can be expected.

The tangential component $\Delta c_u'/u = \psi$ is of the order of 0.28; and the reaction, as expressed by equation 14.7, is about $R = 0.85$. The low pressure rise in the stationary blades permits the use of constant section stationary blades (not twisted) and omission of the interstage seals with little damage to the gross efficiency.

In this type of compressor no stationary guide vanes are required ahead of the first-stage impeller. The discharge from the last stage is axial, and the stationary vanes of the last stage are identical with the rest of stages. The last-stage discharge velocity is moderate, leading to moderate discharge losses.

(b) **Axial Flow Outlet.** This is represented in Fig. 14.2. In this design the flow is given counterprerotation ahead of the impeller. The flow is straightened by the impeller action and leaves the impeller axially. From an inspection of the velocity diagrams it is noticed that,

TABLE 1.   IMPELLER BLADING PROPERTIES

Type of Blading	Reaction R	$R^2 + (1-R)^2$	Basic Efficiency, %	c_m, ft./sec.	u_2, ft./sec.	ϕ	ψ	ω_s
Symmetrical	0.50	0.50	94.0	700	1200	0.70	0.31	2.02
Axial inlet	0.85	0.82	92.4	400	750	0.62	0.28	2.01
Axial outlet	1.10	1.22	90.6	200	500	0.465	0.23	2.00

for the same axial flow velocity, the relative velocities in this design are the highest of the three types. This imposes limitations as to the maximum rotative speed, owing to the adverse effect of a high Mach number. Thus, although for a given blade curvature and peripheral velocity this type will generate the highest head, at the maximum speed the axial flow outlet type produces the lowest head per stage.

The low rotative speed and low specific speed (low axial velocity) lead to larger physical dimensions. This type has been used in the past for low capacity units such as are encountered in closed-cycle gas turbine schemes (reference 4), and is not favored in modern designs. The disadvantages of low head per stage are partly compensated by a smaller stage spacing (smaller blade chord length) and lower velocity at final discharge.

The reaction of this type is about $R = 1.10$ indicating that the impeller has to produce more than stage pressure rise and also has to compensate for the pressure drop taking place in the stationary blades of the preceding stage. With full pressure across the blade this type has a higher leakage loss through the running peripheral clearance than the other two types of blading. Also, since more than full stage pressure is generated by the impeller, this type of blading gives the highest axial thrust of all blade forms. The comparative axial and peripheral velocities are given in Table 1.

(c) **Symmetrical or 50 Per Cent Reaction Velocity Diagrams** (**Fig. 14.3**). This type of velocity diagram provides prerotation with the impeller so that $\alpha_1' = \beta_2'$; $\alpha_2' = \beta_1'$; $c_1' = w_2'$; and $c_2' = w_1'$. Owing to the symmetry of the diagram, reaction $R = 0.5$. This is by far the most popular type of blading. It has been pointed out that this type of blading permits a maximum rotative speed and maximum head per stage, within the same Mach number limitations, owing to a lower relative velocity w_{ave}'/u.

A further increase in prerotation, and decrease of the relative velocity, would increase the average absolute velocity and thus shift the danger of local sonic velocity from the impeller to the stationary vanes.

At the best efficiency point the hydrodynamic losses consist almost entirely of the profile drag or skin friction losses of the impeller and the stationary vanes. Assuming that the loss is proportional to the average relative velocity squared, i.e., in our case drag loss is proportional to $(c_{ave}'^2 + w_{ave}'^2)$, it can be shown that it is proportional to $R^2 + (1 - R)^2$, values of which are given in Table 1.

The calculated basic efficiencies of the different types of blading, accounting only for the profile drag losses, are given in the accompanying tabulation (reference 13).

50 per cent reaction	94.0 per cent
90 per cent reaction	92.4 per cent
110 per cent reaction	90.6 per cent

The advantage of the symmetrical velocity diagram in this respect is apparent. Owing to symmetry, the impeller and stationary blades effect the same fluid deflection. Thus the same profiles can be used but of opposite hand (mirror image). Inherently of higher specific speed, the symmetrical blading results in higher axial velocities (up to 700 ft./sec.) higher rotative speed, higher head per stage, smaller frontal area, a lower number of stages (for a given compression ratio), and a minimum weight. All these features make this design particularly desirable for the aviation gas turbine application. Peripheral velocities in excess of the acoustic velocity (over 1200 ft./sec.) have been used successfully. The Mach number based on the relative velocity is less than unity for the above conditions.

The fact that the blade curvature is the same for the impeller and stationary blades ($\alpha_1' - \alpha_2' = \beta_2' - \beta_1'$) permits use of the maximum possible deflection for both blades at the same time, thus achieving the maximum output from the compressor at the optimum efficiency.

Some disadvantages of the 50 per cent reaction blading may be pointed out: (a) the necessity of having an extra set of stationary blades ahead of the first-stage impeller and (b) high final outlet velocities requiring a more elaborate diffuser to reduce the velocity efficiently. However, since the number of stages and over-all size and weight of this type is lower than any other type, the above disadvantages are well compensated.

14.3 STAGE DESIGN PROCEDURE

(a) **Basic Considerations.** Before discussing the several phases of stage design the entire design procedure will be outlined to indicate the steps involved.

1. The design is made for one set of head-capacity conditions, or design point, which in general is assumed to be the point of best efficiency. The shape of the head-capacity characteristics, including the surge point and maximum flow, is estimated from previous experience and available typical performance data (such as given in references 2, 5, and 8).

2. The design is established for one design diameter first. For this it is convenient to select the mean effective diameter because at this diameter the head generated is equal to the total integrated head irrespective of whether free vortex or full forced vortex patterns of flow and load distribution along the radius are assumed. The mean effective diameter also divides the flow into two equal parts.

3. For a given application the type of blading, i.e., axial inlet, axial outlet, or 50 per cent reaction (symmetrical), is predetermined. Also the type of blade loading along the radius, which determines the blade twist (discussed later), is decided.

Since the 50 per cent reaction blading has proved advantageous as to efficiency, speed, and maximum output, and the majority of known and modern high pressure axial compressors are of this type, most of the discussion will be devoted to the symmetrical blading.

4. For design purposes the rate of flow or capacity should be reduced to the inlet volume (c.f.m.) and the compression ratio, or temperature rise, converted to the polytropic head. The speed in revolutions per minute should be tentatively selected. By dividing the total required head equally among the several stages, the specific speed n_s is calculated. The number of stages is adjusted to bring the specific speed in the desired range consistent with the type of blading preferred.

5. For the performance specific speed thus established, the hub ratio, the head coefficient ψ, the capacity coefficient ϕ, and optimum stage

efficiency are fixed in a rather narrow limit by existing experimental knowledge.

When the hub ratio and head and capacity coefficients are tentatively selected, the over-all features of the compressor (number of stages, outside diameter, and stage spacing) can be established without going into the details of the blade design.

6. When, for multistage axial compressors, a maximum head per stage and a minimum number of stages is the aim, steps 4 and 5 may

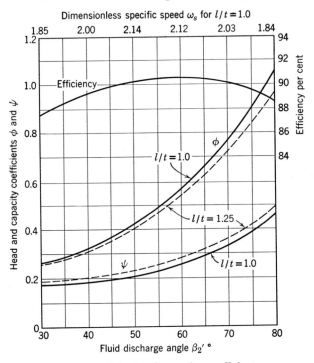

Fig. 14.4.   Head and capacity coefficients.

be by-passed and the stage head coefficient ψ and flow coefficient ϕ are selected from experimental data after the fluid discharge angle β_2' and the chord/spacing ratio l/t are settled.   Figure 14.4, based on the Howell data (reference 2) gives such information.   Drawing up the dimensionless velocity triangle completes the design of the blade at the design diameter.

7. Physical dimensions of the stage are determined as shown in Art. 14.3d.

8. Blade shapes are established for all radii following the accepted load distribution.

The design method presented below follows that accepted by the British National Gas Turbine Establishment (N.G.T.E.), as evidenced by the published articles by Howell and others (references 2, 5, 6, 7, 8, and 14), but it is modified in form to agree with terms, notation, and style of this book.

(b) **Cascade Test Data.** Selection of the actual blading is made from available cascade tests where the fluid deflection angles $\epsilon = \beta_2' - \beta_1'$ were measured rather than lift. Here β_1' is the fluid entrance angle. At the design point, this is also the blade entrance angle $\beta_1 = \beta_1'$ and the angle of incidence is assumed to be zero.‡ Angle β_2' is the fluid exit angle. The difference between the blade discharge angle β_2 and the fluid angle β_2' is called "fluid deviation."

$$\beta_2 - \beta_2' = \delta \tag{14.9}$$

For this Howell proposed an empirical relation

$$\delta = m(\beta_2 - \beta_1) \sqrt{\frac{t}{l}} = \beta_2 - \beta_2' \tag{14.10}$$

where

$$m = 0.23 \left(\frac{2l_c}{l}\right)^2 + 0.002(90 - \beta_2') \tag{14.11}$$

and l_c is the location of the maximum camber. Since, for the design point, $\beta_1 = \beta_1'$, the following relation between the fluid deflection, deviation, and blade curvature can be written.

$$\epsilon = \beta_2' - \beta_1' = (\beta_2 - \beta_1) - \delta \tag{14.12}$$

Relationships expressed by equations 14.9, 14.10, and 14.11 have been simplified by several investigators. Thus for a circular arc camber line ($l_c = 0.5$) and a value of β_2' about 75° equations 14.10 and 14.11 reduce to what is known as Constant's formula.

$$\delta = 0.26(\beta_2 - \beta_1)\sqrt{t/l} \tag{14.13}$$

For an average value of $l/t = 1$ this equation becomes

$$\beta_2 = \beta_2' + 0.35\epsilon \tag{14.14}$$

$$\beta_2' - \beta_1' = 0.74(\beta_2 - \beta_1) = \epsilon \tag{14.15}$$

‡ Note that the angle of incidence ($\beta_1' - \beta_1$) and the blade setting angle (β_2) are taken in respect to the blade entrance and exit angles and are not related to the chord angle. The chord angle plays a prominent part in the airfoil theory.

In the last form the relationship shows that for an assumed l/t ratio of unity the blade succeeds only in deflecting the fluid 74 per cent of its own curvature.

(c) **Selection of the Fluid Discharge Angle.** Figure 14.4 shows the attainable stage efficiency with different fluid exit angles. The efficiency is a maximum near $\beta_2' = 55$ to $60°$. This alone is sufficient reason for selecting β_2' in this range. Besides, it has been established experimentally that impellers with $\beta_2' > 60°$ show a more rapid drop

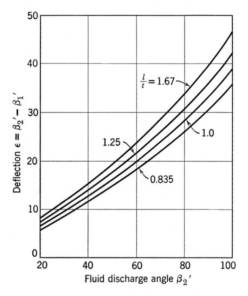

Fig. 14.5.   Fluid deflection angle.

of efficiency from its optimum value at higher speeds (or higher Mach numbers). It has also been established that for a given efficiency impellers with $\beta_2' = 60°$ produce a maximum head per stage, or heads higher than those produced by the impellers with $\beta_2' > 60°$. Thus angles higher than $60°$ have no advantage.

Figure 14.4 also shows ϕ and ψ values for two values of l/t (1.0 and 1.25). The average British designs have $l/t = 1.10$.

The impeller blade is determined by the blade curvature $(\beta_2 - \beta_1)$ and the blade setting angle in respect to the plane of rotation, β_2. To find these the deflection angle ϵ is read off Fig. 14.5 for a selected value of l/t. Then $\beta_1' = \beta_1$ are found from

$$\epsilon = \beta_2' - \beta_1' \tag{14.16}$$

The discharge angle β_2 now can be found from equations 14.10 and 14.11 for known values of β_2', β_1, l_c/l, and l/t.

Now the input velocity triangle can be drawn in the dimensionless form by expressing all velocities as ratios to the peripheral velocity ($u_m = 1$ at the mean effective diameter) and using the value of $\phi = c_m/u_m$ from Fig. 14.4. The value of $\Delta c_u'/u_m = \psi_i$ from the velocity triangle should be multiplied by the value of hydraulic efficiency $e_h \approx 0.90$ to obtain the value of ψ selected tentatively from Fig. 14.4.

The 10 per cent stage hydraulic loss is made up approximately of 4 per cent blading drag loss (both stationary and impeller), 2 per cent

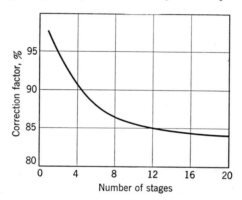

Fig. 14.6. Output correction factors.

for annulus friction, and the remaining 4 per cent in additional secondary losses in the actual stage (non-existing in the tunnel cascade flow).

For multistage performance the value of the head coefficient is multiplied by another correction factor Ω, values of which are given in Fig. 14.6. This accounts for the reduction of head produced on account of an uneven axial velocity distribution. Figure 14.7 shows that after the first three or four stages the axial velocity profiles become "peaky." After four stages, additional stages have little effect upon the velocity distribution.

In Art. 3.7f the effect of the uneven meridional velocity distribution on the theoretical head produced has been treated analytically, and the correction factors arrived at in a numerical example are not inconsistent with the values of Ω given in Fig. 14.6.

(*d*) **Physical Dimensions.** The peripheral velocity at the design impeller diameter is found from

$$\psi = Hg/u_m{}^2 \tag{14.17}$$

and the mean effective diameter can be found for a known r.p.m. from

$$u_m = (D_m \times \text{r.p.m.})/229 \qquad (14.18)$$

where D_m is in inches. The outside diameter D_o and the hub diameter D_h are established from

$$D_m = D_o{}^2(1 + \nu^2)/2 \qquad (14.19)$$

where ν is the hub ratio D_h/D_o tentatively selected at this point. This ratio has to satisfy the continuity equation given below.

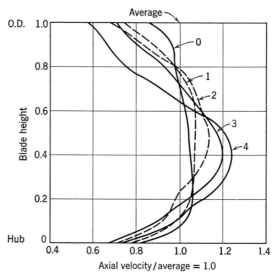

Fig. 14.7.   Axial velocity distribution, first four stages.

The average axial velocity c_m is known from

$$c_m = \phi u_m \qquad (14.20)$$

This should satisfy the continuity equation

$$c_m = \frac{\text{c.f.m.} \times 2.4}{(\pi/4)D_o{}^2(1 - \nu^2)} \qquad (14.21)$$

where D_o is in inches. It may be necessary to revise the hub ratio tentatively selected and review the diameters D_o and D_h. The peripheral speed at the outside diameter should be within the limit for the blade material.

The blade height (length) is now fixed by

$$b = (D_o - D_h)/2 \qquad (14.22)$$

The number of blades is decided upon from several conflicting considerations; efficiency, cost, weight, and strength. The number of blades determine the chord length l for a known l/t ratio. The aspect ratio b/l and blade thickness affect the blade strength, particularly as to tendency to vibrate. A longer chord means longer stages. Since it is universal practice to make loose blades and attach them rigidly to the hub, the maximum number of blades is restricted by the blade mounting arrangement. For efficiency and cost a minimum number of blades are favorable.

The blade thickness expressed in per cent of the chord length is selected entirely for strength reasons. At the design diameter the

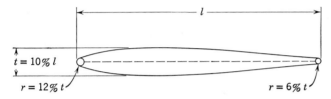

Station	0	1.25	2.5	5.0	7.5	10	15	20	30	40	50	60	70	80	90	95	100	
Upper and lower	0	1.65	2.27	3.08	3.62	4.02	4.55	4.83	5.00	4.89	4.57	4.05	3.37	2.54	1.60	1.06	0	% of l

Fig. 14.8.   Airfoil C4 thickness distribution; all values, per cent of l.

maximum blade thickness is from 10 to 15 per cent of the chord length. Hydraulically, a minimum thickness is preferred. It leads to a higher maximum Mach number corresponding to the maximum rate of flow of the compressor (cascade choking). This should be distinguished from the critical Mach number beyond which efficiency begins to decrease below a certain predetermined level owing to local compressibility effects.

The blade profile is drawn for the known inlet and outlet angles using either a circular arc or a parabolic curve for the camber line. The method of construction of the camber line was presented in Chapter 13. The thickness distribution along the camber line is selected from several profiles known for efficiency. Figure 14.8 shows the airfoil thickness distribution of British profile C4. When the actual maximum thickness is determined all the coordinates of the thickness profile are reduced or increased in the same proportion.

The thickness ordinates are plotted normal to the camber line, the stations being taken along the camber line and not along the chord.

14.4 BLADE TWIST

Introduction. Selection of the blade profile $(\beta_2 - \beta_1)$, the blade-setting angle (β_2), and the chord/spacing ratio l/t at any other than the design diameter is based on an assumption of the load distribution or the value of the head produced along the blade. The chord/spacing ratio usually increases toward the hub, which is the case when l is kept constant. In any case the blade thickness and chord length are determined by strength considerations in order to keep the bending stress at the root within permissible limits of the material used.

Selection of the pattern of load distribution along the radius determines the blade twist and has an immediate effect on the critical Mach number and maximum rotative speed. Thus it is directly connected with the maximum head produced by a stage. It is this consideration that determines the selection of the blading profiles along the radius. The optimum efficiency (at the most favorable speed) is next in importance. In practice some sacrifice in efficiency is allowed at the maximum operating speed. There are several blade forms in use known as: (1) free vortex, (2) constant reaction, (3) half-free vortex, and (4) forced vortex or solid rotation. The tangential velocity distribution along the radius follows a certain law, and thus velocity triangles, Euler's and input, can be drawn without going through the design procedure outlined in the preceeding article for the mean effective diameter. Euler's velocity triangle really determines the blade entrance and exit angles at any desired diameter. The input triangles are drawn to determine the head produced at each radius. Note that any of the above patterns of flow prescribing the load distribution along the blade can be applied to any of the types of blade design, however this discussion will be confined to the symmetrical or 50 per cent reaction blade at the design diameters.

(a) **Free Vortex Pattern of Flow.** In this pattern the tangential velocity distribution, both at inlet and outlet along the radius, follows the law

$$c_{u1}'r = \text{Constant} \tag{14.23}$$

$$c_{u2}'r = \text{Constant} \tag{14.24}$$

This means that the change in the tangential velocity is inversely proportional to the radius

$$\Delta c_u'r = \text{Constant} \tag{14.25}$$

which leads to the condition that the head generated at all radii is the same

$$\Delta c_u' u = gH = \text{Constant} \qquad (14.26)$$

In the early stage of axial flow impeller theory it was a general belief that the free vortex pattern of flow was a necessary requirement to have a stable orderly flow through the impeller. With any other tangential velocity distribution, it was thought, cross flows would result, thus adversely affecting the efficiency. It is obvious that the condition defined by equation 14.26 is not satisfied by any other mode of flow through the impeller, although optimum efficiencies equal or exceeding those obtained with free vortex design are on record.

A constant axial velocity is assumed, as a rule, for the free vortex blading design. In a multistage compressor this is never realized, as is shown in Fig. 14.7, with any type of blading. Thus the requirement of equation 14.26 is not met in actual machines.

$\Delta c_u'$ and c_m being known, the blade entrance and exit velocity triangle can be drawn for any of the three profile designs shown in Figs. 14.1, 14.2, and 14.3. There is no need to draw the input velocity triangle as the head produced is assumed constant along the radius.

Figure 14.9 shows velocity triangles at three diameters for a 50 per cent reaction triangle at the design diameter. Note that reaction is increasing from the hub to the tip of the blade. Thus the advantages of the 50 per cent reaction design are not fully realized. This type of load distribution was only an intermediate step toward the constant reaction blading.§

In Art. 1.3 it has been shown that a free vortex is only one mode of circular fluid motion out of a great many, all of which are stable. In Chapter 4 a detailed comparison was made between the free and forced vortex pattern of flow through a stage. As far as the blade twist is concerned, the half-free vortex and constant reaction blades fall between the free and forced vortex blades. Thus their characteristics are intermediate between those extremes.

(b) **Constant Reaction Blade.** As the title implies the blade profiles at any radii are arrived at by assuming a constant reaction and symmetrical velocity triangles at all radii. Usually $\Delta c_u' r = \text{Constant}$ is assumed at all radii. Since all velocity triangles are symmetrical, they can be drawn for a given axial velocity c_m and known value of $\Delta c_u'$. Note that the free vortex requirement is not satisfied either at the impeller inlet or impeller discharge. In Fig. 14.9 the tangential

§ Early British designs "Anne," "Ruth," and "Freda" had 50 per cent reaction *only at the hub* and free vortex load distribution along the blade (reference 2).

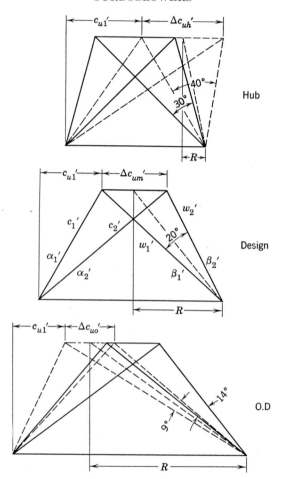

Fig. 14.9.   Constant reaction velocity triangles, solid lines; free vortex, dashed
lines (data by Howell).

components of the absolute velocity at the impeller outside diameter
and the hub have the following approximate ratios.

$$\frac{c_{u1o}'}{c_{u1h}'} = \left(\frac{D_o}{D_h}\right)^{2.0} \quad \text{and} \quad \frac{c_{u2o}'}{c_{u2h}'} = \left(\frac{D_o}{D_h}\right)^{\frac{1}{2}} \quad (14.27)$$

Thus we find a superforced vortex velocity distribution at the impeller
entrance and half-forced vortex at the impeller discharge.‖

Constant's statement (reference 6) is significant in this connection:

‖ These two types of vortex are tabulated under items 6 and 9 on Table 1, p. 5,
Chapter 1.

"This departure from free vortex blading deserves some comment. We had for some time suspected that the losses in a forced vortex might not be appreciably different from those in a free vortex." And in the next paragraph we find: "The general conclusion that was drawn from these test results and from the various other researches that were proceeding on the same subject, was that it was possible to impose on the flow through a compressor or turbine a forced vortex having any angular momentum distribution over a comparatively wide range without serious changes in the blading efficiency."

Carter's statement (reference 7) is more specific on this subject: "Radial equilibrium will be established with any arbitrary type of blading but it has been argued, rather erroneously, that the most efficient form would be that in which radial equilibrium was automatically satisfied without any radial flow."

Both statements are of particular interest as apparently they were arrived at by reasoning different from that given in the article 1.3.¶

By comparing free vortex blading with constant reaction blading in Fig. 14.9 it becomes evident that the advantages of the symmetrical velocity triangle and 50 per cent reaction are non-existent in the free vortex blading except at one radius. Reaction and Mach number, based on the relative velocity, increase between the design and outside diameters of the impeller.

Also note that the free vortex blade is more curved; thus at the hub the fluid deflection is $\beta_{2h}' - \beta_{1h}' = 40°$ while for constant reaction $\beta_{2h}' - \beta_{1h}' = 30°$. The free vortex blade is more twisted at the same time, thus

For free vortex

$$\beta_{2h}' - \beta_{2o}' = 61°$$

$$\beta_{1h}' - \beta_{1o}' = 11°$$

¶ The author's pronouncements on the subject date back to 1943 (*A.S.M.E. Trans.*, Aug., 1945, p. 465; May, 1948, p. 305). The forced vortex pattern of flow for an axial blower was used prior to 1928 by Schmidt (reference 4, Chapter 13). Ponomareff (reference 3, p. 306) himself an adherent to the free vortex theory admits "that the forced vortex flow pattern may be successfully used, as well as many other patterns, in designing of an axial-flow compressor." Martinuzzi, on the other hand, states, "The fact that constant-reaction, half-reaction, and solid rotation blading can give quite reasonably high efficiency shows that the premises of continental (free vortex) theory are not necessarily infallible. Consequently, a critical examination is desirable." (*A.S.M.E. Trans.*, May, 1949, p. 331.) This has been done by British designers, who had based their early designs on the free vortex reasoning. Later deviations from the free vortex theory and an introduction of patterns of flow which violate this theory were arrived at in way of progress based on the improvements in performance.

For constant reaction

$$\beta_{2h}' - \beta_{2o}' = 25°$$

$$\beta_{1h}' - \beta_{1o}' = 25°$$

The Mach number varies little along the blade length in a constant reaction design, whereas it varies considerably for free vortex blading. This affects the blade thickness distribution. Free vortex blades have to be thin at the places of high Mach numbers, i.e., at the tips of the blades, whereas constant reaction blades can be made of uniform thickness and width.

(*c*) **Half-Free Vortex Blading.** This occupies a middle position between the free vortex and constant reaction blading. It is obtained by dividing the sum of various fluid angles of the free vortex and constant reaction by two. Hydraulically this form of blading falls between the first described two. Having no advantages of its own this type of blading was only an intermediate step from the free vortex to the constant reaction type.

Below are compiled some figures on the relative performance of the three types of blading from the original Howell paper (reference 2). All three were designed for the tabulated identical conditions.

c.f.m.	39,500	Reaction at design diam.	0.50
Axial velocity, ft.	500	Discharge angle at O.D.	56°
Impeller O.D., in.	23	Mach number at O.D.	0.72
Hub ratio	0.695		

The results are given in the accompanying tabulation.

	Free Vortex	Half Vortex	Constant Reaction
r.p.m.	7500	8500	9500
Head per stage, ft.	5000	5750	6350
Specific speed n_s	2500	2570	2650
Chord length, in.	1.0	1.2	1.5

Howell suggests that free vortex and half-vortex blading may be used when a lower rotative speed is desired. But this could be accomplished without sacrificing any of the advantages of the constant reaction blading by using a different hub ratio and thus achieving a desired variation of specific speed as discussed in Art. 14.6.

(*d*) **Forced Vortex Blading.** This is also known as "solid rotation," since all particles of fluid rotate with the same angular velocity as if they were parts of a rigid body. It is evident that the tangential components of the absolute velocity vary directly as the radius and that the head generated varies directly as the square of the radius. In the current literature the term "solid rotation" is used to designate several types of blading differing widely as to degree of reaction or blading load distribution. They can be described in three groups:

1. Blading that provides a forced vortex pattern of flow ahead of the impeller (reference 10). Half-free vortex blading mentioned above is approximately of the solid rotation type, i.e., c_{u1}' varies directly as the radius. Any desired blade load distribution (variation of $\Delta c_u'$) can be combined with the solid body prerotation.

2. Forced vortex pattern of flow is at the discharge from the impellers, and that means that c_{u2}' varies directly as the radius. The degree of prerotation and blade load distribution can still vary subject to a limitation that $c_{u1}' + \Delta c_u' = c_{u2}'$ at all radii.

3. When both c_{u1}' and c_{u2}' vary directly as the radius, $\Delta c_u'$ follows the same law. Then the pattern of flow becomes full forced vortex flow throughout the whole stage. This has been treated in detail in Chapter 4, and also in Chapter 13 mostly in connection with a design with no prerotation ahead of the impeller. Full forced vortex pattern of flow can be combined with any degree of prerotation or any degree of reaction. Figure 14.10 shows velocity triangles (Euler's), one at the outside diameter, the other at the hub and drawn for 50 per cent reaction at all radii and forced vortex flow before and beyond the impeller. The diagram embodies the principle outlined in Chapter 4 (Figs. 4.8 to 4.11) and otherwise is self explanatory.

In addition to the advantages associated with the symmetrical diagrams at all radii a forced vortex design offers the advantage of a considerably higher integrated head than is possible with the free vortex layout ($\Delta c_u'r = $ Constant). Thus, if in both types the head generated at the hub is the same, then the total integrated head of the forced vortex impeller is expressed by the formula

$$H_{\text{forced}} = H_{\text{free}} \times \tfrac{1}{2}\left(1 + \frac{1}{\nu^2}\right) \tag{14.28}$$

Thus, for instance, for a hub ratio of 0.70,

$$H_{\text{forced}} = H_{\text{free}} \times 1.52$$

Equation 14.28 is based on equation 4.10, Chapter 4.

Although, in the above example, the head at the periphery is about twice that at the hub (disregarding the effect of clearance and the stationary wall), the blade sections near the blade tip are not overloaded as can be seen from the following considerations from Chapter 4.

*The dimensionless head $\psi = Hg/u^2$ is constant at all radii, which means
that energy applied to the fluid per foot of peripheral velocity is constant.*
Therefore, if the blade chord is constant at all radii, the load on the
blade profile is the same along the blade length.

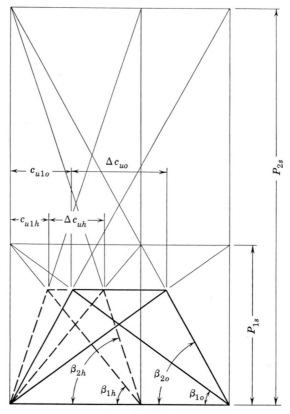

Fig. 14.10.   Forced vortex 50 per cent reaction Euler's velocity triangles; solid line
at O.D.; dashed line at hub.

To produce the extra head the blade curvature at the tip is higher
than it is at the hub or

$$(\beta_{2o} - \beta_{1o}) > (\beta_{2h} - \beta_{1h})$$

This is the reverse of the condition of blading with the constant reaction and constant head along the blade.   Obviously at some intermediate type of blade loading it is possible to have both stationary
and rotor blades of constant curvature only slightly twisted from tip
to hub.

Low pressure tests ($u = 275$ ft./sec.) show an impeller efficiency equal to or exceeding that of best known designs, i.e., 95.0 per cent. The possibilities and limitations of forced vortex multistage compressors have not been investigated, judged from the lack of published reports.

Of particular interest, of course, is the effect of Mach number at high rotative speeds. Although a greater curvature of the blade tip tends to lower the critical Mach number, it is possible that a compromise design (constant Δc_u along the radius, for instance) may lead to a higher compression ratio without sacrificing efficiency.

Advantages in efficiency and quietness of operation are claimed for impellers with an increasing loading of the blades from the hub to the periphery (reference 12) but experimental proof of the claim is lacking.

Although we may not have information on the latest British designs of axial flow compressors for some time, it becomes apparent (through statements such as made by Carter** that the requirement of a constant head along the blade has been abandoned. This may only mean that higher load is applied to the blade toward the tip as the blade at the root was already loaded to the stalling limit.

In full forced vortex pattern of flow fluid enters the impeller under a head which increases parabolically from hub to tip of the blades. The impeller raises this head, still maintaining a square paraboloid of head distribution from hub to periphery. In the stationary blades the tangential component of the absolute velocity is reduced to its inlet value, the pressure increasing accordingly. Thus the inlet distribution is restored] at a higher pressure level, the process repeating from stage to stage. The last row of stationary blades takes out all the tangential component of the absolute velocity, and the flow leaves the last stage axially. The change of momentum (velocity into pressure) occurs in the stationary vanes on the molecular scale without "cross flows."

The fluid rotates with a constant angular velocity which is lower than that of the impeller. The fluid angular velocity is a maximum when it leaves the impeller, and it is a minimum when fluid leaves the stationary blades. With the rotor running at constant angular velocity, a constant angular velocity of the fluid is the easiest thing to imagine and the most natural to expect.

(*e*) **Average Axial Velocity.** A constant axial velocity is commonly assumed for all types of blading design. This is never realized even under the most favorable conditions (single stage). In multistage

---

** "In practice we usually have to adopt a design having a radial variation of circulation along the blade." (Reference 7, p. 26.)

compressors, after three or four stages, a velocity distribution is reached having a maximum to minimum ratio of two to one as shown on Fig. 14.7. Under such conditions the question arises: How much faith can be put in designs when one of the basic assumptions is not fulfilled in practice even approximately?

The answer lies in the fact that the average axial velocity in its dimensionless form $c_m/u = \phi$ should be looked upon as an "over-all" design factor connecting the rate of flow with the size of the stage. Some of such design constants in use are expressed in terms of a fictitious non-existent velocity, which, however, serve the same purpose as ϕ. Examples of such factors were given in Chapter 6, from which equations 6.22 and 6.24 are repeated below, and are applicable primarily to centrifugal and mixed flow impellers.

$$\delta_r = (Q/R_2{}^2)(1/u_2) \tag{6.22}$$

$$\delta = (4Q/\pi D_2{}^2)(1/u_2) = \delta_r/\pi \tag{6.24}$$

In the above equations, R_2 and D_2 are the outside impeller radius and diameter, Q is the rate of flow or capacity of the machine, and u_2 is the peripheral velocity at the impeller outside diameter. The properties of such design constants are: (1) for a given design the capacity coefficient (or constant in any of the above forms) remains constant for all homologous machines; (2) for machines of consistent design the variation of the capacity constant is continuous for different specific speeds. Thus the capacity coefficient ϕ (and ψ) form a basis for evaluating the performance of a continuous series of designs in terms of controlling design quantities.

Designs of mixed flow impellers are based on such average "over-all" capacity coefficients, although it is definitely known that the meridional velocity through the impeller is not uniform on account of a 90° turn at the impeller inlet. However, such design methods resulted in perfection of hydraulic forms of impellers, which show efficiencies in excess of 90 per cent in the centrifugal pump and water turbine fields. Single stage blowers of later design are approaching this mark very rapidly.

It may be mentioned here that in the case of the simplest flow pattern in a circular pipe, where the velocity distribution can be considered as known in terms of Reynolds number, its performance is expressed in terms of design factors based on the average velocity, or "over-all" characteristic of the pipe, in the form of a friction loss coefficient.

Attempts have been made in some designs to prescribe an axial velocity distribution different from the constant average velocity, mostly in order to satisfy the "radial equilibrium" or free-vortex conditions. Any such provisions to control the axial velocity distribution have shown very little effect upon the ultimate velocity distribution of multistage compressors.

(*f*) **Stationary Blades of Constant Curvature.** These blades have been used without any detrimental effect on the optimum efficiency. Constant (reference 6) reports 90 per cent efficiency with the design "Freda," which had untwisted stationary blades, all alike for nine stages. The impeller design was of the free vortex type at the impeller approach with 50 per cent reaction at the hub. Ponomareff (reference 3) shows 88 per cent efficiency with constant curvature stationary blades, in a twenty-stage compressor having axial inlet impeller blading and free vortex load distribution.

It is possible to design an impeller which would require constant curvature stationary blading. This leads to the condition $\Delta c_u' = $ Constant along the radius, which corresponds to the type of vortex given by item 5, Table 1, Chapter 1. This type is perfectly stable as are the several known types already quoted and has been tried on an actual design with a normal efficiency (reference 11).

(*g*) **Staging.** As the gas progresses from stage to stage its volume is reduced. Since the average axial velocity remains essentially the same (it reduces slowly) the area of the annulus should be reduced to accommodate the same mass of flow. This can be accomplished either by increasing the hub diameter with constant blade tip diameter, or by keeping the hub diameter constant and reducing the blade outside diameter. Hydraulically this results in a decrease of specific speed from stage to stage, a decrease in the blade aspect ratio (b/l), or ratio of the blade length (height) to the chord length, and an increase in the hub ratio. All these factors tend to reduce the stage efficiency and set the practical limit to the number of stages in a single unit. Constant (reference 14) sets a compression ratio 6:1 as a limit for a single unit after which compounding should be resorted to. Use of two mechanically independent compressors in series results in a more flexible turbine operation with greater freedom from the danger of surging. In land and marine applications compounding makes it easier to use intercoolers.

Hydraulically compounding permits selection of a more favorable specific speed, type of blading, and hub ratio by changing speed and diameter of the high pressure compressor.

It would be possible to improve the hub ratio for high pressure stages of a multistage compressor by using lower specific speed velocity diagrams with lower values of $\phi = c_m/u$, thus changing from constant reaction to axial inlet and to axial outlet blading. Since temperature of the fluid is increasing from stage to stage this scheme would not incur any danger of Mach number effects. However, such a design would introduce considerable manufacturing difficulties owing to the variety of blading, with little advantages to compensate them, as the two latter types of blading are inherently less efficient than 50 per cent constant reaction blading.

A number of designs are known having efficiencies among the highest which use identical blades for all stages, set at the same angle and cut to suit. The British "Freda" design previously referred to is of this type.

(*h*) **Experimental Results.** There are a number of design factors and physical dimensions which do not enter directly into the design calculations but which have an important bearing on the hydraulic and mechanical performance of axial flow compressors. Practical limitations for such factors have been established experimentally. The proper selection of the values to suit a particular design requires experience and knowledge of the effects of such factors on the performance of a complete unit. The most important among such factors are:

1. *Mach number* is defined as w_1'/a, where w_1' is the entrance relative velocity and a is the acoustic velocity corresponding to the inlet temperature. The critical Mach number is about 0.70 to 0.75; a further increase of speed results in rapid deterioration of efficiency.

The effects of Mach number are reduced by: lower camber and thickness of the blade, location of the camber at 0.5 of the chord, and sharpening of the inlet edges of the blades (reference 16).

As a result of extensive high speed testing, the British use a circular arc for the camber line on their later designs as it gives a better performance at high Mach numbers. The parabolic blading although giving higher choking flow (maximum capacity) had appreciably lower critical Mach number (reference 18).

2. *Reynolds number* $Re = lw_{ave}'/\nu$ where w_{ave}' is the average relative velocity, l is the chord and ν is the kinematic viscosity of the fluid. In normal designs $Re \geq 300,000$. Values of Re below this lead to a reduction of efficiency.

With low head and low speed impellers, w_{ave}' is low, and changing l, the chord length, without changing the spacing ratio l/t is the only means to increase Re. For that reason fan impellers have a few long vanes and long hubs.

3. *Hub ratio* varies from 0.6 to 0.85. A number of existing high pressure compressors have hub ratios from 0.7 to 0.82.

For a given type of blading, say 50 per cent constant reaction, variation of the hub ratio is the only means to get a variation of specific speed n_s. This may be necessary when designing a single-, two-, or three-stage compressor, as it may be found impossible to use the specific speed adopted for multistage design. Variation of the discharge angle β_2 (or β_2') does not produce appreciable variation of the specific speed (Fig. 14.4); this finding is in agreement with centrifugal blower experience.

4. *The chord/spacing ratio* varies from 1.0 to 1.25 at the design diameter. A constant width blade results in an increase of l/t from tip to the hub, inversely as the hub ratio. Thus, if $l/t = 1.0$ at the outside diameter, with a hub ratio 0.7, the ratio $l/t = 1.425$ at the hub for a constant l blade.

It has been pointed out that axial inlet and axial outlet blades have a maximum Mach number at the blade tips. To improve the critical Mach number of these blades, the blade thickness is reduced from the blade root to the tips, and hence for mechanical reasons the chord length has to be reduced. This in turn reduces the maximum load carrying capacity of the blades.

5. *The running radial clearance* between the blades and the stationary shell is 1 to 2 per cent of the blade height. This equals approximately 0.001 in. per inch of the impeller outside diameter. Doubling this clearance will reduce the efficiency about two to three points.

6. *The axial clearance* between the stationary and moving blades varies from 0.2 to 0.5 of the chord length, higher speeds requiring larger clearances.

7. *The number of blades.* For a given impeller diameter and selected l/t ratio the actual chord length determines the number of blades. A greater blade curvature ($\beta_2 - \beta_1$) and higher speed call for a longer chord. For that reason in the axial outlet type of blading, owing to lower curvature and lower maximum speed, a shorter chord can be used. Manufacturing methods and strength considerations have an important bearing on the selection of the chord length and number of blades. To date no simple rule has been devised connecting the several variables involved.

Several existing designs of the constant reaction type have about two blades per inch of impeller diameter.

14.5 REVIEW OF BRITISH DEVELOPMENT OF AXIAL COMPRESSORS

(*a*) **Four Steps in Progress.** The design method and data presented in this chapter are based on British publications, issued over a 10-year period, that describe the development of the British gas turbine under the direction of the National Gas Turbine Establishment (N.G.T.E.). Although data on the latest British designs may not be known for some time, a study of their reports indicates a gradual adjustment of their theoretical reasoning as experimental knowledge was accumulated. Several steps in the evolution of the British design methods are very significant and will be reviewed here.

1. (a) The value of 50 per cent reaction velocity triangles was realized very early. However, on early designs, the symmetrical velocity triangle was used at the hub only.

(b) Free vortex velocity distribution ahead and past the impeller was provided.

(c) Constant head was assumed along the radius.

(d) Euler's two-dimensional theory was used as a basis of theoretical reasoning in connection with a constant axial velocity assumption.

(e) Cascade test data in terms of fluid deflection and deviation were used for velocity diagrams instead of single airfoil theory and single airfoil data in terms of lift coefficient and chord angle.

2. (a) The 50 per cent reaction velocity diagrams were placed at the mean blade diameter.

(b) The free vortex pattern of flow ahead and past the impeller was still used.

(c) Constant head along the blade was retained.

3. (a) Constant 50 per cent reaction used along the blade.

(b) *Free vortex pattern of flow before and after the impeller was abandoned.*

(c) Constant head along the blade was retained.

4. (a) Constant 50 per cent reaction along the blade retained.

(b) *Free vortex pattern was entirely abandoned.*

(c) *Constant head (or constant circulation) along the blade was discarded in favor of increasing the blade load toward the tip (blade was always fully loaded at the hub).*

There is little information available on the last or fourth stage of the development. The trend toward the forced vortex or solid rotation pattern of flow is evident. But limitations imposed by the maximum Mach number may require a compromise design such as constant tangential velocity increment along the radius.

Note also that in later stages of the development new blade forms were tested by the British in special experimental units, single-stage and multistage. Some of them were operated on water at suitable speeds. This offered a considerable advantage over tests of cascades in wind tunnels as the blade performance was established in its normal rotary operation requiring no further corrections.†† This is in agreement with the normal practice in the field of centrifugal and axial flow pumps and water turbines; i.e., to test all new impeller designs in suitable casings, using models when testing full-size units, is not practical. The progress in British development was evident in improvement of efficiency to about 91 per cent polytropic, production of a maximum output for a given size and weight of the unit and increasing the compression ratio to over 7:1 in one unit without sacrificing efficiency.

In retrospect it can be said that there were two circumstances that retarded the progress of the development of the high pressure axial flow compressor:

1. Early publicity connected with axial outlet blading (reference 1). This type of blading proved to be inferior to several other possible types.

2. A preconception that the free vortex pattern of flow was the only one which was stable under conditions of flow existing in the axial flow stage. Stated differently, it was a fallacy to believe that any deviation from the free vortex pattern of flow in an axial compressor is injurious to the stage efficiency. A constant head along the blade is a part of the free vortex pattern of flow.

The literature on the subject in the United States is very scarce and originates, with few exceptions, from sources not connected with the industry. Therefore, it neither represents the state of the art nor suggests any trends in the design. The government sponsored research programs have been dispersed amongst several institutions with unavoidable duplications of efforts resulting in conflict of ideas and lack of continuity in planning. The published results are fragmentary, and it is impossible to piece them together into any kind of consistent design method or detect any degree of progress.

The European Continental practice (Swiss and German) is characterized by (1) use of airfoil theory and lift coefficients as a basis of design; (2) free vortex pattern of flow and constant head along the blade; (3) use of relatively low impeller discharge angles and low values of the capacity coefficients (reference 5, p. 455).

The early Continental designs were based on the axial outlet velocity triangles (Reaction > 1.0); while for later multistage compressors an

†† Constant's statement on this subject is of interest: "Unless some new base profile is introduced, the basic data now available are probably adequate and little further routine wind tunnel testing will be necessary. Our wind tunnels are, therefore, being diverted to other uses and attention is being concentrated to an increasing extent on the performance of rotating machinery" (reference 18).

axial inlet (reaction, about 0.9) were adopted. The symmetrical velocity triangles (reaction, 0.5) if used are applied only at the design diameter with a constant head distribution along the blade. The constant reaction designs (0.5) are treated with reservations as conflicting with the free vortex theory which is considered the only sound basis for the design of turbomachines. The forced vortex, or "solid rotation" is not mentioned in the latest writings on the subject (reference 19).

(b) **Conversion Formulas.** One of the difficulties encountered in following the literature on axial flow compressors is the lack of generally accepted definitions of the head and capacity coefficients. Table 2 contains coefficients in use and conversion factors in terms of

TABLE 2. CONVERSION FORMULAS FOR HEAD AND CAPACITY
COEFFICIENTS FOR AXIAL FLOW IMPELLERS

No.	Conversion Formula	Numerical Value for $\nu = 0.7$	Definition of Coefficient
1	$\phi = \phi_m$	1.0	$\phi = \phi_m = c_m/u_m$
2	$\psi = \psi_m$	1.0	$\psi = \psi_m = gH/u_m^2$
3	$\phi = \phi_{\mathrm{ave}} \sqrt{2A}/B$	1.015	$\phi_{\mathrm{ave}} = c_m/u_{\mathrm{ave}}$
4	$\psi = \psi_{\mathrm{ave}} B^2/4A$	0.485	$\psi_{\mathrm{ave}} = 2gH/u_{\mathrm{ave}}^2$
5	$\phi = \phi_o(2/A)^{1/2}$	1.16	$\phi_o = c_m/u_o$
6	$\psi = \psi_o 1/A$	0.667	$\psi_o = 2gH/u_o^2 \approx 2\Delta p/\rho u_o^2$
7	$\phi = q_s \dfrac{4}{\pi^2(2 - A) \sqrt{A}}$	0.925	$q_s = Q/nD_o^3$
8	$\psi = C_p \dfrac{2}{\pi^2 A}$	0.136	$C_p = \Delta p/\rho n^2 D_o^2$
9	$\psi = \psi_T(e_p B^2/4A)$	0.437 ($e_p = 0.90$)	$\psi_T = 2C_p\Delta T/u_{\mathrm{ave}}^2 = 2\Delta p/\rho u_{\mathrm{ave}}^2 e_p$

u_m is peripheral velocity based on the mean effective diameter.
u_{ave} is peripheral velocity based on the average diameter.
u_o is peripheral velocity based on outside diameter.
ΔT is measured stage temperature rise.
e_p is stage polytropic efficiency.
$A = 1 + \nu^2$.
$B = 1 + \nu$.
$\nu = D_h/D_o$ hub ratio.

the hub ratio and head and capacity coefficients adopted in this book. One column contains the numerical values of the conversion factors for the hub ratio 0.7 to give an illustration of the order of the conversion factors.

14.6 SPECIFIC SPEED OF AXIAL FLOW COMPRESSORS

This is referred to the first stage performance. When used as a part of the gas turbine plant, specific speed of the compressor always can be selected by adjusting the speed of the unit and number of stages within the desired range. Thus a majority of British designs have specific speed n_s of approximately 2800 based on the inlet volume in c.f.m. Changing the fluid discharge angle β_2' does not produce a marked difference in specific speed.

(a) **Hub Ratio.** However, when the number of stages of a compressor is small (say, two, three, or four) or when designing a single-stage axial blower and the selection of speed is restricted, it may be necessary to resort to a specific speed different from that adopted for multistage designs. There are two means to vary specific speed of an axial flow stage: (1) by changing the hub ratio and (2) by changing the blade solidity. By referring to equation 13.9 reproduced below

$$n_s = 2495[(1 - \nu^2)/(1 + \nu^2)]^{\frac{1}{2}}\omega_s \qquad (13.9)$$

it will be seen that for a constant dimensionless specific speed ω_s different specific speeds can be obtained by selecting the hub ratio. For example, if with the hub ratio 0.7 specific speed $n_s = 2800$ is obtained, by using $\nu = 0.75$ specific speed will drop to $n_s = 2300$ approximately. But since values of ϕ and ψ are functions of the hub ratio the above relationship is approximate only. It has been shown in Art. 6.4b that when impeller discharge angle is varied, holding the impeller profile (or hub ratio) the same dimensionless specific speed ω_s remains constant.

Actually there is a slight variation of ω_s for different fluid discharge angles as shown on the upper scale in Fig. 14.4 for $l/t = 1.0$. By using $l/t = 1.25$ the dimensionless specific speed ω_s is reduced; for instance, for $\beta_2' = 60°$, $\omega_s = 1.89$, as compared with $\omega_s = 2.12$ for $l/t = 1.0$.

(b) **Solidity.** Increasing or decreasing the blade solidity (l/t) affects the values of ϕ and ψ and hence ω_s. Thus, different specific speeds can be obtained. For instance, by referring to Fig. 14.4, if the blading is changed from $l/t = 1.0$ to $l/t = 1.25$, the specific speed will decrease inversely approximately as $\sqrt{1.25}$. However, variation of l/t should be used with great discretion as the blade performance is intimately related to the l/t ratio. An increase of $l/t > 1.25$ leads to excessive friction losses. On the other hand, a reduction of $l/t < 1.0$ may lead to stalling with the high discharge angles. Also with a low l/t ratio the number of blades may be reduced to increase the Reynolds number.

(c) **Degree of Reaction.** By referring to Table 1 it will be noticed that the degree of reaction has no bearing on the specific speed as w_s is essentially the same for the three types of blading. Thus variation of the performance specific speed n_s can be obtained by variation of the hub ratio according to equation 13.9 quoted above. It has been suggested that the axial outlet type of blading be used to improve the blade aspect ratio (b/l) for the high pressure stages of a multistage compressor. However, the same result can be obtained with constant reaction blading by merely using lower values for the discharge angle. Thus, the good features of the constant reaction blading are not sacrificed.

(d) **Blade Loading.** By referring to Art. 14.4c, it will be observed that a different load distribution along the blade, for the same velocity triangle at the design diameter, results in a minor variation of the specific speed. Again, the same or a greater variation of specific speed can be realized as shown above while retaining the 50 per cent reaction at all radii.‡‡

14.7 EXAMPLES AND APPLICATION OF AXIAL FLOW COMPRESSORS

(a) **Field of Application.** Although developed primarily for gas turbine application, axial flow compressors gradually find their way into other fields to compete with multistage centrifugal compressors. High efficiency is the only advantage of axial flow compressors which remains valid and of importance for the stationary installations. Small size and light weight are of not much value for such installations, particularly in view of the fact that they are not reflected in the price of the units which is of the same order as that of centrifugal compressors. On the other hand disadvantages of axial compressors are: a limited operating range, greater vulnerability to corrosion and erosion, and susceptibility to deposits. All these account for the reluctance of the users of such equipment in accepting axial flow compressors for services where centrifugal compressors were used heretofore.

Since size and weight are of little importance in the stationary installations, there is no point in operating axial compressors above the optimum efficiency speed, at which these machines are normally rated (Fig. 14.19).

(b) **Axial Flow Compressors for Blast Furnaces.** Owing to their limitations, only a few axial compressors are in use outside the gas turbine application. Since axial compressors are in par-

---

‡‡ Howell suggests utilizing blading of different load distribution to obtain some speed variation (Fig. 93, reference 2). None of British writings on the axial flow compressors use the concept of specific speed for classifying their designs. Also the hub ratio as a type number is not utilized in their discussions perhaps because their problems at the time were restricted only to one application, i.e., aircraft jet propulsion.

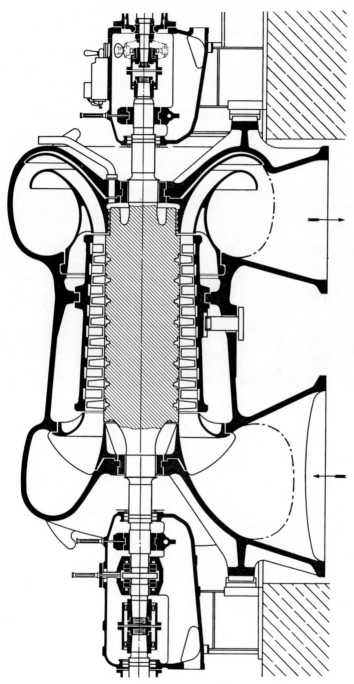

Fig. 14.11. Sulzer axial flow compressor.

ticular suited for large volumes at moderate pressures, blast furnace service was the first field invaded in Europe by axial compressors with a marked degree of success. Elaborate controlling devices were developed to permit volume variation required for this service.

Figure 14.11 shows a Sulzer eight-stage axial compressor with the rotor made out of a one-piece forging with constant hub diameter. The reduction of the blade height for high pressure stages is accomplished by reducing the diameter of the casing. A curved vaneless diffuser is provided beyond the last stage leading the flow into a discharge collecting chamber of constant area. Several such units were

Fig. 14.12. Escher Wyss axial flow compressor.

sold for blast furnaces. Two ten-stage units sold to a large French steel mill are rated 74,200 c.f.m., 40 p.s.i.a., 6900 hp. variable speed motor drive through a step-up gear at 5680 r.p.m. Nine units ranging from 13,000 to 125,000 c.f.m. were installed by this firm for blast furnace service, driven by steam turbines or synchronous motors, except one unit (59,000 c.f.m.) which is driven by a Sulzer gas turbine operating on blast furnace gas.

Figure 14.12 shows an eight stage Escher Wyss axial compressor, sold for blast furnace service, rated at 57,300 c.f.m. at 31.75 p.s.i.a. motor driven through a speed increaser at 4900 r.p.m. This machine has been in successful operation since 1949. Two steam-turbine driven units were on order at the time of this writing. Note that in this compressor the rotating blades are mounted on individual disks on a heavy shaft. No seals are provided between the rotor and the stationary blades. Due to a small pressure rise across the stationary blades, omission of seals does not incur any appreciable loss in efficiency with axial inlet or axial outlet impeller blading. A long straight-walled vaneless diffuser leads the flow from the last stage to the discharge nozzle. In this machine, the outside diameter of the stationary blades is constant, but the rotating disks have larger diameters toward the last stage.

Figure 14.13 shows a seven-stage Escher Wyss axial compressor with impeller blades automatically adjusted to meet variable head-capacity requirements at constant speed. Although this particular machine was built for a wind tunnel application, the same design is offered for blast furnace service. When there is much more gas available than

Fig. 14.13. Escher Wyss seven-stage axial flow compressor with automatically adjustable blades.

required for the gas turbine drive a variable pitch compressor run at constant speed can be coupled to drive an alternator. Note that an axial outlet permits an efficient recovery of pressure at discharge.

Figure 14.14 shows a Brown Boveri axial compressor with an axial outlet. The rotating blades are mounted on the several disks, two stages on each, the disks are bolted together to form a continuous drum with close running clearances between the drum and the stationary blades. The drum is of constant diameter.

Brown Boveri lists three steam-turbine-driven axial flow blowers among fifteen blast-furnace blowers built in 1952.

In 1953 Brown Boveri reported a sale of six axial flow compressors for blast furnace service with capacities up to 105,000 c.f.m. These units were synchronous-motor driven and equipped with recovery gas turbines for capacity control. The initial cost and space requirements for axial flow compressors were lower than those for centrifugal compressors of the same rating.

Figure 14.15 shows a U.S.S.R. axial compressor. The rotating blades are mounted on a hollow cylinder of constant diameter with stub shaft pressed in on each end. The casing is made of two pieces bolted together. There is no attempt to recover the pressure beyond the last stage. The design is based on symmetrical blading profiles.

Figure 14.16 shows a large Escher Wyss turbocompressor consisting of a low pressure axial flow part and a centrifugal high pressure part with a cooler in between. The unit is rated of 117,000 c.f.m. of air, at 100 p.s.i.g., at 3000 r.p.m., 22,000 hp. for compressed air supply.

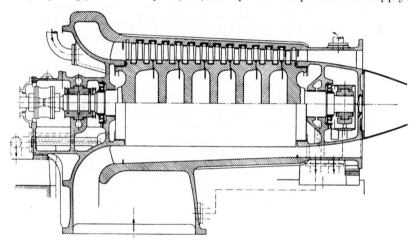

Fig. 14.14.   Brown Boveri axial compressor.

Use of the axial flow compressor for the low-pressure part permitted selection of a better speed for the high pressure part and the driver.

Among other applications of the axial flow compressors in Europe can be mentioned: supercharging of Diesel engines, wind tunnel, compressing gases in chemical industry and others.

(c) **Axial Flow Compressors in U.S.A.** The number of axial flow compressors built for services other than gas turbine is very small. Allis Chalmers list one four-stage compressor for a 50,000 c.f.m. steam turbine driven at 5800 r.p.m. for natural gas booster service. The largest unit built by Allis Chalmers for the last wind tunnel at Langley Field, Va., is a seven-stage compressor rated at 870,000 c.f.m. at 1320 r.p.m. The impeller diameter is 130 in. Figure 14.17 shows an Allis Chalmers axial flow compressor. The hub of constant diameter is a two-piece hollow cylinder with flanged stub shafts at each end.

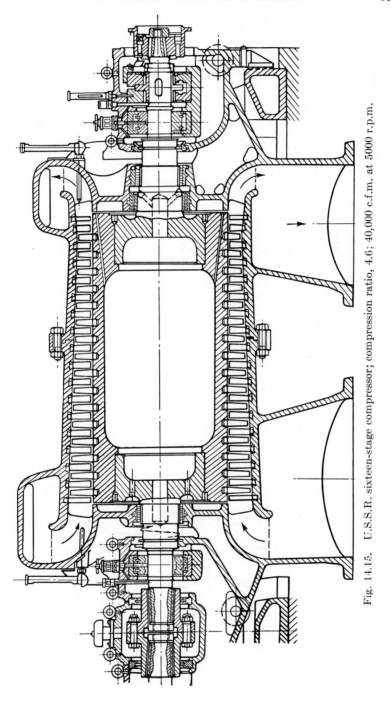

Fig. 14.15. U.S.S.R. sixteen-stage compressor; compression ratio, 4.6; 40,000 c.f.m. at 5000 r.p.m.

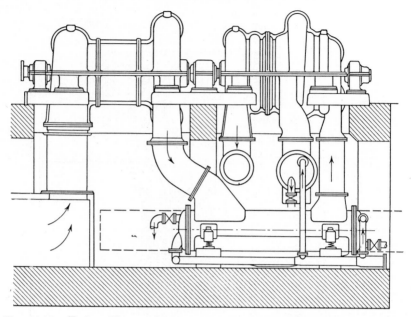

Fig. 14.16.   Escher Wyss turbocompressor for compressed-air supply; 117,000
c.f.m., 100 p.s.i.g., 3000 r.p.m., 22,000 hp.

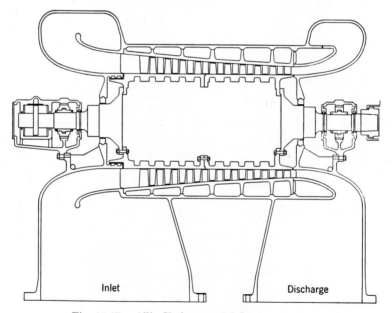

Inlet   Discharge

Fig. 14.17.   Allis Chalmers axial flow compressor.

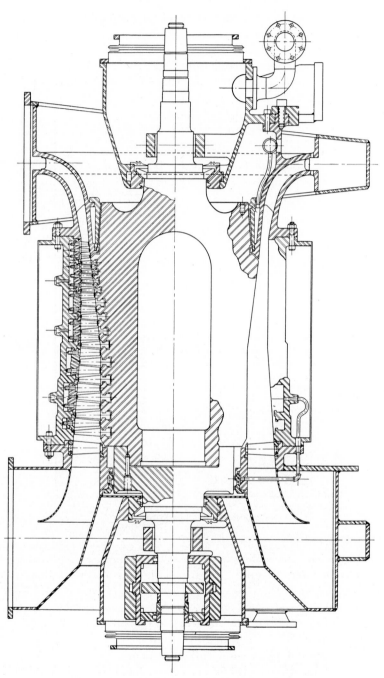

Fig. 14.18. Clark axial flow compression.

Figure 14.18 shows a cross section of a Clark axial flow compressor, and Fig. 14.19 represents a typical performance of a thirteen-stage unit at 15,000 r.p.m.

Several units have been installed by this firm including one 17,000 c.f.m. compressor for a discharge pressure of 100 p.s.i.a. realized in

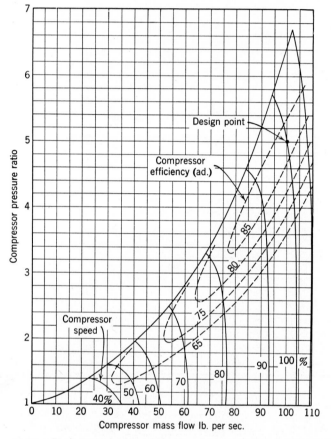

Fig. 14.19.   Performance of axial flow compressor shown in Fig. 14.18.

two casings with intercooling between low and high pressure casings. A 50 per cent reaction type of blading with constant head along the blade is employed in the Clark Bros. Co. design of axial compressors.

Description of axial flow compressors used in connection with gas turbine power plants is outside the scope of this book and is found in a number of publications covering gas turbines.

Figures 14.20 and 14.21 show the performance of a six-stage compressor at several speeds with 50 per cent reaction blading, published by Friedrich (reference 18). The compression ratio on atmospheric air is 3:1 at 24 cu.m./sec. capacity (1 cu.m./sec. = 2120 c.f.m.) with efficiency of 82 per cent. The optimum total (shaft) efficiency is over 90 per cent at a Mach number 0.65 based on the outside peripheral

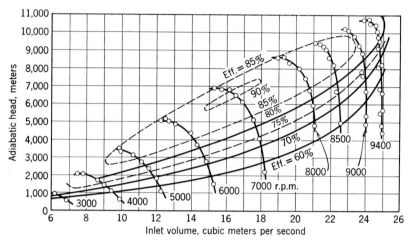

Fig. 14.20. Performance of a six-stage axial compressor (Friedrich).

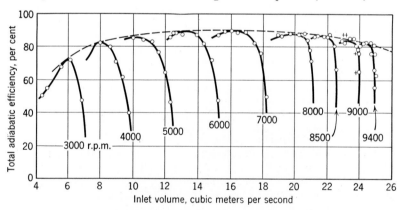

Fig. 14.21. Total adiabatic efficiency of the six-stage compressor (Friedrich).

velocity. Efficiency remains 90 per cent at Mach number 0.77. The change of the slope of the head-capacity characteristics and reduction of the operating range with the increase of speed is very pronounced. It should be noted that the head coefficient at the best efficiency point at several speeds does not remain constant, it has a maximum at the optimum speed of 7000 r.p.m. decreasing on both sides of this point partly owing to impaired stage matching at compression ratios other than the design point. The decrease in efficiency at higher speeds is caused by the increased losses at higher Mach numbers and stage mismatching. As the lower speeds the effect of Reynolds number accounts for the lower efficiency.

In general, at the optimum speed higher impeller discharge angles result in a flatter characteristic curve and a greater capacity range. At the same time the peak efficiency point tends to occur near the surge point.

REFERENCES

1. Keller, *Axial Flow Fans*, McGraw-Hill, 1937.
2. Howell, "Design of Axial Compressors," W.E.I. No. 12, *Inst. Mech. Engrs. Proc.*; reprint by *A.S.M.E.* under the title "Development of The British Gas Turbine Jet Unit," 1947; p. 462.
3. Ponomareff, "Axial Flow Compressors for Gas Turbines," *A.S.M.E. Trans.*, May, 1948, p. 295.
4. Keller, "The Escher Wyss-AK Closed Cycle Turbine," *A.S.M.E. Trans.*, Vol. 68, 1946, pp. 791–812.
5. Howell, "Design of Axial Compressors," p. 452, reference 2.
6. Constant, "The Early History of the Axial Type of Gas Turbine Engine," reference 2, p. 421.
7. Carter, *Three-Dimensional-Flow Theories for Axial Flow Compressors and Turbines*. Lectures on the Development of Internal Combustion Turbines, Inst. Mech. Engrs. Reprinted by A.S.M.E. 1949, p. 261.
8. Howell and Bonham, "Overall Stage Characteristic of Axial Flow Compressors," *Inst. Mech. Eng. Proc.*, Vol. 163, 1950, pp. 235–248.
9. Eckert, Weinig, and Kobel, "The Design of 50% Reaction Compressors and Results of Tests of Individual Stages," U. S. Navy Dept. *BuShips* 338, May, 1946, Part B, Vol. 2.
10. Bowen, Sabersky, Rannie, "Investigation of Axial Flow Compressors," *A.S.M.E. Paper* 49-A-102.
11. Kahane, "Investigation of Axial Flow Fan and Compressor Rotors," *N.A.C.A. Tech. Note* 1652.
12. Adamtchik, U. S. Patent 2,524,870, Oct. 10, 1950.
13. Brunner and McNair, "Blading for Axial Flow Compressors," *A.S.M.E. Paper* 50-A-113, Fig. 2.
14. Constant, "The Gas Turbine in Perspective," reference 8, pp. 185–192.
15. Eckert, *Ladeeinrichtungen für Verbrennungs-Motoren*, Franckh'sche Verlag, Stuttgart, 1952, p. 38.
16. Dickman, "Pfeilung von Schaufeln bei Axial-Stufen Nahe der Schallgrenze," *Z.V.D.I.*, Bd. 99, No. 31, 1952, p. 1019.
17. Constant, "The Application of Research to the Gas Turbine," *Eng.*, Jan. 9, 1953, p. 62.
18. Friedrich, "Axialverdichter," Konstruktion, Heft 12, 1951, S. 374.
19. Eckert, *Axialkompressoren und Radialkompressoren*, Springer, Berlin, 1953.
20. Schnee, Theory of Gas Turbines, Maschgis, 1950, U.S.S.R. (in Russian).

CHAPTER 15

Special Problems
and Application of
Blowers and Compressors

15.1 WEIGHT OF FLOW CONTROL

The head-capacity and efficiency curves at constant speed represent an inherent characteristic of a blower or compressor which is determined completely by the design elements used for the impeller and casing. Such curves, established at one speed by test, can be calculated for any speed with due regard to the effect of Reynolds and Mach numbers. The operating point (A, Fig. 15.1) on the head-

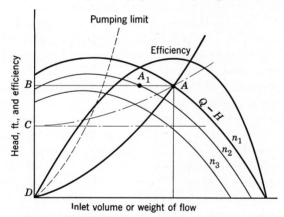

Fig. 15.1. System characteristics.

capacity curve is determined by the system characteristic representing the head variation of the system as a function of weight of flow. This may be a line parallel to the axis of capacity (AB) as is the case when the discharge piping is short and all of the blower head is utilized as pressure. On the other hand all the blower head may be used to overcome pipe line friction as in the natural gas pipe lines. In this case the system characteristic is a parabolic curve (AD) passing through the origin of the blower characteristics. If only part of the head developed by the blower is utilized for overcoming the pipe friction

319

and the rest is available as pressure at the destination point, the system characteristic is a parabolic curve drawn above the capacity axis (AC). If the head-capacity requirements change, the operating point moves along the blower head-capacity curve and a new system characteristic results. The operating point is an intersection of the two characteristics in every case.

Variation of the head-capacity requirements (system characteristics) may be caused by a variation of the demand for gas at constant pressure by the process, or, a constant amount of gas may be required at a variable pressure owing to increased resistance to the flow, as happens, for instance, with blast furnaces depending on the run of the furnace. On the other hand, variable quantities of gas at different pressures may be required by the process, as is typical for the steel production processes. Variation of the blower output to meet the head-capacity demand of the system requires special controls to regulate the volume, pressure, or both. These operate on several different hydraulic principles, depending on the type of blower, driver, and application.

The design and application of governors and various controls for turbomachinery have developed into a major independent engineering field, which is beyond the scope of this book. However, several methods of blower regulation will be described briefly to point out some of the control principles with which the blower designer is most likely to be concerned.

(*a*) **Speed Control.** When a blower is driven by a variable speed driver such as a steam or gas turbine, a series of head-capacity curves can be obtained with the operating point remaining on the system characteristic curve. In this way constant head or constant capacity can be realized within a certain range fixed by the pumping limit of the unit. The capacity at which pumping starts varies approximately directly as the speed. Should lower rates of flow be required, some other means, such as throttling of the inlet, may be employed. Determination of head-capacity curves at several speeds is accomplished by the application of the affinity laws discussed in Arts. 2.4 and 7.3*b*. Speed variation of turbine-driven compressors is the most practical and economical way to control capacity. Speed variation of motor-driven units is rarely used, owing to the extra cost of slip ring motors and electric losses involved.

(*b*) **Throttling Discharge Pipe.** This is the method universally used for controlling capacity of centrifugal pumps. It is used on blowers to establish the head-capacity curve during the performance test. The lowest capacity is limited by the pumping point. The power demand remains on the constant speed b.hp. curve at any rate of flow. For that reason this method is not used on an actual installation as head-capacity reduction can be accomplished, and power saving realized, by throttling the inlet pipe.

(c) **Throttling Inlet.** This is the simplest and most practical way to vary the rate of flow of a blower. Since the system characteristic beyond the blower discharge remains unchanged, the operating point based on the impeller discharge volume also remains essentially the same and the reduction of weight of flow is accomplished by a reduction of the inlet gas density. Although throttling takes place at constant enthalpy, it is accompanied by a loss of energy $(T_o \Delta s)$ as has been pointed out in Art. 7.2d. This loss is smaller than that which occurs when throttling the blower discharge because the same weight of flow takes place at a higher volumetric capacity of the impeller and at a better hydraulic (polytropic) efficiency. The pumping capacity in terms of inlet c.f.m. (or weight of flow) is reduced in proportion to the density decrease, whereas the pumping capacity based on the impeller discharge volume remains the same.

Figure 15.2 shows power requirements for the three above-described methods of rate of flow control plotted against the inlet volume or weight of flow in per cent of the design point. Curve CD on the upper figure represents the test pressure ratio versus inlet volume. The curve CD on the lower figure represents the normal test power curve. Curve A is the power with inlet throttled while curve B is power with speed variation, both for constant pressure ratio $8:1$.

(d) **Operation at Capacities below the Pumping Point.** A partial reduction of the pumping limit (pumping c.f.m.) is accomplished with inlet throttling and speed control. To operate at still lower capacities, compressors are sometimes equipped with a blow-off valve, which permits operation at a lower c.f.m. than the critical. The valve is adjusted mostly manually so that the sum of the volumes discharged into the system and by-passed to atmosphere (if it is an air compressor) or back to the inlet, is above the pumping limit. The power required to drive the machine remains the same, thus the power applied to the by-pass volume is wasted. When the noise from the blow-off valve is objectionable, special silencers are provided.

An extension of the operating range is possible by by-passing only certain stages, instead of all stages, and thus reducing the power waste. Figure 15.3 shows an Escher Wyss five-stage compressor with a hand-operated valve by-passing the flow after the second stage. The same by-pass valve can be arranged for automatic operation.

(e) **Recovery Gas Turbine.** When the cycle of operation of a compressor is such that considerable quantities of gas are by-passed for

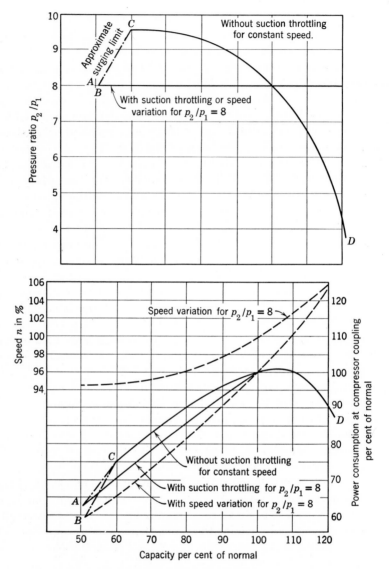

Fig. 15.2. Head-capacity control by speed variation and inlet and discharge throttling (Escher Wyss).

extended periods of time, it has been found practical to provide recovery gas turbines (two-stage) mounted on the same shaft so that gas reexpands through the gas turbine on its way to the inlet. When no gas is by-passed the turbine incurs a loss. Therefore, to justify the use of recovery turbines a careful study is made of the working

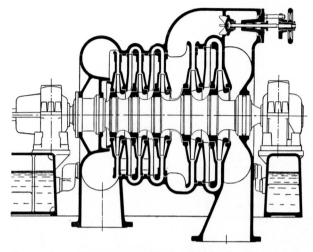

Fig. 15.3. By-passing certain stages with the aid of a hand-operated valve or by automatic control (Escher Wyss).

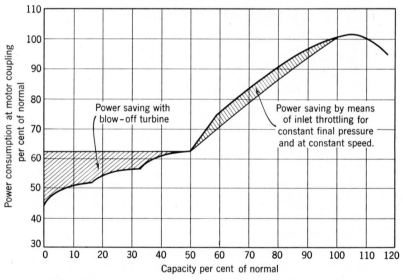

Fig. 15.4.   Power saving with blow-off turbine (Escher Wyss).

schedule of the compressor to determine whether power recovery from the blow-off is sufficient to compensate for the additional loss and complications.   Figure 15.4 shows the power recovered from blow-off at capacities below the pumping point of 50 per cent of the rated capacity.   Figure 11.6 shows a gas turbine mounted on the inlet side of a Brown Boveri isotherm compressor.

(*f*) **Cut-Off Capacity Control.** For large central compressed-air installations in Europe* working on extensive distributing pipe systems with large storage capacity, it has been found practical to cut off the compressor from the system when the capacity falls below the pumping point. The compressor runs at shut-off with atmospheric pressure at the discharge and vacuum throughout the stages by throttling the inlet. When the pressure in the system drops below a predetermined value, the compressor is put back on the line. This method is equally

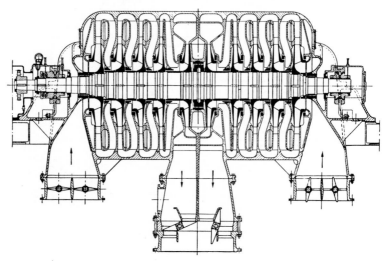

Fig. 15.5a. Double-inlet five-stage compressor (GHH); c.f.m. = 144,000 maximum.

applicable to steam and electric drive. The change from on and off the line is accomplished without undue shock. Power demand at the unloaded condition is of the order of 8–10 per cent of the normal. Under the proper application, this method of control has proved itself as most economical and foolproof (reference 1).

(*g*) **Double-Flow Blowers.** Figure 15.5a shows a Gutehoffnungshütte (GHH), Germany, double-flow blast furnace blower rated at 144,000 c.f.m. at 42.7 p.s.i.a. and provided with special valves on the inlet and outlet discharge flanges which permit cutting off one half the unit when the capacity approaches the pumping limit of the whole unit.   In this manner the pumping limit is reduced to one half that of

* The following firms, for example, furnish such control equipment: Demag, Gutehoffnungshütte, British Thomson-Houston.

the complete unit or to about 20 per cent of the rated capacity.   For the lower capacity of 108,000 c.f.m. the same firm has built double-flow machines with vaned diffusers (reference 1).

Figure 15.5b shows a Demag double-flow blast furnace blower rated at 35,000 c.f.m.   The two halves of the blower are manifolded externally so that they can be operated in parallel or in series, thus increasing the operating range of the blower.

(h) **Inlet Guide Vanes.**   Figure 15.6 shows a four-stage Allis Chalmers blower equipped with inlet guide vanes at each stage.   These vanes are adjusted manually to reduce the capacity and to increase the

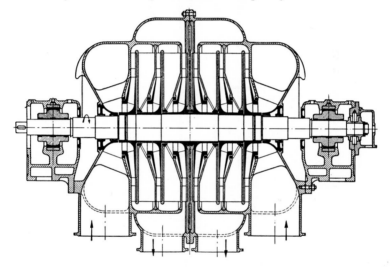

Fig. 15.5b.   Demag double flow blast furnace blower, 35,000 c.f.m., arranged for series-parallel operation.

stable operating range.   Although the primary role of the guide vanes is to provide prerotation ahead of each impeller and thus to reduce the head-capacity, the same vanes act also as a throttle to reduce the flow rate by reducing the gas density at the same time.

Figure 15.7 shows a single-stage blower with inlet guide vanes and Figure 15.8 shows performance with different vane positions.   The action of the vanes is mostly that of a throttle rather than guide vanes to control the prerotation.   Variation of the flow is accompanied by a drop of efficiency.   Even in a neutral position the inlet vanes incur an additional hydraulic loss at the impeller approach.   The effectiveness of inlet guide vanes is reduced at high inlet velocities.

In designs such as are shown in Fig. 15.9, part of the return channel vanes are arranged in the interstage packing ring (seal).   By changing

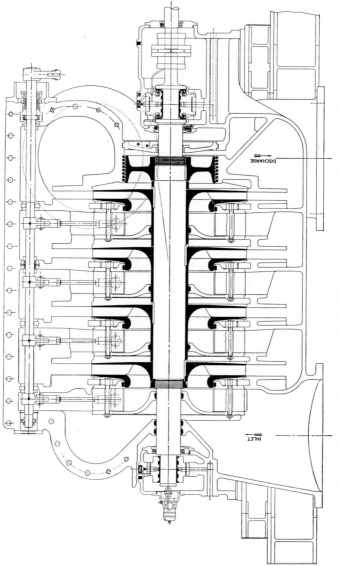

Fig. 15.6. Allis Chalmers four-stage blower with inlet guide vanes in each stage.

the shape of this portion of the vanes some degree of prerotation ahead of the impeller inlet can be induced. However, just as in the case of guide vanes ahead of the impeller inlet of a single-stage blower (Fig. 15.7) such stationary guide vanes are ineffective in producing counter

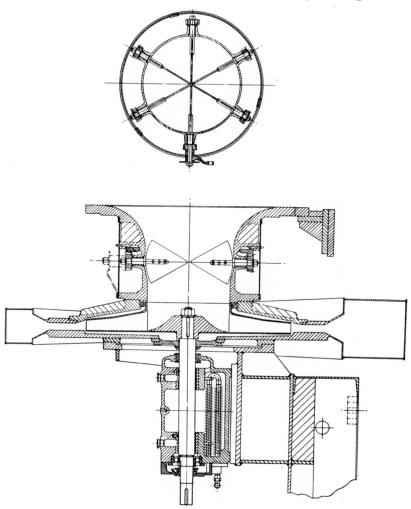

Fig. 15.7. Ingersoll-Rand single-stage blower with inlet guide vanes.

rotation and thus are incapable of increasing the output of a stage. Reduction of head-capacity by this means is always accompanied with a reduction in efficiency, thus indicating that a reduction of the output results primarily from the throttling effect of the guide vanes and a reduction of gas density. Therefore the method has no advantage over throttling the inlet of the whole machine as discussed above.

(*i*) **Power Wheel.** Figure 15.9 shows an Ingersoll-Rand blast furnace blower equipped with a power wheel. This is a reaction turbine wheel, placed between the inlet guide vanes and the first stage impeller inlet, intended to utilize the kinetic energy of the flow from the guide

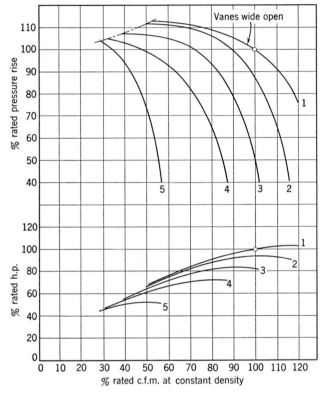

Fig. 15.8. Pressure-volume control with inlet vanes (Allis Chalmers).

vanes in addition to the pressure drop through the wheel. At the rated capacity and with guide vanes radial the flow through the power wheel is radial and exerts no torque on the wheel. Since extra power is required to drive the power wheel under all operating conditions the benefits from the wheel have to compensate for this additional power.

The same units are available with inlet guide vanes only (first stage) and the power wheel omitted. Special tests have shown that use of the inlet vanes at the first stage reduces the power about 10 per cent throughout a wide range of operation as compared with the simple

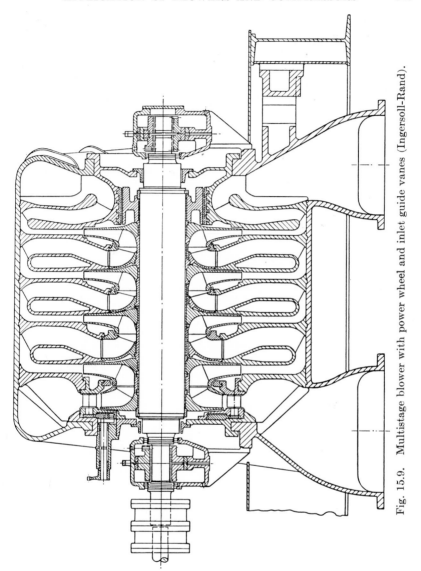

Fig. 15.9.   Multistage blower with power wheel and inlet guide vanes (Ingersoll-Rand).

inlet pipe throttling.   This is because prerotation unloads the first-stage impeller and guide vanes produce more uniform velocity of approach to the first-stage impeller than is possible with a simple throttle of the inlet pipe (Fig. 15.10).

(*j*) **Adjustable Diffuser Vanes.**   Figure 15.11 shows a six-stage Brown Boveri blower provided with adjustable diffuser vanes in second,

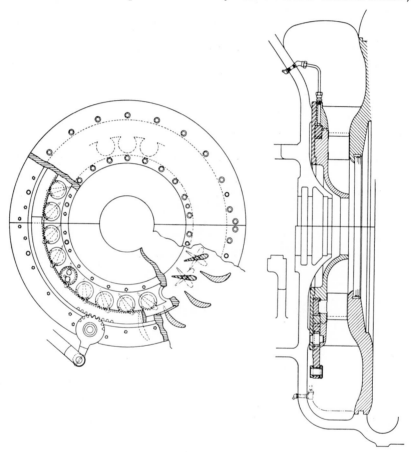

Fig. 15.10.   Adjustable first-stage inlet guide vanes (Clark).

fourth, and sixth stages.   Figure 15.12 shows the detail of the adjusting vane mechanism.   For the average blast furnace conditions the pumping limit may be moved by these controls to about 20 per cent of the rated capacity.   Figure 15.13 shows performance of a blast furnace blower at two speeds for eight positions of the diffuser vanes. Points *a*, *b*, *c*, *d*, *e*, and *f* are operating points for different runs of the furnace.   About 55 per cent of the blast furnace blowers furnished by Brown Boveri since 1929 to 1953 are equipped with movable diffuser vanes (reference 2).

Since the atmosphere in blast furnace plants often contains a large amount of dust, it is recommended that air filters be provided on the

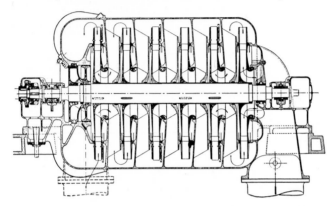

Fig. 15.11.   Brown Boveri compressor with discharge adjustable vanes.

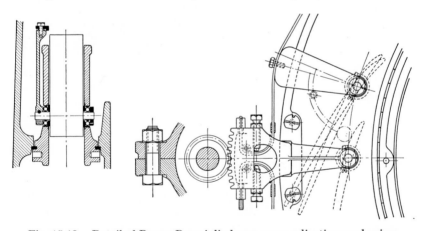

Fig. 15.12.   Detail of Brown Boveri discharge vanes adjusting mechanism.

inlet pipes to protect the parts of the vane-adjusting mechanism from erosion and clogging.

(*k*) **Adjustable Impeller Vanes.**   Escher Wyss have developed a multistage axial compressor for motor drive at constant speed with adjustable impeller vanes, which are operated manually or automatically while in operation.   One seven-stage unit of this type was installed for a wind tunnel (Fig. 14.13).   The same design is intended for blast furnace service at a constant speed drive by a gas turbine utilizing the blast furnace gas. The excess power developed by the gas turbine is used to drive an alternator. The adjustable vane control provides sufficient head-capacity range to meet the requirements for air of the blast furnace (reference 3).

(*l*) **Two-Speed Gear Increasers.** A variation of speed has been obtained in several isolated cases in Europe by using two-speed speed

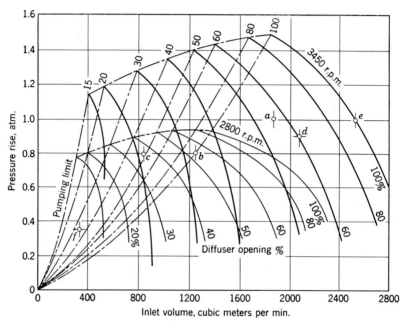

Fig. 15.13. Head-capacity control with adjustable diffuser vanes for blast furnace blowers (data by Kluge).

increaser. Change of speed is performed manually by engaging either one of the two couplings of the gear speed increaser (reference 3, p. 6).

Remarks on Controls. Several of the described head-capacity controls developed in Europe, and frequently used in connection with full automatic governing devices, are little known in the United States. High cost of power and fuel relative to labor and material and high cost of fuel in comparison with hydroelectric power justify elaborate power-saving devices in Europe, but the same equipment would not be practical in this country. As a result, speed control, inlet throttling, and inlet guide vanes to a limited extent, are the only controls which are used in the United States.

15.2   SPECIAL DESIGNS AND APPLICATION OF BLOWERS AND COMPRESSORS

The Compressed Air and Gas Institute (an association of the manufacturers of compressed air equipment) gives a list of applications of compressed air in the "Compressed Air Handbook, 1947," extending over 17 pages.   An equally impressive list could be compiled of applications of blowers and compressors handling vapors and gases other than air.   For a great majority of applications standard manufacturers' designs are used, whereas in others special materials or mechanical details (such as high pressure seals) are called for.   They are

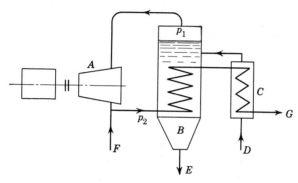

Fig. 15.14.   Heat pump process.

described in the trade literature.   However, there are several more recent applications of centrifugal compressors, mostly in the field of chemical engineering, which presented new hydraulic and thermodynamic problems, the solution of which led to new designs.   The largest capacity and highest compression ratio blowers and compressors belong to this class.

(*a*) **Heat Pumps.**   This term is applied to compressors used for vapor compression (mostly water) and utilizing the heat of compression for heating purposes.   The process is economically practical when there is plenty of hydroelectrical energy available, but there is scarcity of fuel, coal, or oil.   By far a great majority of heat pumps are used in evaporating plants for concentration of solutions containing water such as common salt ($NaCl$), sugar, fruit juices, and a great number of chemicals.   The heat of vaporization is taken from the solution at low pressure and temperature and raised to a higher pressure and temperature.   The heat effect produced by the heat pump requires from three to fifteen times less electric energy than would be necessary by direct

electric heating.   Escher Wyss estimate that heat pumps installed
by this firm alone save about 500,000 tons of coal a year.

Figure 15.14 shows a diagram of the heat pump operation in an
evaporating plant.   A compressor A draws vapor from the evaporator
B at a pressure p_1 and discharges it at a pressure p_2.   Heat of evaporation boosted from the temperature T_1 to T_2 is utilized for heating the
solution in the evaporator B, while the vapor is condensed.   On its
way out of the evaporator the condensate is further cooled in the heat-
exchanger C by the incoming fresh weak solution at D.   The concentrated solution is withdrawn from the evaporator at E.   Fresh steam
to provide the balance of heat required by the process may be introduced at F.   The condensate leaves the system at G.   A Ts diagram

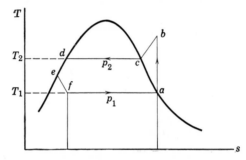

Fig. 15.15. Ts diagram of heat pump.

of the process is shown in Fig. 15.15.   Compression takes place along
ab; the vapor is cooled and condensed along bcd, the condensate is
cooled along de; evaporation of water proceeds along efa.   In Art.
11.6 it was pointed out that in multistage compressors used as heat
pumps, injection cooling is used in preference to external water cooling,
as removal of heat by cooling water would upset the heat balance of
the process.

At the pressures used in thermocompression processes the water
vapor has a density considerably lower than air.   This leads to larger
compressor machinery and a greater number of stages to realize the
same compression ratio.   As a result the largest single-casing compressors and the greatest number of stages per casing (13) are found in
heat-pump applications.   Escher Wyss built one unit for 140,000 c.f.m.
at the inlet of the low pressure part consisting of three stages, double-
flow type, motor driven.   The high pressure part consists of two casings connected in series and driven by a common motor.   The low
pressure half handles 90,000 c.f.m., has four stages, double flow;
whereas the high pressure half has seven stages single flow.   When

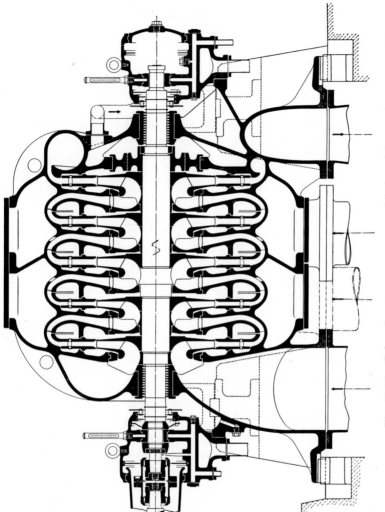

Fig. 15.16.   Sulzer five-stage compressor with three inlet nozzles.

handling air, the same compressor aggregate would produce a compression ratio of 14:1. This is higher than any compressed air supply units yet designed (up to 10:1). Perhaps the largest compressed air supply unit was built also by Escher Wyss. It is rated at 118,000 c.f.m., 100 p.s.i.g. pressure, requiring 22,000 hp. at 3000 r.p.m., consisting of two casings, the low pressure unit being an axial flow compressor (Fig. 14.16).

(b) **Heat Pumps in Paper Mills.** The heat pump principle is utilized in blowers used in paper mills as vacuum pumps for removal of moisture from the paper. Hot air at low relative humidity is used for

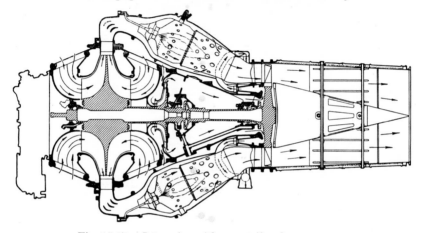

Fig. 15.17.   Jet engine with a centrifugal compressor.

drying the paper below the dry end of the machine. Widely different vacua are required at the various suction points of a paper machine. Since the vacuum generated is increasing from stage to stage, multistage compressors are provided with several suction nozzles to provide the different vacuum requirements. Figure 15.16 shows a Sulzer five-stage compressor with three inlet nozzles. Up to eight stages may be required for such applications. Only moderate peripheral velocities are employed (about two-thirds of normal multistage practice). A maximum vacuum in excess of 20 in. Hg is realized in this manner, which is sufficient for the process requirements. Compressors, used as vacuum pumps in paper making, replaced vacuum pumps of the water-ring type at a power saving of 40 to 60 per cent, in addition to other advantages (reference 6).

(c) **Centrifugal Compressors for Aircraft Gas Turbines.** Although the primary object of this book is the presentation of the theory and design methods of compressors other than those used with gas turbines, a brief description of the centrifugal compressors as developed by Whittle, in England, is included to point out several features which contributed to the success of this compressor. A detailed report on the development of the Whittle compressor was published by Cheshire (reference 7). Figure 15.17 shows a diagram of the jet engine with a centrifugal compressor. Figure 15.18 represents the isometric view of the impeller and Fig. 15.19 of the diffusion casing. The character-

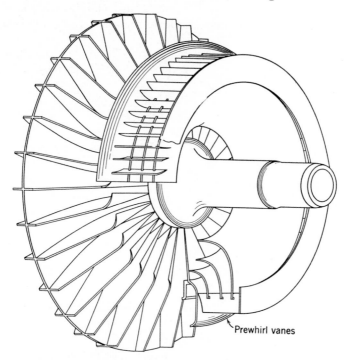

Prewhirl vanes

Fig. 15.18.   Impeller with two sets of inlet guide vanes.

istic curves appear on Fig. 15.20. An adiabatic efficiency of 80.0 per cent was realized at a compression ratio of 4.5:1. This corresponds to a polytropic efficiency of about 83 per cent. At a compression ratio of 3:1, the adiabatic efficiency rises to 83 per cent. The important data on this compressor is given in the accompanying tabulation.

Maximum r.p.m.	16,750
Impeller diameter, in.	20.68
Impeller eye diam., in.	11.81
Impeller hub diam., in.	5.5
Impeller width at discharge, in.	1.74
Diffuser entrance diam., in.	24.0
Number of impeller vanes	29.0
Impeller peripheral velocity, ft./sec.	1,512

The performance, as stated, was achieved by means of several refine-
ments of the hydraulic design such as: (1) assurance of a uniform air
distribution at the impeller entrance by use of three concentric bell-
shaped baffles as shown on Fig. 15.17; (2) providing prerotation vanes
ahead of the above three baffles to reduce the relative velocity at
entrance and to increase the entrance impeller angle; (3) adoption of a
long radius profile for the impeller; and (4) use of a flat walled diffuser
channel essentially of the same proportions presented as most favorable

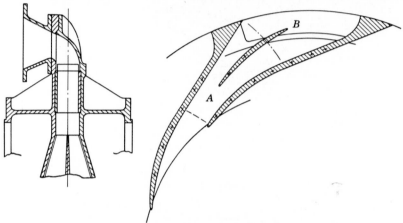

Fig. 15.19.   Diffuser channel of Whittle compressor.   The vane AB was omitted
in final design.

in Chapter 9.   Radial impeller vanes with the inlet part bent to satisfy
the entrance velocity triangles are used for the reasons of strength
at such extremely high peripheral velocities.   Impellers are milled
out of solid stock.   Note that the number of impeller vanes (twenty-
nine) satisfies the author's rule of thumb $z = \beta_2°/3$, given in Art. 6.4.

The beneficial effects of the bell-shaped baffles at the entrance to
the impeller of a low head axial flow blower were reported by Ponomareff (reference 3, Chapter 14).

Figure 15.21 shows a single inlet impeller used on the deHavilland
Ghost jet propulsion unit.   Because the impeller has a straight central
(axial) inlet no inlet guide vanes are employed.   The impeller has
nineteen vanes, 33.5 in. diameter, is operated at 10,200 r.p.m., 1500
ft./sec., tip speed.   The diffuser has twenty vanes.   Note that
impeller passages, milled out of solid stock, are proportioned in agreement with Fig. 6.13.

(d) **Turbochargers.**   Turbocharger units comprising a single-stage
blower and gas turbine driven by exhaust gases are used in connection

with the Buchi system of pressure charging and scavenging of Diesel engines.   In this system the compressed air delivered by the turbocharger scavenges the hot residual gases left in the cylinder at the end of the exhaust stroke and replaces them with cooler fresh air.   Besides, it fills the cylinder with an air charge of higher density at the end of the

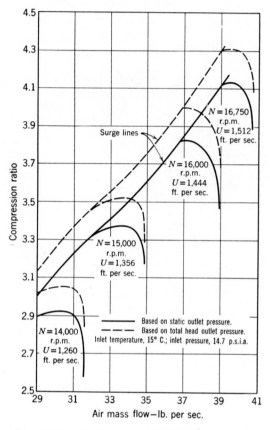

Fig. 15.20.   Performance of Whittle compressor.

suction stroke.   This permits the combustion of a correspondingly greater amount of fuel and a higher output.

Scavenging the combustion space with cool air effects a considerable degree of cooling of the cylinder and for this reason a greater amount of fuel can be burned, and greater power developed, with supercharging without harmful effects on the engine from excessive heat.   The speed and output of the turbocharger vary automatically with the load on the engine.

Figure 15.22 shows an Elliott turbocharger. The blower impeller is mounted on the shaft with the gas turbine wheel so that the axial thrust of one very nearly balances that of the other. The residual unbalance is taken up with a grooved thrust collar on the turbine end. There is another collar bearing provided on the radial bearing on the blower end to limit the endplay. The closed type of impeller is a precision aluminum casting and has a 90° impeller discharge angle.

Fig. 15.21. Single-inlet impeller of the de Havilland Ghost jet engine.

The radial bearings are of the sleeve type, steel backed and babbit lined, pressed into the intermediate casing part. The oiling system is independent of the engine oiling, with its own oil pump. The intermediate casing, between the blower and turbine casings, forms a water jacket with a water temperature rise of 30°F. at full load. A complete line of turbochargers is available for ratings from 225 to 2700 hp. The turbine speeds range from 12,000 to 29,000 r.p.m.

Figure 15.23 shows a Brown Boveri turbocharger (reference 8) for low pressure operation with a compression ratio 1.5:1. For the high pressure type with pressure ratio up to 2.2 an open impeller is used for a greater mechanical strength. Note that ball bearings are used for radial and thrust bearings which are "elastically mounted." A complete line of turbochargers is available for four-stroke Diesel engine outputs from 150 to 5500 hp. manufactured on a mass production basis in a special plant. Low pressure and altitude turbocharging results in 50 per cent power increase over uncharged engines at sea level. High pressure charging brings 120 per cent power increases over uncharged engines at sea level. The specific fuel consumption

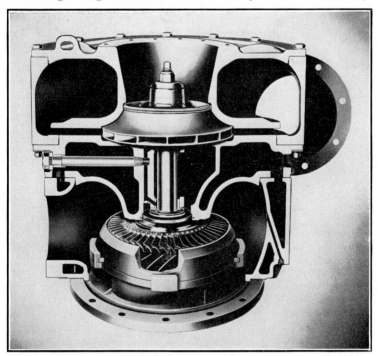

Fig. 15.22.   Elliott turbocharger.

of charged engines is lower, partly owing to the improved mechanical efficiency from the increased output and partly owing to an increase of thermal efficiency. High pressure charging requires an air cooler, usually mounted on the engine. The oil lubricating system is independent of the engine, each bearing having its own disk oil pump to lift oil to the bearings.

The maximum impeller peripheral velocities up to 1600 ft. per sec. were realized with open impellers for military aircraft engine supercharging, requiring a compression ratio up to 5:1. Such impellers employ radial vanes and almost symmetrical shrouds (web) for mechanical strength.

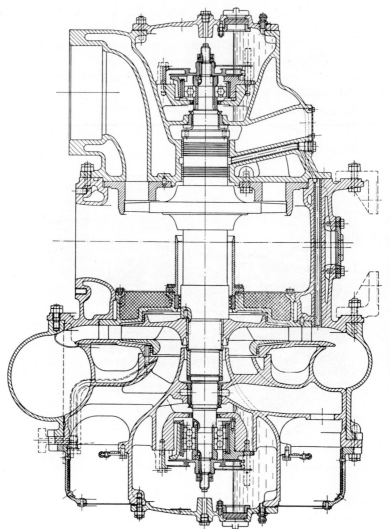

Fig. 15.23.   Brown Boveri turbocharger.

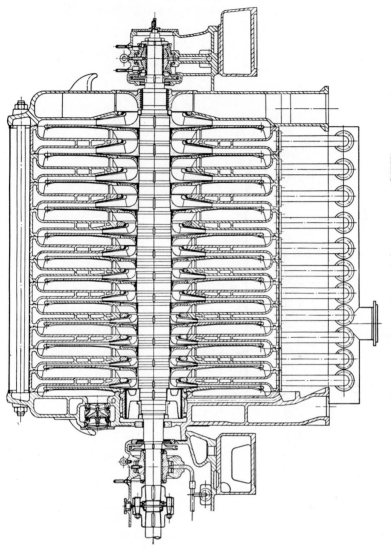

Fig. 15.24. Internally cooled compressor (GHH).

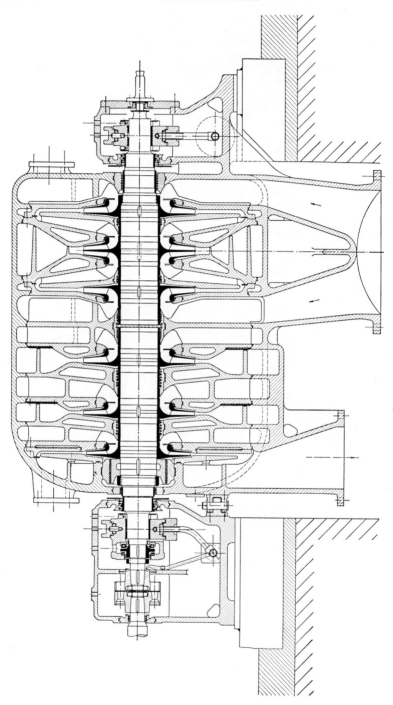

Fig. 15.25a.   GHH five-stage compressor.

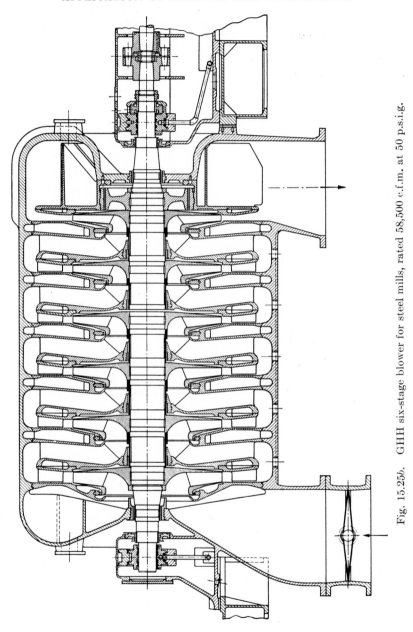

Fig. 15.25b. GHH six-stage blower for steel mills, rated 58,500 c.f.m. at 50 p.s.i.g.

15.3 EXAMPLES OF BLOWERS AND COMPRESSORS

Figure 15.24 shows a GHH twelve-stage internally cooled compressor of old design, but still in use. The casing outside diameter is increased to increase the cooling surface. The same firm has a complete line of

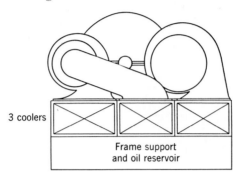

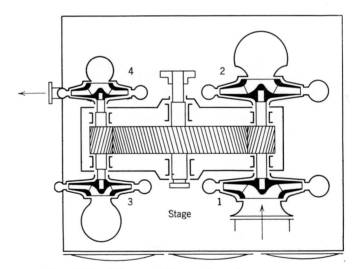

Fig. 15.26. Diagram of Demag four-stage compressor.

externally cooled compressors. Figure 15.25a shows a five-stage compressor. The first two low pressure stages are double flow, the high pressure stages are single flow. There is a cooler after the second, third, and fourth stages, mounted on both sides of the casing. The first and last stages have vaneless diffusers, whereas the balance have volute casings.

Figure 15.25*b* shows GHH six-stage uncooled compressor with all impellers of the same diameter and vaned diffusers in all stages except the final.   Note that diffuser profile is slightly divergent on the elevation view and that the diffuser vanes are accessible for cleaning.

Figure 15.26 shows a four-stage Demag compressor with three external coolers mounted in the base below the compressor.   The step-up gear is built into the unit.   Impellers are mounted on two shafts running at different speeds.   In this manner specific speed of the third and fourth stages is increased by increasing the speed as

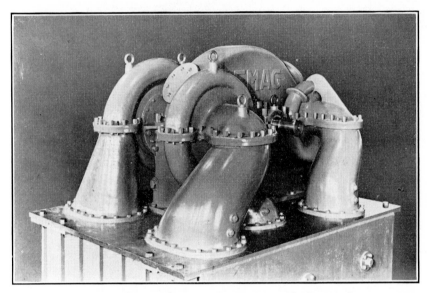

Fig. 15.27.   Demag four-stage compressor with three coolers.

compared with the first two stages.   The casings are of volute type. In five sizes a range of 5000 to 15,000 c.f.m. is covered for compression ratios up to 8:1 for air.   The design is very compact and light and self-contained, requiring simple and small foundations.   Higher efficiencies (66 per cent isothermal gross efficiencies for larger sizes) have been realized with this design as compared with older multistage slow running compressors for the same output.   Figure 15.27 shows the photograph of the same unit.

Figure 15.28 shows GHH gas circulating turbocompressor rated at 240 c.f.m. and pressure rise from 4270 to 4550 p.s.i.g. used in the manufacture of ammonia.   The complete unit including motor is included in a shell subjected to full pressure of the gas, thus requiring no stuffing

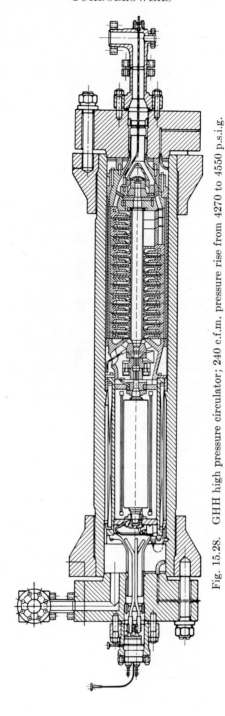

Fig. 15.28. GHH high pressure circulator; 240 c.f.m. pressure rise from 4270 to 4550 p.s.i.g.

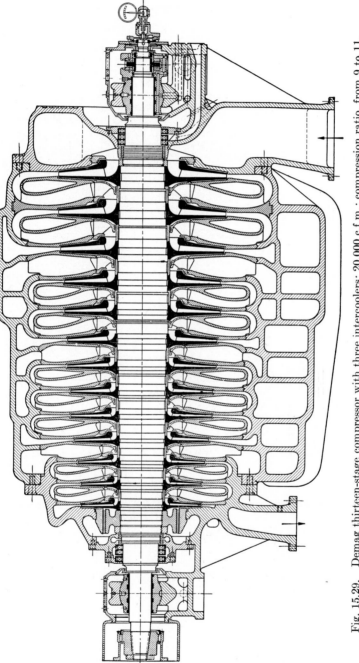

Fig. 15.29.   Demag thirteen-stage compressor with three intercoolers; 20,000 c.f.m.; compression ratio, from 9 to 11.

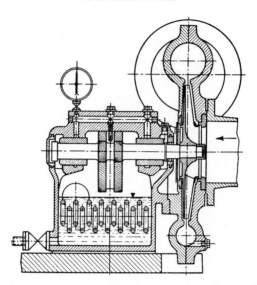

Fig. 15.30.   Demag single-stage blower mounted on the speed increaser.

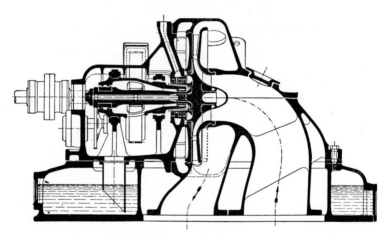

Fig. 15.31.   Sulzer single-stage high speed blower, with radial impeller mounted
on the speed increaser.

boxes or seals.   Both motor and compressor have ball bearings fed
with grease from outside.   The motor cooling is accomplished by the
inlet gas.

Figure 15.29 represents what is believed to be the largest compressor
with a maximum number of stages in one casing designed for 20,000
c.f.m. and compression ratio of 9 to 11, for chemical works.   The
maximum peripheral velocity is 1015 ft./sec.   The operating speed

is above the first critical speed.   Cooling is accomplished in three intercoolers mounted on one side of the casing.

The largest multistage compressors are believed to be two units furnished by Demag, Duisburg, to the United States, rated at 234,000 c.f.m.   The largest multistage blowers for blast furnace service were built by GHH, Germany, rated at 164,000 c.f.m. at 21.4 to 36.5 p.s.i.g. pressure.

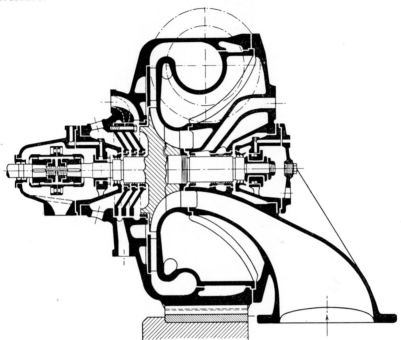

Fig. 15.32.   Sulzer single-stage blower with two-bearing construction for direct turbine drive.

Figure 15.30 shows a Demag single-stage volute blower with the impeller overhung on the gear speed-increaser shaft.   It is quite common in Europe for blower manufacturers to produce their own gears.   This type of blower is built in sizes from 250 to 14,500 c.f.m. and compression ratio up to 1.7.

Figure 15.31 shows a Sulzer single-stage blower with bottom inlet and outlet nozzles.   The impeller with 90° discharge angle is of open construction built up of two pieces for manufacturing reasons, the vanes of the two parts being perfectly matched and streamlined. The maximum impeller tip velocity is 1000 ft. per sec.   A vaned diffuser is used for high efficiency.   Note that 50 cycle power in Europe imposes a limitation as to maximum speed for direct motor driven blowers, therefore speed increases are used for high head units almost universally.

Figure 15.32 shows a Sulzer single-stage blower similar to the above but with two-bearing construction for direct steam turbine drive. The vaned diffuser is discharging into an off-set volute collecting

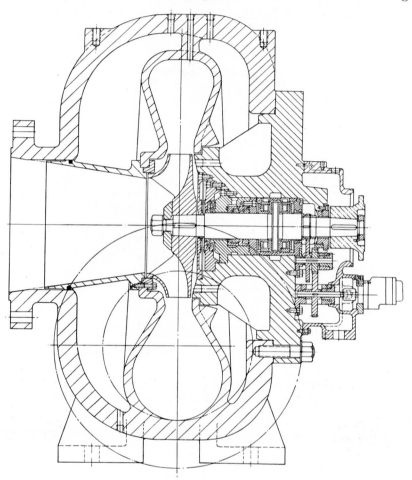

Fig. 15.33.   Ingersoll-Rand natural gas pipe line booster.

chamber. The unsymmetrical volute casing does not incur excessive losses on account of low velocities beyond the diffusers.

Figure 15.33 shows an Ingersoll-Rand natural gas pipe line booster designed for 14,000 c.f.m., 4000 ft. head at 5000 r.p.m., gas turbine driven (5000 hp.) at a maximum speed of 5500 r.p.m. The volute casing proper is cast integral within a cylindrical shell to withstand the working pressures up to 900 p.s.i.g.   Two or three units are used in series to produce the total station compression ratio, limited by the driver horsepower.   A low impeller discharge angle (25°) is used for high efficiency.

Figure 15.34 shows a De Laval impeller used in a high capacity (19,000 c.f.m.) natural gas pipe line booster driven by a 5000 hp. gas

Fig. 15.34.   Mixed flow impeller for De Laval natural gas pipe line booster.

turbine at a maximum speed of 5500 r.p.m.   This impeller is milled out of solid stock by a process developed for high speed turbochargers. The impeller vane layout is such that sections by planes normal to the axis are radial, thus exerting no bending stresses on the vanes.

For moderate impeller peripheral speeds aluminum or bronze impellers have been made having the same mechanical properties. The slope of radial sections is adjusted by rotating several flow lines about the axis of rotation as discussed in detail in the following

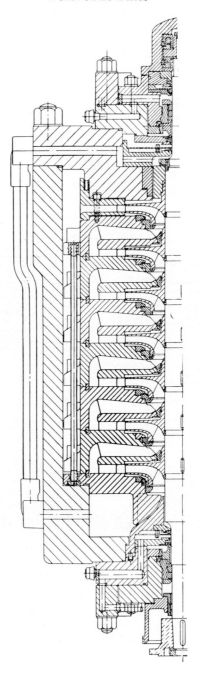

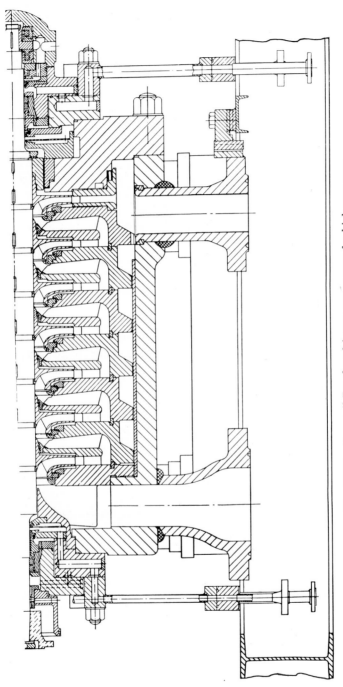

Fig. 15.35. Ingersoll-Rand multistage compressor for high pressures.

chapter. Using a lower impeller discharge angle and reducing the number of vanes lead to a better efficiency.

Figure 15.35 shows an Ingersoll-Rand seven-stage compressor for high pressures. The pumping element proper is enclosed in a steel barrel to withstand high pressures. Pressures up to 2000 p.s.i. of natural gas were realized with compressors of this type, using seven units in series with intercoolers in between for repressuring oil fields. Low angle impeller and vaned diffusion casings were used for high efficiency, comparable to that obtainable with modern centrifugal multistage pumps (Fig. 7.4).

The British Thomson-Huston Co. have built high pressure multistage compressors for compressed air supply for coal mines in sizes 5000 to 25,000 c.f.m. and pressures 80 to 100 p.s.i.g., steam turbine driven. The units are built in one casing with ten to thirteen stages, with three external coolers assembled in one housing and bolted to and below the lower half of the compressor casing. Compressors have vaned diffusers and impellers with radial vanes and axial inlet of welded construction and are operated at 1000 ft. per second peripheral velocity. To facilitate the running of the rotor through the first critical speed one of the spherically seated self-aligning bearings is mounted on a flexible support. The *British Thomson-Huston Bulletin*, 1950, lists fifteen units built for compressed air supply. In the same bulletin are listed among others two 60,000 c.f.m. blast furnace blowers to operate against 15 to 30 p.s.i.g. pressure, when operated at 3200 to 4000 r.p.m.

They are the largest units for this service built in England. They have vaneless diffusers and impellers with radial vanes. The blower casing is made of sections bolted together and provided with internal water cooling.

REFERENCES

1. Kluge, *Kreiselgebläse und Kreiselverdichter*, Springer, Berlin, 1953, pp. 132, 214.
2. Haller, "Turbo-blowers in Blast-Furnace Plants," *Brown Boveri Publ.* 2273E, 1952, p. 33.
3. *Escher Wyss Publ.* 22010, 1953, p. 12.
4. *Escher Wyss Mitt.*, 1946/47, p. 49.
5. *Escher Wyss News*, 1941, p. 20.
6. *Sulzer Tech. Rev. (Switz.)* No. 1, 1951, p. 21.
7. *Development of the British Gas Turbine Jet Unit*, reprint by A.S.M.E. 1947, p. 426.
8. *Brown Boveri Rev.*, Nov., 1950, pp. 408–469.
9. Bruno Eckert, *Ladeeinrichtungen für Verbrennungsmotoren*, Franckh'sche Verlag, Stuttgart, Germany, 1952.
10. General Electric Co., *Supercharger Symposium Lectures*, 1943, River Works, West Lynn, Mass.

CHAPTER 16

Design of
Mixed Flow Impellers

16.1 STATEMENT OF THE PROBLEM

The layout of a mixed flow impeller on the drawing board is the most complicated drafting problem in centrifugal blower design. Two methods are in use. The first, or old, method is one in which the vane entrance and discharge tips are developed on a cone as a plain cylindrical vane and then transferred to the plan view, from which the vane pattern sections are constructed. In the second, or new, method, the vane plane development with true angularity, vane length, and thickness is assumed, and then the vane flow lines are replotted on the plan view. This method, called by Kaplan "the method of error triangles," will be discussed in this chapter as it has definite advantages over the old cone development.

The design of a centrifugal impeller can be divided into two parts. The first is the selection of proper velocities and vane angles needed to obtain the desired performance with the best possible efficiency. The second is the layout of the impeller for the selected angles and areas. The first phase of the design will not be discussed here. For a given set of basic design elements it is possible to make several layouts that will differ in performance. Therefore, for best results, experience and skill are necessary to represent graphically the requirements for best efficiency.

The following are the minimum basic design elements necessary to define the impeller proportions; see Figs. 3.1a and 3.1b.

1. Radial velocity at the impeller eye, c_{m1}.
2. Radial velocity at the impeller discharge, c_{m2}.
3. The impeller peripheral velocity u_2 at the discharge or impeller diameter D_2.
4. The vane angle at entrance, β_1.
5. The discharge angle β_2.

These quantities are sufficient to construct Euler's velocity triangles, the impeller profile, and the vane plan view.

357

16.2 GEOMETRICAL RELATIONSHIPS

Before the development of mixed flow vanes is described, several geometrical definitions and statements will be given which are necessary for further discussion.

a. The angle α between two intersecting planes A and B (Fig. 16.1) is equal to the angle between the two normals CO and DO drawn at any point on the common line of intersection of the two planes. Evidently both of these normals lie in a plane normal to both plane A and plane B. Traces of the normal plane on planes A and B (lines EO and FO) form an angle α.

b. If two planes A and B (Fig. 16.2) have an angle α between them and are sectioned with another plane C normal to plane A, the traces

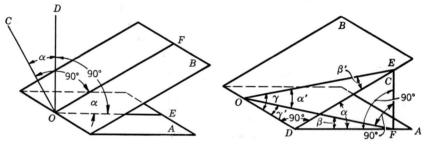

Fig. 16.1. Angle between two planes. Fig. 16.2. Angle projections on a plane.

of plane C on planes A and B (lines OF and OE respectively) will form an angle α' which is related to the angle α in the following way:

$$\tan \alpha' = \tan \alpha \cos \beta \qquad (16.1)$$

where β is an angle between the plane C and a plane normal to both plane A and plane B. If EDF lies in a plane normal to both A and B, then

$$\tan \alpha = EF/DF \qquad \tan \alpha' = EF/OF \qquad OF \cos \beta = DF$$

Hence

$$\tan \alpha'/\tan \alpha = DF/OF = \cos \beta$$

c. If an angle γ on a plane B (Fig. 16.2) is projected on plane A, its projection angle γ' will be given by the relation

$$\tan \gamma' = \tan \gamma \cos \alpha \qquad (16.2)$$

because

$$DE/OD = \tan \gamma \qquad DF/OD = \tan \gamma' \qquad DF/DE = \cos \alpha$$

and

$$\tan \gamma'/\tan \gamma = \cos \alpha$$

d. Similarly, it can be shown that

$$\tan \beta \cos \alpha = \tan \beta' \qquad (16.3)$$

Note that when one side of the angle is parallel to or coincides with *OD*, the common line of intersection of planes *A* and *B*, the angles in projection are smaller; but, if none of the angle sides is parallel to the line of plane intersection *OD*, the angle in projection (β on plane *A*) is greater than the projected angle β' on plane *B*.

The same definitions and theorems apply when one or both of the planes are replaced by curved surfaces except that tangent planes drawn at a common point on both surfaces are substituted for curved surfaces.

16.3 PLAIN VANE FAULTS

If the vane shown in Fig. 16.3 is laid out so that the entrance angle is β_1 on the plan view for the flow lines near the front and back shrouds,

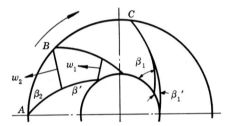

Fig. 16.3.   Plain vane impeller.

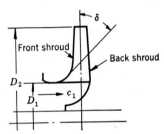

Fig. 16.4.   Profile of a plain vane impeller.

the true angle between the vane and peripheral velocity at the entrance edge near the front shroud will be considerably greater than β_1 and is given, according to Art. 16.2*c*, by the equation

$$\tan \beta_{1f} \cos \delta = \tan \beta_1 \qquad (16.4)$$

where δ is the angle between the tangent to the front shroud at the entrance edge (Fig. 16.4) and the plane normal to the impeller shaft axis.   Thus, if $\beta_1 = 20°$ and $\delta = 45°$, which is quite usual for a plain vane impeller, $\beta_{1f} = 27°$.   But, since the peripheral velocity is constant for all points along the entrance edge, the vane angle should be constant for all points on the entrance edge to agree with the velocity triangle.   To be equal in space, the angle β_1' at the front shroud should be smaller on the plan view, so that

$$\tan \beta_1' = \tan \beta_1 \cos \delta \qquad (16.5)$$

This is shown in Fig. 16.3, vane C. It means that the vane should have a double curvature. Thus a plain vane impeller should have both shrouds normal to the shaft axis; such a condition seldom exists. With curved shrouds a mixed flow vane is necessary for "shockless entrance" even if the vane entrance edge is parallel to the axis.

In addition, if the front shroud is curved it is impossible to avoid sharp corners between the vane and the shroud with a plain vane; therefore the vane is extended into the impeller eye (Fig. 16.5) so that the entrance edge is no longer parallel to the axis, and the vane is curved so that the angles between the vane and the shrouds are nearly 90°.

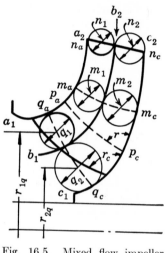

With such a vane, different entrance angles will be required for several flow lines, such as a_1a_2, b_1b_2, and c_1c_2 (Fig. 16.5), for shockless entrance. The entrance angle varies in such a way that the vane becomes more nearly normal to both shrouds. The higher entrance angles required with mixed flow vanes result in wider openings between the vanes, which are necessary for high specific speed impellers. Thus it follows that plain, single-curvature vanes can be used only with narrow impellers with both shrouds nearly normal to the axis and curved very little at the impeller eye. Such impellers are suited only to small blowers.

Fig. 16.5.   Mixed flow impeller profile.

16.4   MIXED FLOW IMPELLERS

To make a mixed flow vane pattern it is necessary to have drawings of the impeller and vane profile showing the layout of the front and back shrouds, the impeller vane entrance and exit edges, and the vane sections along contour lines on several planes drawn normal to the axis. The following points will be given consideration in developing the profile of an impeller of the mixed flow type.

a. Extending the impeller vanes at the entrance into the impeller eye tends to improve efficiency by giving a greater overlap to the vanes and reducing the impeller outside diameter required for a given normal head. Shock losses take less power when the shock occurs at a smaller diameter, and disk friction will be less.

The effect of the impeller eye diameter on the total head will be seen from a consideration of the equation for the input head.

$$H_i = (u_2 c_{u2} - u_1 c_{u1})/g$$

In a normal design it is impossible and inadvisable to suppress completely fluid prerotation at the impeller entrance; therefore c_{u1} is not equal to zero. In that case the subtractive term is smaller for lower values of u_1, and for a fixed outside diameter of the impeller the total head will be higher for smaller impeller entrance diameters. However, there is a limit to extending the vanes into the impeller eye, beyond which further extension will reduce rather than improve the efficiency. This is because it is difficult to avoid sharp corners between the vanes and shrouds; and, since vanes take up a considerable portion of the eye area, unnecessary vane friction is added, and the cleaning of the impeller casting becomes difficult. To provide the necessary entrance area a larger eye diameter is required.

b. The profile of the impeller is drawn for given radial velocities c_{m1} at the entrance and c_{m2} at the discharge in such a way that the change from c_{m1} to c_{m2} is gradual.

c. The entrance edge of the vane on the profile is a circular projection of points that are not in one plane but are brought into the plane of the drawing by rotation about the axis of the impeller shaft. Similarly, the flow lines $a_1 a_2$, $b_1 b_2$, and $c_1 c_2$ (Fig. 16.5) are circular projections of the paths of the water particles if they follow the vane in the manner prescribed by the design. The flow lines $a_1 a_2$ and $c_1 c_2$ represent the true radial sections through the impeller shrouds at the same time. The shroud curvature should be as gradual as possible to minimize uneven pressure and velocity distribution.

The edge of the vane is drawn so that the angles formed with the shrouds on the elevation view are about 90°.

d. The flow lines are one set of construction lines used for the vane development on the drawing. The number of flow lines necessary to define accurately the vane surface depends on the width of the impeller and the actual impeller size. This is a matter of experience. The flow lines are drawn in such a way that the surfaces of revolution formed by these lines divide the flow into equal parts. Following water turbine practice, in which mixed flow impellers were first developed, it is assumed that the meridional velocity is constant along normals to the flow lines ($n_a n_c$, $m_a m_c$, $p_a p_c$, and $q_a q_c$, Fig. 16.5) and equal to the average velocity. From this it follows that the meridional velocities for several points along the entrance edge of the vane are the same only if the entrance edge coincides with one of the normals.

The normals are drawn first by eye. Then they are divided into parts (Fig. 16.5); n_1, n_2; m_1, m_2; q_1, q_2; so that

$$2\pi r_{1q}q_1 = 2\pi r_{2q}q_2 \qquad (16.6)$$

or

$$r_{1q}q_1 = r_{2q}q_2$$

where r_{1q} and r_{2q} are the radii of the centers of gravity of sections q_1 and q_2. This is repeated for every normal.

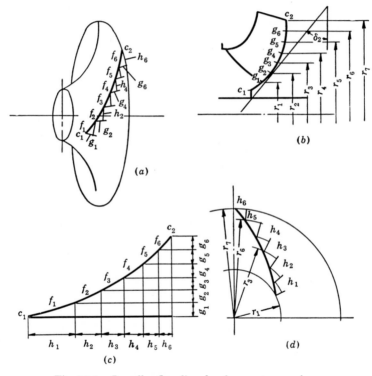

Fig. 16.6. Impeller flow line development on a plane.

For wide and large impellers requiring four or five flow lines, the work of adjusting the sections to comply with equation 16.6 requires much time and a great deal of patience. Accuracy within 3 to 5 per cent should be considered satisfactory.

16.5 METHOD OF ERROR TRIANGLES

The principle of this method of plotting the flow lines on the plan view will be described now. In Fig. 16.6a, suppose a flow line c_1c_2 is shown in perspective on a surface of the back shroud of an impeller.

By cutting the surface with a number of parallel planes, the curve c_1c_2 can be divided into sections $f_1, f_2, \cdots, f_6$. The intersection of the planes with the surface of the shroud will form a number of parallel circles. Through the points of intersection of the curve c_1c_2 with the parallel circles, a number of meridional planes may be drawn which will section the shroud surface along the curved lines $g_1, g_2, \cdots, g_6$. These lines, together with the sections of the parallel circles $h_1, h_2,$ $\cdots, h_6$ and the curve c_1c_2, form a number of curved triangles called by Kaplan "error triangles." Now suppose all these curved triangles are cut and transferred to a plane so that sections $h_1, h_2, \cdots, h_6$ of the parallel circles are arranged along horizontal parallel lines. The sections $g_1, g_2, \cdots, g_6$ of the curved vertical sides will become flat vertical lines, and the curves $f_1, f_2, \cdots, f_6$ will form a plane development of the curve c_1c_2, Fig. 16.6c. Obviously the greater the number of sections drawn through the flow line, the more accurate the plane development of the curve will be. The angles the curve c_1c_2 makes with the parallel circles are the same on the plane development. Also, the length of the flow line c_1c_2 in the development is very nearly equal to the true length of the flow line in space.

On the elevation view, the flow line c_1c_2 will appear as shown in Fig. 16.6b where $r_1, r_2, \cdots, r_6$ are the radii of the parallel circles. A plan view of the flow line c_1c_2 can now be drawn; Fig. 16.7d. Each point of the curve in the plan view is located by radii $r_1, r_2, \cdots, r_6$. The displacement $h_1, h_2, \cdots, h_6$ of one meridional plane with respect to an adjacent one along the parallel circle is shown without distortion on the plane development, Fig. 16.6c, and appears in full length on the plan view, Fig. 16.6d. The intersections of the meridional planes with the parallel circles determine the points of the curve in the plan view.

To apply the method of error triangles to the impeller vane layout the following procedure is followed.

a. The elevation view, or profile, of the impeller is drawn as described previously. The flow lines are drawn, Fig. 16.7a.

b. The vane development on a plane, Fig. 16.7b, is drawn to correspond to the profile and the vane angles at entrance and discharge. The vane thickness is shown on the plane development, Fig. 16.7b.

To draw the vane development divide one of the flow lines a_1a_2 into a number of parts and then lay out the same distances along the rest of the flow lines, points $1a, 2a, \cdots, 8a; 1b, 2b, \cdots, 10b; 1c, 2c,$ $\cdots, 11c$. In this way all the error triangles on the development will be of the same height. Parallel lines spaced g_1, g_2, g_3, etc., apart are drawn for the vane development on a plane, Fig. 16.7b. The vane development is first sketched in between the parallel lines limiting the flow lines on profile $1a$, $8a$; $1b$, $9b$; and $1c$, $10c$ for the flow lines a_1a_2, b_1b_2, and c_1c_2, respectively. The vane thickness is also shown for the flow line c_1c_2 on Fig. 16.7b. This does not have to be the same for all flow lines or constant along the same flow line. The desired degree of streamlining can be given to the vane. Also, for molding

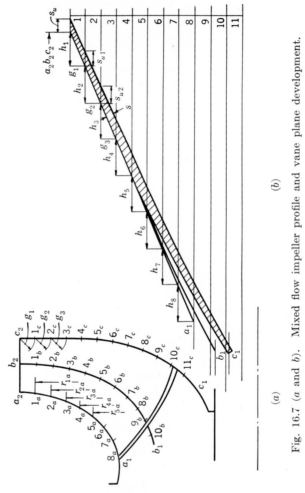

Fig. 16.7 (a and b). Mixed flow impeller profile and vane plane development.

reasons or strength, the vane thickness may vary from one flow line to the other. Although for the development it is more convenient to draw vane sections a certain distance apart, it is found helpful to put the vane development of several flow lines into their true relative positions, Fig. 16.7b. The inlet ends of the developed flow lines should arrange themselves evenly spaced, and the tips of flow lines should form a smooth curve to assure that the edge projection on the plan view will also be a smooth curve. Then the triangles are drawn for one side of the vane only, say the leading face, a_1a_2, Fig. 16.7b.

c. The vane sections are transferred from the development to the plan view, Fig. 16.7c. An arbitrary starting point having been chosen,

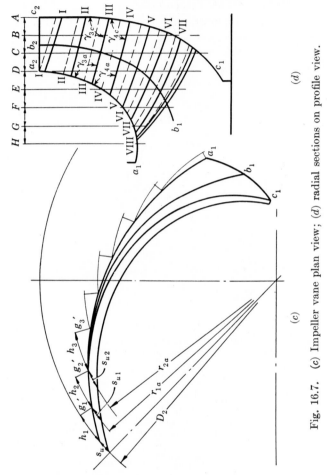

Fig. 16.7. (c) Impeller vane plan view; (d) radial sections on profile view.

curved triangles are drawn. The arcs of parallel circles are drawn with radii taken from the elevation view for points $1a$, $2a$, $\cdots$, $8a$, etc. The displacement of one point with respect to the other is taken from the vane development (h_1, h_2, $\cdots$, h_8). By joining the points with a curved line, the plan projection of the flow line is obtained.

To draw the back side of the vane, the vane thickness is laid off from points $1a$, $2a$, $\cdots$, $8a$ along the parallel circles arcs taken from the vane development (s_{u1}, s_{u2}, etc.).   The flow lines b_1b_2 and c_1c_2 are plotted on the plan view in the same way.

d. The flow lines on the elevation and plan view are the first set of construction lines used for plotting the vane pattern sections.   As a second set of construction lines, a number of uniformly spaced (1, II, III, etc.) radial sections are drawn on the plan view, Fig. 16.7e.   The intersections of the flow lines, with the radial sections for both front and back of the vane, are plotted on the elevation view from the plan view, Fig. 16.7d.   If the radial sections on the elevation view do not form smooth lines, uniformly spaced, it is an indication that the change

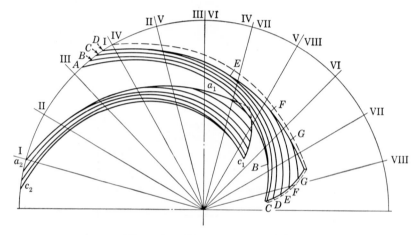

Fig. 16.7e.   Vane pattern sections.

in vane angularity on the vane developments was too abrupt for one or more of the flow lines.

An alternate method of drawing the second set of construction lines may be mentioned.   In this, the flow lines on the elevation view are divided into an equal number of parts and the corresponding points 1a, 1b, 1c; 2a, 2b, 2c, etc., Fig. 16.7a, should form smooth curves on the plan view also.   These curves are used for the second set of construction lines for plotting the vane pattern sections.   The advantage of this method is that no additional points are plotted, and those already on the drawing utilized.

e. The next step is to draw the vane pattern sections A, B, C, $\cdots$, H, Fig. 16.7d.   The vane is divided into a suitable number of boards the number depending on the vane dimensions.   Vane sections are drawn on the elevation view and then plotted on the plan view, the intersections of the board planes being located with the radial sections

or any other construction lines.   To avoid confusion of lines it may
be advisable to separate the views of the front and back sides of the
vane by showing the front side of one vane and back sides of the next
vane, Fig. 16.7e.   In this way the channel between the two vanes will
be defined.

The contour lines or the vane pattern sections on the plan view
completely determine the shape of the vanes.   If boards of the proper
thickness are cut along these lines and stacked in the proper order and
the corners of the boards are shaved off, the vane surface will be
obtained for the front and back sides.

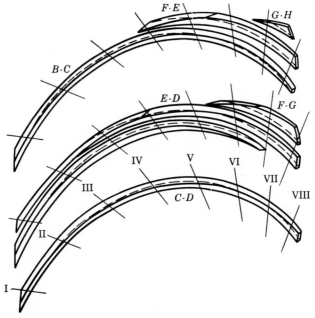

Fig. 16.7(f).   Vane pattern sections.

There are two ways to use these vane sections for building the impeller pattern.   In one, a sectional core box is made for a single-vane
channel.   A number of cores equal to the number of vanes are made
and assembled into one core, for the whole impeller.   For this arrangement, views of the front and back sides of the vane as shown on Fig.
16.7e are sufficient.

In the second method, used mostly for smaller impellers, one core
is made for the whole impeller.   This core is usually baked with
metal vanes in place and is then broken to remove the vanes, after
which the parts of the core are pasted together.   For a pattern of this

type a wooden vane is first made, from which metal vanes are cast for the core box. To build the wooden vane, the vane sections are cut to the proper shape and thickness, and, when they are glued together in the proper order and their corners are shaved off, they will give the vane shape.

The vane section drawings are obtained by placing the two views of the front and back sides of the vane in their proper relative position, one on top of the other. From this the vane sections can be picked out for each board, Fig. 16.7f. Although only outer contour lines are necessary to cut the boards, the inside lines are also shown because they assist in locating the boards in their correct position. Also the radial lines I, II, III, etc., are shown on the vane section as additional guides in the assembly of the vane from the board sections.

f. Hydraulically, the best form of the impeller channel is obtained when the true angles between the impeller vanes and shrouds are close to 90°. When the impeller profile is curved considerably, this becomes difficult to accomplish. The channel form may be improved by tilting the vane with respect to the shrouds. This is done by moving the flow lines on the plan view, Fig. 16.7c, through a certain angle, which will change the angle between the vane and the impeller shrouds without changing the vane angularity.

When heavy vanes are used, a slight inclination of the vanes to both impeller shrouds at the discharge results in quieter pump operation because the discharge from the individual impeller channels against the volute tongue is smoother. With thin streamlined vanes and ample space between the impeller and volute tongue, this consideration becomes unimportant.

To obtain a true picture of the impeller channel normal to the flow, the channel section should be drawn normal to some average flow line which passes somewhere in the middle of the channel. This section is not normal to either of the shrouds or vanes, as neither the shrouds nor the two adjacent vanes are parallel. It is difficult to draw such a section on the drawing. However, to find the angles between the vanes and both shrouds, the radial sections I, II, III, etc., Fig. 16.7e will give a satisfactory approximation. It will be shown that the angles between the shrouds and the vane radial sections on the elevation view (γ_{4a}' and γ_{4c}', Fig. 16.7d) are very nearly equal to the true angles in space between the vane and shroud surfaces γ_{4a} and γ_{4c}, or, more accurately,

$$\tan \gamma_{4a}' = \tan \gamma_{4a} \times \cos \beta_{4a}$$

$$\tan \gamma_{4c}' = \tan \gamma_{4c} \times \cos \beta_{4c} \qquad (16.7)$$

where β_{4a} and β_{4c} are the vane angles at section IV, Fig. 16.7d, taken for illustration.

This follows from the fact that the plane normal to the flow line $a_1 a_2$ intersects the plane normal to the peripheral velocity (radial plane) at an angle β, according to the definition of the angle between the two planes. Thus, the true angle γ_{4a}, between the vane and shroud taken in the plane normal to the flow line, if projected on the radial plane IV making an angle γ_{4a} to the normal plane, will be reduced as given by equation 16.7. It should be noticed that, if γ is 90° (tan γ = ∞) or near it, its tangent is a very large number and $\gamma' \approx \gamma$. Several values of γ and γ' for different values of β are given in the accompanying tabulation.

γ/γ'	$\beta = 20°$	$\beta = 30°$	$\beta = 45°$	$\beta = 60°$
85°	84.7	84.3	83.0	80.0
80°	79.4	78.5	76.0	70.6
75°	74.1	72.8	69.3	61.8

Because the shrouds are not parallel, it is impossible to make angles between one vane and both shrouds 90° without excessive vane bending. But, γ is seldom smaller than 75°; γ' on the elevation view, always will be, within a few degrees, equal to γ, the true angle between the vane and shrouds in space.

g. The vane angle β for any point on the flow lines appears on the plan view reduced to β' so that

$$\tan \beta' = \tan \beta \cos \delta \tag{16.8}$$

where δ is the angle between the tangent to the flow line at that point on the elevation view and the plane normal to the impeller axis. Thus, for instance, in Figs. 16.7a,b,c,d for triangle 3,

$$\tan \beta = g_3/h_3 \qquad \tan \beta' = (r_{2a} - r_{3a})/h_3$$

but

$$(r_{2a} - r_{3a})/g_3 = \cos \delta_3$$

hence

$$\tan \beta' = \tan \beta \cos \delta_3$$

It has been found that in practice three flow lines will be sufficient for a vane layout in the majority of cases. Furthermore, the vane construction can be simplified by drawing the middle flow line as a curve equally spaced from both shrouds. For small and narrow impellers the middle flow line can be omitted. In that case the radial vane sections (lines I, II, III, etc., Figs. 16.7d and 16.7e) are drawn as straight lines or curves by eye on the elevation view. The accuracy of vane construction is not impaired by these short cuts, as can be proved by comparing layouts made with and without these simplifications.

16.6 APPLICATION OF METHOD OF ERROR TRIANGLES TO THE DESIGN OF PLAIN VANES

For a given entrance angle β_1 and discharge angle β_2 it is always possible to draw a vane as a circular arc with a single radius. However, such a vane has serious disadvantages. Figure 16.8 shows the construction. From an arbitrary point A on the circle of the impeller outside diameter, draw one line AM at an angle β_2 to the radius AC. At point C, construct an angle $\beta_2 + \beta_1$ to the radius AC. The line will intersect the impeller eye circle at B. Draw a line AB to intersect the impeller eye circle at D. Draw a perpendicular line in the middle of AD to intersect line AM at M. MA will be the radius of the arc to give an angle β_2 at discharge and an angle β_1 at entrance.

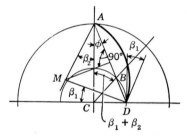

Fig. 16.8. Plain vane drawn as a circular arc.

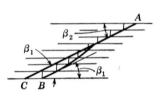

Fig. 16.9. Development of the vane in Fig. 16.8.

The proof of this construction may be of interest.

$$\beta_1 + \beta_2 + \phi = \angle CBD = \angle CDB$$

$$\beta_2 + \phi = \angle MAD = \angle MDA$$

By subtraction

$$\beta_1 = \angle CDB - \angle MDA = \angle MDC$$

The method of error triangles can be advantageously applied to the analysis and construction of the plain vane. In Fig. 16.9 AB is the development on a plane of the vane in Fig. 16.8 obtained by the use of error triangles. It will be noticed that the change in vane angularity is irregular. First, the vane angle increases rapidly, then slowly decreases to the discharge angle. This form of vane is not considered the most efficient. A vane with a gradual change in the vane angle, AC in Fig. 16.9, is preferred. To get a better vane shape for the plain vane impeller, it pays to draw first the vane development on a plane and then to replot it on a plan view by the method of error triangles. Although this method takes more time, its systematic use permits improving the vane shape to get the best performance.

REFERENCES

1. Kaplan and Lechner, *Theorie und Bau von Turbinen-Schnelläufern*, R. Oldenbourg, Munich, 1931, pp. 125–129.
2. Schaefer, *Kreiselmaschinen*, Julius Springer, Berlin, 1930, pp. 29–37.
3. Quantz, *Kreiselpumpen*, Julius Springer, Berlin, 1930, pp. 18–20.
4. Pfleiderer, *Die Kreiselpumpen*, Julius Springer, Berlin, 1932, pp. 266–279.
5. Camerer, *Vorlesungen über Wasserkraftmaschinen*, Wilhelm Engelman, Leipzig, 1929, pp. 274, 275, 369.

INDEX